# Stone by Stone

A Guide to Building Stone in the Northern Ireland Environment

# Stone by Stone

## A Guide to Building Stone in the Northern Ireland Environment

Joanne Curran, Patricia Warke, Dawson Stelfox,
Bernard Smith, John Savage

Appletree Press

**First published in 2010 by Appletree Press Ltd**
The Old Potato Station, 14 Howard Street South, Belfast BT7 1AP

**T** +44 (0) 28 9024 3074, **F** +44 (0) 28 9024 6756
**E** reception@appletree.ie, **W** www.appletree.ie

Published in association with Consarc Design Group



A catalogue record for this book is available from the British Library.

**Stone by Stone – A Guide to Building Stone in the Northern Ireland Environment**

ISBN: 978 1 84758 141 9

Copy-editor: Jean Brown
Designer: Lisa Smyth
Production Manager: Paul McAvoy

9 8 7 6 5 4 3 2 1

AP3642

For further information on the Natural Stone Database for Northern Ireland please visit:

**www.stonedatabase.com**

# Contents

Gasworks, Ormeau Road, Belfast

Guild Hall and Northern Bank, Londonderry

## About the Contributors

**Joanne Curran** BSc, PhD

Joanne Curran is a geologist and project manager for Stone Conservation Services, Consarc Design Group. Since completing her PhD in 1995 she worked as a Research Fellow at Queen's University on a range of building stone research projects and stone analysis on key buildings including the Albert Memorial, St George's Market, Stormont and the Lanyon Building at Queen's.

She was appointed in 2001 to project manage the Knowledge Transfer Partnership (KTP) Programme to link stone research at Queen's University Belfast with Consarc Conservation. This project won a National award and culminated in the creation of a specialist department Stone Conservation Services, a consultancy providing technical advice, survey, testing and analysis for conservation projects. Now company supervisor for a second KTP Programme between Queen's and Consarc set up to apply the latest non-destructive monitoring techniques to building and monument conservation.

She worked as project manager of the 'Natural Stone Database Project' for the Northern Ireland Environment Agency which recorded the condition of stonework of listed stone buildings and monuments throughout Northern Ireland. This project was completed in January 2008 with the launch of an on-line database of stone buildings throughout Northern Ireland (**www.stonedatabase.com**).

She is a former Associate Lecturer for the Open University and Queen's University Belfast and is Treasurer of Earth Science 2000, a charity dedicated to the promotion of Ireland's geological heritage.

**John Savage** FIOC, ICIOB, MIWMT, LICW

After leaving school John worked as a cabinet maker and joiner for the first ten years of his career and in 1987 won the Northern Ireland Skill Build competition in joinery and second place in the UK finals.

In 1993 he was appointed Clerk of Works for the stonework cleaning, restoration and ancillary works to Belfast City Hall, (1994 to 1996). After working with Dawson Stelfox on the restoration of the Custom House, John took up a position with Consarc Design Group and was made an Associate of the company in 2002 and set up Stone Conservation Services with Dawson Stelfox and Joanne Curran.

Over the last number of years he has project managed the conservation and restoration of some of the most important historic buildings in Northern Ireland. These include: Belfast City Hall, St George's Market, the Albert Memorial, Christchurch, Centre of Excellence, College Square, Holycross Church in Ardoyne, Ballymena Town Hall and St Malachy's Church in Belfast.

He is a member of the Ulster Architectural Heritage Society and acts as an industry advisor on several research projects with Queen's University.

**Bernard Smith** BSc, PhD, C.Geog

Bernard Smith is Professor of Tropical Geomorphology in the School of Geography, Archaeology and Palaeoecology, Queen's University Belfast where he has worked since 1979. Previously, he lectured in northern Nigeria after obtaining both his undergraduate degree and PhD at the University of Reading. His main research interest is the study of stone decay processes in natural and built environments across a wide range of climatic zones. He is a member of the Weathering Research Group within Queen's and was recently elected Vice-Chair of the British Society for Geomorphology.

His research on urban stone decay includes studies in Venice, Budapest, Prague, Rio de Janeiro, Dublin and Belfast and he has acted as an adviser to the Getty Conservation Institute on salt weathering mechanisms. Collaboration with Consarc Design Group has included a number of UK Research Council projects and inputs into the conservation of key structures in Belfast such as the Albert Clock, St George's

Gargoyle, Albert Memorial Clock

Albert Memorial, Belfast

Market, Parliament Buildings at Stormont and the Lanyon Building at Queen's. These links are all designed to combine the practical expertise of Consarc with the research potential of the University and have been exemplified in the joint creation of the on-line 'Natural Stone Database for Northern Ireland'.

Prof. Smith's interests in the conservation of built heritage are complemented by a concern for natural heritage. He is a member of the statutory advisory Council for Nature Conservation and Countryside (CNCC), sits on the management committee of the Giant's Causeway World Heritage Site and acts as a World Heritage evaluator for UNESCO.

**Dawson Stelfox** DL, MBE, Hon DSc, Hon DUniv, BSc Arch, Dip Arch, RIBA, FRIAI

Dawson Stelfox is a Conservation Architect ( AABC and RIAI Grade 1) and Chairman of Consarc Design Group and Stone Conservation Services. He is currently President of the Royal Society of Ulster Architects (RSUA) and is a former convenor of the RSUA Conservation Committee. A former member of the Historic Buildings Council for Northern Ireland, Dawson has been involved in the restoration of a large number of key historic buildings including the Albert Memorial, Parliament Buildings, the Custom House, Lanyon Building at Queen's University and many churches. Project Director on two KTP programmes with QUB School of Geography and Industry Partner on a number of university research programmes on stone weathering. He is co-author of

Queen's University Belfast

*Traditional Buildings – A Homeowners Guide*, with Dick Oram.

**Patricia Warke** BSc, PhD
Patricia Warke is a lecturer in the School of Geography, Archaeology and Palaeoecology at Queen's University Belfast. A geomorphologist by training, her PhD research involved investigation of rock weathering in contemporary hot arid environments with particular emphasis on the role of inheritance effects in development of present-day weathering phenomena. Since appointment as lecturer in 1999 her research interests have grown to include study of general decay dynamics of stone in built structures, both archaeological and historical, which in turn has stimulated a focus on development of condition classification systems for buildings and ancient monuments based on the Staging System approach used in medicine. As a member of the Weathering Research Group she has been involved in a wide variety of pure and applied research projects investigating stone properties, and the factors controlling the breakdown of stone in buildings under a wide range of environmental conditions.

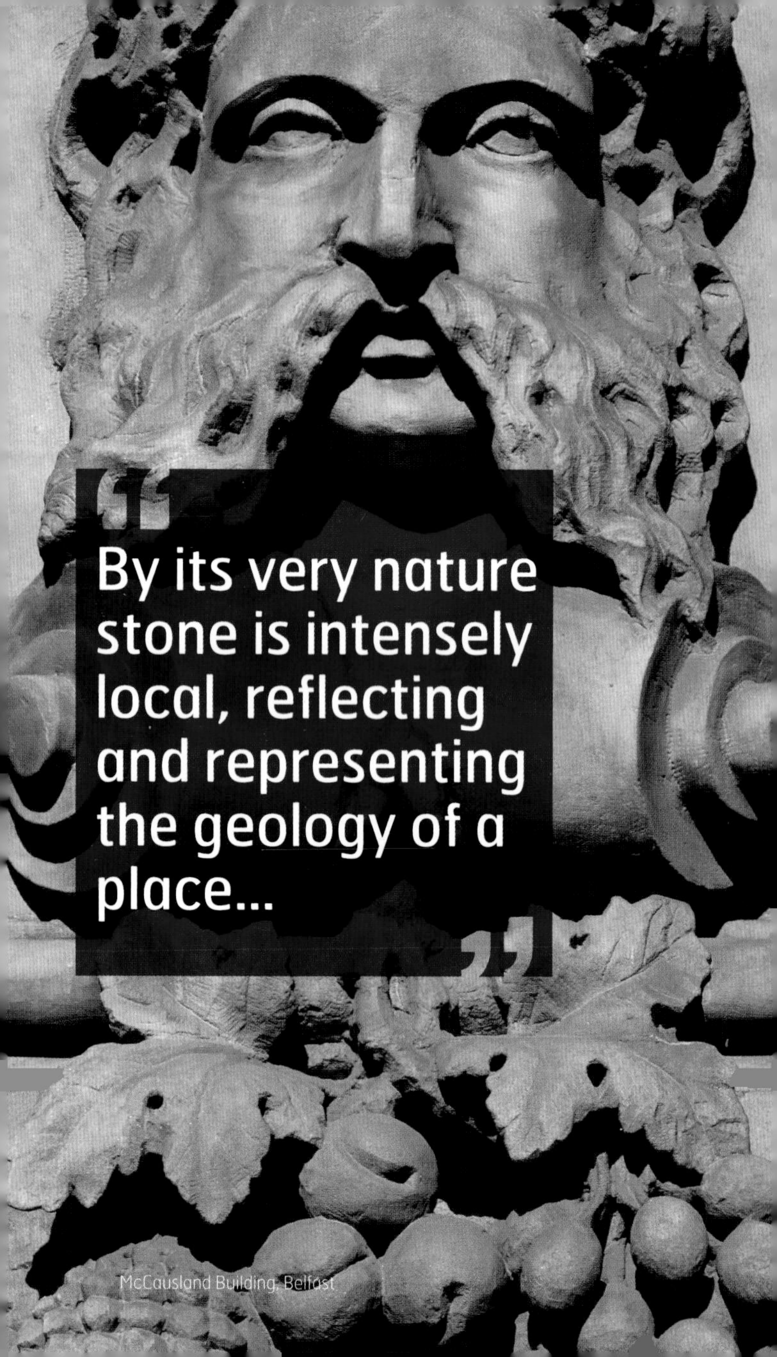


McCausland Building, Belfast

Dawson Stelfox

# Foreword

Stone is the quintessential elemental building material – used for millennia but remaining in the vanguard of innovative design and construction – representing quality, longevity and a commitment to future posterity.

Stone is the canvas for extraordinary masonry skill and craftsmanship and today it combines ancient hand-carving skills with the latest computer controlled saws and cutting tools. By its very nature stone is intensely local – reflecting and representing the geology of a place, the opportunity offered for re-establishing lost practices and skills of vernacular construction, reducing transport costs and emissions, and founding new and exciting architecture in the spirit of place in which they sit, at the same time providing local employment and skill development. As we move into a world of uncertain climatic conditions, with rising global temperatures, there is also an argument for returning to high thermal mass buildings – warm in winter, cool in summer, linked to ground, water or sun-based energy, and stone construction offers an easy way to achieve high thermal mass.

But stone is also a complex material and hard lessons have been learnt from its inappropriate use and combination with other materials. Millions of pounds have been spent repairing unnecessary problems arising from poor practice in detailing and understanding of materials such as spalling of soft stones used with hard pointing mortars, delamination of sandstone which had been wrongly bedded, corrosion of stone due to airborne pollution etc. Failure can be catastrophic and costly, and our gradually warmer and wetter climate is throwing up new challenges of weathering to understand. Some paving stones become slippery and dangerous – while others remain robust and safe. Some stones in some conditions remain sharp and pristine for centuries, whilst others erode and lose definition within decades.

Understanding how and why this happens is not just an academic exercise. Years of serious research in the universities have now been matched with experience from architects, stonemasons, building surveyors and geologists to form a practical understanding of how and why stone in building weathers and decays, and more importantly, how to prevent and repair this damage, vital to sensitive heritage conservation projects and new buildings alike.

For the last five years specialists in the School of Geography, Archaeology and Palaeoecology at Queen's University Belfast (QUB) have been working with Conservation Architects at Consarc Design Group to marry stone weathering research with practical conservation projects on many of Belfast's most important listed buildings including the Albert Memorial Clock, St George's Market and many churches. This collaboration led to the formation of Stone Conservation Services, a research-based consultancy and also to the setting up of the Northern Ireland Stone Database Project, funded by the EU Special Programmes through the Northern Ireland Environment and Heritage Service (now Northern Ireland Environment Agency or NIEA) and supported by QUB and Consarc Design Group.

This book is one of the outcomes of that project designed to complement the web-based database. It is aimed at building owners, architects, surveyors and engineers, and all those who have a responsibility for the care, repair and restoration of stone buildings – as well as those who are just interested in the place where they live.

It is a field guide, intended to be used on site to identify stones, weathering and defects, and to help optimise repair and restoration specifications. It also guides the sourcing of stone for both repairs and for new buildings, all aimed at ensuring stone is used more appropriately in repairing the buildings of the past, and creating the landmarks of the future.

## About this Book

The primary purpose of this book is to be a practical working guide to identifying, assessing and specifying stone and stonework, to encourage good practice and informed decision making. It charts the transition from rock in the ground to building stone, from the quarry to the high street.

Granite in the Mourne Mountains as rock in the ground and stone in the wall.

The layout of the book is designed to make the information accessible and relevant for a range of requirements. The name of the book comes from our adoption of a rigorous approach to stone identification, analysis and repair – a **'stone by stone'** approach which recognises the full range of factors such as geology, orientation, environment and use that together make each stone unique.

The key to a successful process is to start by accurately identifying the stone and other materials used. The field guide in Building Stones of Northern Ireland helps in the identification and sourcing of the main building stone types used in Northern Ireland, explaining their key characteristics. From that, depending on your needs or interest, you can move on to explore the theories underpinning stone decay and condition assessment in the Theory Section or the practice of stone specification and repair in the Practice Section. The final chapter, Monitoring and Maintenance, addresses maintenance issues and is primarily aimed at building owners and managers and is designed to counter the regrettable fact that much damage to stone is done by a lack of proper maintenance.

This book complements the Natural Stone Database for Northern Ireland (**www.stonedatabase.com**) which details the use of stone and its condition in over 2000 buildings and monuments in Northern Ireland, providing an invaluable source of information for building owners and users.

Stone carving, St Anne's Cathedral, Belfast


## Acknowledgements

We would like to acknowledge the following people and agencies for their help in the production of this book.

Firstly, Claire Foley and Brian McKervey from the Northern Ireland Environment Agency (NIEA) and Garth Earls and Ian Mitchell from the Geological Survey of Northern Ireland (GSNI) for their support, advice and encouragement during the development of the Natural Stone Database for Northern Ireland – a project funded by an award from the European Union and which provided the stimulus for this book. We must also thank the GSNI and the Geological Survey of Ireland (GSI) for permission to reproduce bedrock geology maps.

Secondly, thanks must go to Catherine Adamson and Mark Francis who performed the numerous building surveys and initial formulation of the database. Also to Kara Dotter for information on lime mortars.

Thirdly, we are grateful to staff at Queen's University Belfast and Consarc Design Group. The former include Gill Alexander and Maura Pringle for help with diagrams and Pat McBride for preparation of rock samples while the latter include John McNeill for his contribution to the section on Health and Safety issues and Katie Taylor, Eric Hunter, Garth

Gargoyle in Doulting Limestone,
Holy Cross Church, Belfast

Stone and mortar, Carrickfergus Castle

Scrabo Tower, Newtownards, Co. Down

Leaker and Neeltje Harmsen for the production of tables and graphics.

Fourthly, for the graphic design and layout of this publication, we are indebted to the extremely patient Lisa Smyth and to Billy Mol for proofreading and general advice.

Finally, acknowledgement is made of the support and information provided by Rita Harkin and Andrew McClelland from the Ulster Architectural Heritage Society (UAHS).

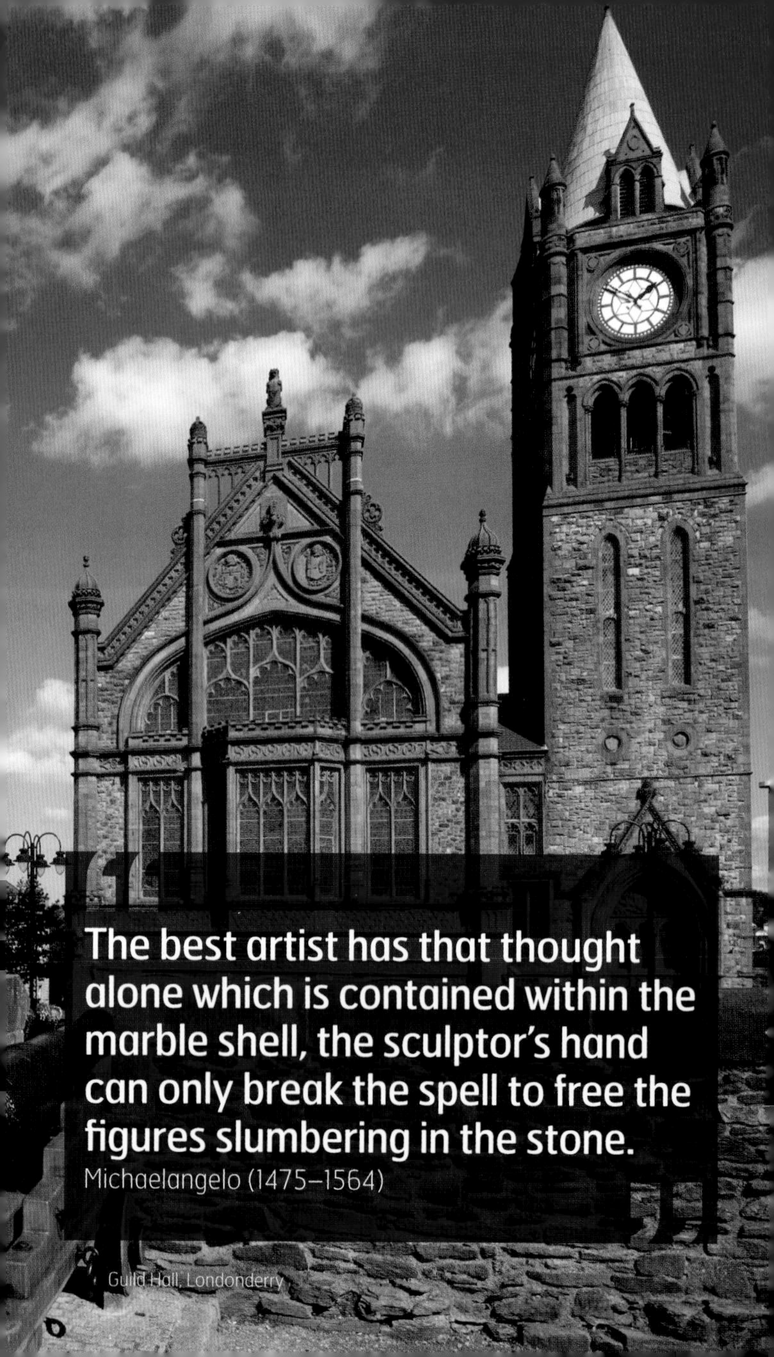


Guild Hall, Londonderry

Dawson Stelfox

# Understanding Stone in Buildings

## Introduction

Stone is a natural, complex material of almost infinitive variety and behavioural characteristics. That is what makes it so attractive as a construction material, but it is also what can lead to a multitude of failings and problems.

Understanding how stone performs in its environment is vital to specifying, repairing and restoring masonry buildings, be it a modern thin skin on a steel frame or an ancient solid walled monument. The level of understanding required can be achieved by analysis and consideration of the building at multiple, overlapping levels:

- Historical integrity, character and the patina of age
- Aesthetics, artistic quality and construction
- Sources, surveys and investigations
- Technical and innovative qualities
- Associated people or events

All this will build up the overarching importance of a stone wall or structure, often expressed through a **'Statement of Significance'**. This provides a baseline against which the impact of repair or replacement techniques can be measured and decisions made as to their desirability or otherwise. Choices are frequently difficult. An ancient weathered stone statue will inevitably decay to the extent of losing its unique markings. Should it be brought into a museum and replaced by a replica? This will preserve the original but it will be disassociated from its real meaning as its

Boa Island figures, County Fermanagh

Sueno's Stone, Forres, Scotland. A Pictish stone that stands 6.5m high and is now enclosed in a climate-controlled chamber to prevent further stone weathering.

location was crucial to its understanding. Should it be preserved in-situ, within a protective enclosure, which will inevitably break its connection to the landscape? Should it be treated with a chemical consolidant to reduce decay? Or, should a copy be made now, before it weathers too much and the original just left to slowly dissolve? All four solutions could be right, or wrong, depending on what emphasis is given to what factor. There are often no easy answers in stonework repair and restoration but those that are there can be gained through a thorough understanding of the building and its context, allied to a rigorous scientific approach, and sound practical knowledge.

**UNDERSTANDING, THEORY** and **PRACTICE** is our three-legged stool for maximising the conservation benefit in stone buildings – take any one away and decisions are suspect – combine all three and some of the best of our buildings – built in natural stone out of necessity or pride or both will now be properly looked after and equipped for the 21st century.

## Historical Integrity, Character and the Patina of Age

"Rain! whose soft architectural hands have power to cut stones and chisel to shapes of grandeur the very mountains"
**Henry Ward Beecher, (1813–1887)**

All buildings age and weather through time, sometimes gracefully, sometimes destructively, and with stone buildings it is invariably both. The weathering and ageing of stone can add to its beauty and character, contributing to its historical integrity, building up a patina of age which is unique, based as it is on a singular combination of geology, time and environment. However, it is not easily measured in any subjective way, and excessive weathering can trigger negative perceptions as it can engender an impression of neglect which can be the start of a downward spiral of decline. These perceptions tend to follow cyclical fashions and the results can be enormously destructive. An example of this is the excessive cleaning of sandstone buildings in Glasgow, amongst other industrial cities, during the 1970s and 1980s. The blackened crusted sandstone, the legacy of a century of heavy industrial pollution, robbed many fine buildings of their visual quality, texture and character, all too frequently leading to demolition or destructive over-cleaning.

The damage caused by over-cleaning created a conservation based backlash and a predisposition against cleaning which is still prevalent today. Excessive cleaning removes the patina of age, causes loss of historic fabric and can start a destructive cycle of decay. Not cleaning, however, can leave destructive organisms in place and more subtly, contribute to a perceived loss of value of a building, contributing to neglect. The decision to clean or not to clean a historic stone building should not be taken lightly, or purely based on the current fashion or aesthetic judgements. It can be one of the most difficult decisions a building owner or their architect can make and there are key bits of information that need to be established before a sound decision can be made. Is the soiling, environmental growth or encrustation causing any actual ongoing decay of the stone? If decay is happening, is it possible to clean minimally to remove only destructive soiling without excessive loss of historic fabric and causing further decay? To answer these questions properly requires a detailed knowledge of the theory and practice of stone weathering and repair and an acceptance that weathering and soiling are an integral part of the story of a historic building.

Dunseverick Castle, County Antrim

## Aesthetics, Artistic Quality and Construction

"Form in early architecture is paralleled by continuity in the megalithic tradition itself, in the use of single stones as monuments, markers and memorials. The constant presence of rude monumentality in rough stone hewn out or picked up from the ground, preventing too close a distinction between its casual and its formal use – gives all stone, even today, a certain potency"
**– from *A Lost Tradition: The Nature of Architecture in Ireland* (Niall McCullough and Valerie Mulvin).**

Stone has been used for generations not just because of its permanence and longevity, but also for its aesthetic qualities and in particular for its ability to be worked, dressed, and carved to express the intent and inspiration of architect, sculptor and mason. The aesthetics of a building thus exist both on the macro scale – the architectural composition, but also down to micro scale – the individual carved stone, a piece of art in its own right, bearing the artistic expression of the mason who created it. The value of a stone building then can be measured both by its overall quality and by the reputation and legacy of the architect, but also by the masons or carvers who worked on it, and their reputation and legacy. Of all trades and crafts, it is in stonemasonry that the hand, eye and intellect of the craftsman become such a vital physical expression in the building. The medieval masons, of course, were the architects and the masters of building, combining their vision of the whole composition with a deep understanding of how it was to be built. It is crucial to the understanding of a stone building to know how it is constructed, how the components are crafted together and how this intricate combination of the parts contributes to the aesthetic and artistic qualities of the completed building.

## Sources, Surveys and Investigations

"There is a close connection between Geology and Architecture; ... The study of Geology is particularly appropriate for the architect, who, in applying the various materials of the Earth's crust in the realisation of his designs, should be familiar with their origin, if he would successfully employ them in securing variety, beauty and the permanency of his structures..."
**William Gray, addressing the Royal Institute of Architects of Ireland, 1869.**

Whereas subjective judgements play an important part in the arrival at a conclusion about historic integrity and aesthetics, there are a range of objective data that are crucial to the understanding of a building. These will be explored more fully in the '**Theory**' section of this book but whereas specialists will inevitably be involved in the detailed studies, it is important that building owners and architects have a general understanding of sources of stones, the need or value of certain surveys and investigations.

The basic checklist of knowledge required is:

- Quarry source
- Technical – geology, porosity etc.
- Key buildings where used – to gather comparative data
- Records on databases and inventories etc.

This generic knowledge, gathered from a 'desk-top' study can then be supplemented with site and building specific surveys and investigations, including information on past cleaning and repair regimes, as detailed later in both '**Theory**' and '**Practice**' sections. All of this information builds up to create a more complete picture of the state of the stone and how it is likely to perform in the future without intervention.

View of the Law Courts and Waterfront Hall, Belfast

## Technical and Innovative Qualities

"Without tradition, art is a flock of sheep without a shepherd. Without innovation, it is a corpse."
**Winston Churchill (1874–1965)**

The value of a building or structure may not just be in its architectural or aesthetic qualities or its historical integrity, but in technical or innovative achievements which can add to, or even be the sole reason for its overall significance.

These could be related to the span and structure of bridges, historically innovative developments, or right up to date with technical developments brought on by the abilities of computer-controlled cutting saws creating intricate three-dimensional shapes as demonstrated by the Diana Memorial Fountain.

The importance of such qualities, particularly in structures which are not aesthetically pleasing or of architectural value, may not be immediately obvious on a visual survey and underline the need for thorough documentary research and an ability to analyse and put in context technical and innovative developments.

## The Diana Memorial, Hyde Park, London.

**Stonemasons – S. McConnell and Sons, Kilkeel.**

The Diana Memorial in Hyde Park, West London opened in 2004, combined the traditional art of stonemasonry with the latest CAD/CAM software and production techniques.

The 'necklace of water', an oval-shaped fountain of Cornish 'De Lank' Granite, was ground-breaking as it was the first to produce an accurate freeform shape from granite cut by the stonemasons Computer-Numerical-Control (CNC) machines.

This was achieved by creating a 3D surface model of every element of the design – including the textured surfaces that produce the variations in the fountain's water flow – which was then converted into data files compatible with the CNC machine.

Once the surface model was complete, it was divided into 545 individual stones produced taking into account foundation levels, drainage locations, joint lines, the limits of the CNC machines and the quarry's output capacity. Over a period of 5 months the stones (which varied in length from 3m to 8m), were cut by S. McConnell and Sons in Kilkeel, Co. Down, finished to 5mm tolerances, delivered to site in West London and slotted into their allocated positions with precise alignment of each section of the 210m circumference.

Belfast City Hall, 1903. Image reproduced courtesy of the Trustees of National Museums Northern Ireland

## Associated People and Events

"People will not look forward to posterity who will not look backward to their ancestors."
**Edmund Burke (1729–1797)**

The final aspect of the layers of understanding of the significance of a building lies not just with the fabric itself but in the extra dimensions added to its historical importance by association with people and events. These can be recorded in many ways – historical databases, photographs, official records etc, but all of it builds up a layer of cultural importance every bit as critical as the building's architectural merit or age. This knowledge can also feed back into understanding the physical fabric, by recording how the building has been adapted, changed or affected by historical events – the fixing of flags or banners for a royal visit or a protest, the effects of a fire or bomb explosion, or evidence of previous repairs and cleaning. We know from historical photographs that the gleaming white Portland limestone of Belfast City Hall had already gone grey before it was even officially opened – the result of the city's notoriously high levels of urban air pollution in the 19th and 20th centuries. We also know, that, it has been cleaned at least twice in its lifetime and that part of it was burnt out in the 1941 blitz and all manner of flags, banners and decorative lights have been fixed to its façades over its first century, all leaving their legacy in physical form. All of this knowledge contributes to its overall significance and this legacy should be considered in any repair or restoration proposals.

## A Checklist of Understanding

Understanding is key to sound decision making, and asking the right questions is key to the knowledge that brings with it that understanding. The whole purpose of this book is to unlock that knowledge and spread that understanding.

What you need to know before making any decisions about what to do with a stone structure:

- Dates of design and construction
- Owners and their other commissions
- Architectural style, influences and legacy
- Architect and their portfolio
- Main contractor and sub-contractors
- Stone carver / sculptor and their works
- Major events in or around the building
- Significant people associated with the building
- Record of previous repairs, cleaning, adaptations and interventions
- The building as it is today with character and patina of age
- Types of stone and physical data
- Quarry sources
- Use in other buildings
- Weathering characteristics
- Climate, environment and aspect
- Construction detailing and associated materials
- Record of weathering and change
- Predictive weathering and decay without intervention
- Intervention possibilities and their effect.

Carving above doorway, St Peter's Cathedral, Belfast

Carved head, McCausland Building, Belfast

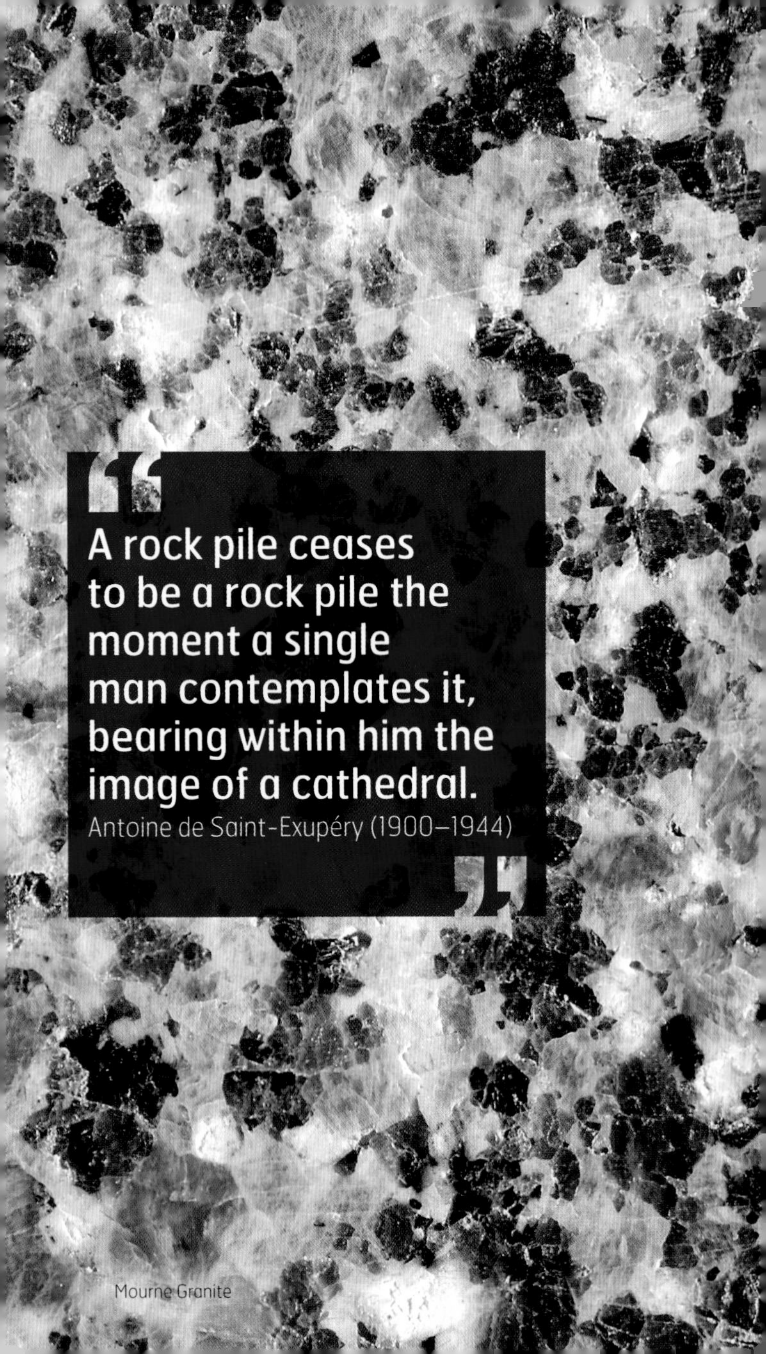
"A rock pile ceases to be a rock pile the moment a single man contemplates it, bearing within him the image of a cathedral."
Antoine de Saint-Exupéry (1900–1944)
Mourne Granite

Joanne Curran and Patricia Warke

# Identifying Stone

## Introduction

We have a long history of using stone for building in Northern Ireland. Our varied geological foundation has provided a wide variety of stone types for use to construct our buildings, monuments, stone walls and bridges.

Until recently, local availability of material dictated the building stone of choice giving each area its own distinctive character. For example, the Mourne granite and greywacke (gritstone) of County Down and the black basalt of County Antrim dominate the random rubble and dressed stonework of buildings and monuments throughout these counties. Scrabo sandstone from Newtownards, with its distinctive pink and yellow hues and bedding, and the buff sandstones of Dungannon and Ballycastle dominate the dressed and intricately carved stonework on much of our ecclesiastical heritage. In Counties Fermanagh and Armagh, the fossil-rich grey and pink limestones have been widely used in both construction of the simplest vernacular buildings and the grandest churches and town halls.

In the north of Ireland the full range of rock types have been used since earliest times but as transport systems developed in the 19th and 20th centuries, stone was moved more widely around the country as well as being shipped in from further afield. For example, Belfast's built heritage has a full range of Scottish Carboniferous sandstones and English Jurassic limestones used from the mid-19th century onwards as the City expanded on the back of a thriving industrial economy. Until the railway network was well established the easiest and most economical way to transport stone was via inland waterways

Dunluce Castle, County Antrim.
Local Antrim Basalt was used to construct the 17th century castle which also sits on a basalt headland

The Braid Ballymena Town Hall, Museum and Arts Complex, County Antrim.
Portland Limestone imported from England used to construct the Town Hall in 1928 and to clad the new Museum and Arts Centre completed in 2007

and by sea rather than overland and today we continue to ship stone from all over the world for cladding of new buildings and paving for public walkways.

The 19th and 20th century Irish architect was knowledgeable about both the use and availability of stone for construction with publications such as *The Practical Geology and Ancient Architecture of Ireland* by George Wilkinson (1845) and Kinahan's *Economic Geology of Ireland* (1889) providing invaluable information about stone resources throughout Ireland. However, today stone is only one of many materials used in construction and for stone in the 21st century the agenda has changed with much of the focus now being on conservation of stone on historic monuments and buildings. Consequently, information regarding best practice for conserving and repairing stonework and specifying stone for new buildings and other new uses needs to be made more widely available in an accessible format. As an initial step towards addressing this need, this handbook supplies an illustrated guide to, and advice concerning the use of stone in Northern Ireland.

In Northern Ireland, natural stone is still widely used in construction of often award-winning new buildings and in conservation of historically important structures. However, there is an increasing emphasis on improving sustainability including the materials used in construction. There is an increased awareness of the energy involved in the production of modern materials such as cement, concrete and glass, together with the rising costs of importing stone from other parts of the world. It should be recognised that indigenous building stone is one of the most sustainable, long-lasting and desirable materials available for construction.

## Rock Types

In order to specify new stone and to conserve existing stonework a basic understanding of the different groups of rock types, how they formed and how they perform as construction materials is essential.

Geologists categorise rocks as being **igneous**, **sedimentary** or **metamorphic**. **Table 1** below shows these three main rock groups and the stone types within those groups that can be found in Northern Ireland.

### Igneous rocks

Igneous rocks are crystalline rocks which form when hot, molten rock (called magma) cools and solidifies. There are two main types of igneous rock, depending on where the magma cooled:

- **Intrusive igneous rocks** form when the magma comes from deep underground and is forced into the upper layers of the Earth's crust but without breaking through to the surface, where it cools slowly to form rocks such as gabbro and granite
- **Extrusive igneous rocks** form when the magma erupts onto the Earth's surface from a volcanic vent or fissure where it cools quickly to form basalt and rhyolite.

#### Texture

Igneous rocks contain randomly arranged crystals (crystalline) and these tend to be large if the molten rock cooled slowly (gabbro, granite), and small if it cooled quickly (basalt, rhyolite).

#### Chemistry

Igneous rocks vary in chemical composition as well as texture. 'Basic' igneous rocks such as basalt, dolerite and gabbro are generally dark grey to black in colour and contain magnesium and iron minerals and feldspar with little or no quartz. 'Acid'

Table 1 **Three Main Rock Groups**

| Igneous | Sedimentary | Metamorphic |
|---|---|---|
| Basalt | Sandstone | Schist |
| Rhyolite | Limestone | Slate |
| Granite | Shale | Marble |
| Gabbro | Conglomerate | Gneiss |

igneous rocks such as granite and rhyolite are composed of the minerals quartz, feldspar and mica. Granites can vary widely in both texture and colour, with common grey and pale red-orange varieties reflecting their feldspar composition.

### Sedimentary rocks

Sedimentary rocks are formed from the deposition and subsequent consolidation (lithification process) of sediment. Particles of rock, minerals or shells settle through the water or air to form layers (strata) of sediment. Over millions of years these layers of sediment build up buried one on top of the other with the sediments slowly becoming bonded together (lithified) to form rock.

Consequently, sedimentary rocks often have a layered appearance with visible bedding and they may also contain fossil remains of animals and plants that were trapped as the layers of sediments were deposited. Limestone, sandstone, shale and mudstone are examples of commonly occurring sedimentary rocks.

#### Sandstone

Sandstone is composed of sand-sized grains (usually quartz), cemented together by minerals such as silica, iron or calcite. Sandstone varies widely in terms of constituent minerals, cement types, grain sizes and pore structures which lead to a wide variety of colours, textures and performances as building stones.

#### Limestone

Limestone is wholly or largely composed of the mineral calcite (calcium carbonate). Most limestone is formed by the deposition and consolidation of the skeletons of marine invertebrates although a few originate as a result of chemical precipitation of calcium carbonate from solution. In their pure form they are usually white but may be coloured by the presence of mineral impurities. For example iron oxide can make limestones brown, yellow or red in appearance whilst the presence of carbon, plant remains and lime mud give a blue, black or grey colour. The texture of limestone varies from coarse to fine-grained and fossils of various sizes may be visible throughout the fabric of the rock.

#### Shale

Shale and mudstone are fine-grained, dark grey sedimentary rocks formed from deposits of silt and clay. Shale has a layered (laminated) structure and is relatively easily split along bedding planes while mudstone tends to have no laminations.

#### Conglomerate

Conglomerate and breccia are also part of the sedimentary group of rocks. They are coarse-grained rocks composed of pebbles and rounded particles (conglomerate) or angular clasts (breccia) bound together in a matrix of finer material.

### Metamorphic rocks

Metamorphic rocks are derived from pre-existing rocks which have been subjected to great heat and/or pressure deep within the Earth's crust but without melting. These conditions can occur when existing rocks (sedimentary, igneous or metamorphic) come into contact with cooling igneous rocks, or at the edges of tectonic plates where very high temperatures and pressures occur as mountains are being formed. Schist, gneiss, slate and marble are examples of metamorphic rocks.

#### Texture

When a rock is metamorphosed the mineral crystals change. Often minerals such as mica become aligned perpendicular to the direction of pressure. When minerals within a metamorphic rock are organised in this way, it is called foliation.

#### Chemistry

Metamorphic rocks may have the same bulk chemical composition as the pre-existing rocks from which they formed. For example, marble is formed from limestone, and its origins are evident through its retention of a predominantly calcium carbonate chemistry.

## Identifying Stone Types: The Decision Making Process

Recognition of stone requires some geological understanding and a little local knowledge. Being able to describe the fabric of a rock can go some way towards its identification.

The fabric of a rock is defined by the size (fine-, medium- and coarse-grained), shape (angular, sub-angular, sub-rounded and rounded) and arrangement of mineral grains (i.e. how densely or loosely grains are packed together). All theses properties combine to form the texture of a rock.

### What's in a name?

A stone can have an assortment of names. Polished gabbros from all over the world are referred to as 'black granites' while limestones are often described as marble much to the perplexity of many geologists. The use of industry names such as 'Blue Pearl' and 'Honey Glow' by stone suppliers can cause further confusion for architects and stone specifiers as such names do not relate to the rock type.

In Europe, in an effort to overcome this confusion and regulate stone names, a BS EN Standard has been compiled for 'Stone

Names' of European rock types that are actively quarried (BS EN 12440:2001 'Natural Stone – Denomination Criteria'). All stone types covered by this scheme have a 'CE' mark or identification so that they can be traced to the quarry of origin.

As shown on **Table 2**, the left-hand column shows the information that can be provided for each stone type; the centre and right hand columns show the entries for Mourne Granite and Cornish Granite (De Lank). Traditional Name, Petrological Family and Quarry information *must* be provided for each rock type (other information is optional).

Our local geology also provides a whole host of names for building stone used in Northern Ireland. Local sandstone, limestone and granite can be described by their geological formation, stratigraphic age, locality or quarry name. For example, sandstone from County Tyrone was used as a popular dimension stone throughout Northern Ireland and **Table 3** illustrates the variety of potential names used to describe it.

Table 2 **Example of Entries From BS EN 12440**

| **Traditional name** | **Mourne Glen Pink** | **De Lank** |
|---|---|---|
| Petrological Family | Granite | Granite |
| Typical Colour | Grey/Pink | Silver Grey |
| Place of Origin | Co. Down, Northern Ireland | Cornwall, England |
| Quarry | Robinson Quarry, Co. Down | De Lank Quarry, Bodmin, Cornwall |

Table 3 **Various Ways of Naming County Tyrone Sandstone**

| **Classification** | **Name** |
|---|---|
| Geological Formation | Millstone Grit |
| Geological Age | Carboniferous (320 Million Years Old) |
| Common Name | Dungannon Sandstone |
| Quarry Name | Carland Stone |

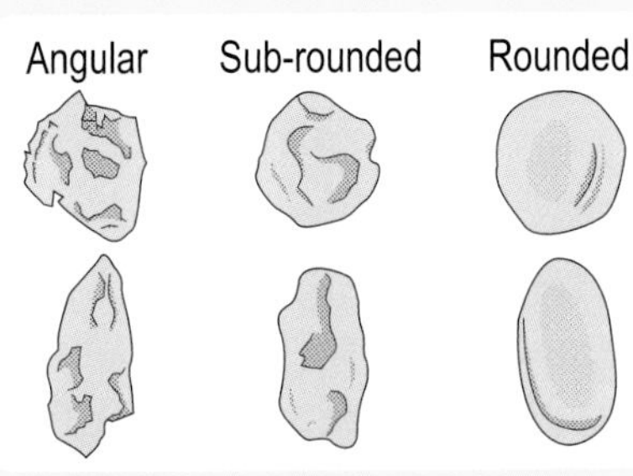


Examples of shape categories from Power's Scale of Roundness

**Grain size and shape**

The diameter of individual grains within a rock is referred to as grain or particle size. This is an important property and one that can be used as an aid to rock identification. There are different categories of grain size as shown in the guides on this page based on the Wentworth Scale which is the most commonly used guide to classifying the grain size of rocks and unconsolidated sediments.

Although this scale provides categories for fine sand and silts less than 0.25mm in diameter these are almost impossible to distinguish with the naked eye and so the grain size categories shown here start at fine / medium sand increasing in size by a constant ratio of 1:2 through coarse sands, granules (very fine gravel) to pebble sized material.

Grain shape is commonly classified using visual comparative schemes as shown above. The degree of particle angularity or rounding often reflects how long sediment was transported before deposition.

**Grain Size Scale**

Fine / Medium sand **0.25mm**

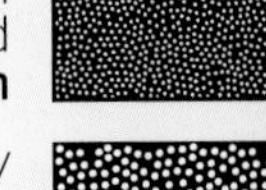

Medium / Coarse sand **0.5mm**

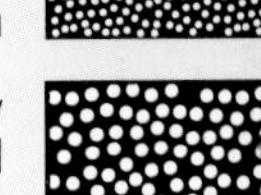

Coarse / Very Coarse sand **1.00mm**

Granules **2.00mm**

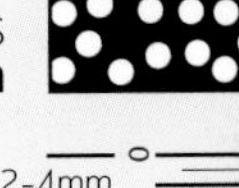

Granules 2-4mm

Small Pebbles 4-8mm

Medium Pebbles 8-16mm

Large Pebbles 16-32mm

Very Large Pebbles 32-64mm

0 10 20 30 40 50 60 mm

## Texture

'Texture' is the term used to describe the physical relationships between particles within a rock. Most rock types have textures that are either made of crystals or made of grains (see below). There are five main types of rock texture: crystalline, granular, fragmental, foliated and fine-grained.

In rocks with crystalline texture, minerals are interlocking while in granular or fragmental rocks grains tend to be more loosely packed reflecting their mode of transport and deposition. A foliated rock texture shows mineral grains or crystals aligned to form visible bands or layers.

Crystalline rocks tend to be harder than those with granular texture. When crystalline rocks break they often fracture along smooth, angular surfaces within individual crystals with the result that broken surfaces of crystalline rocks have many flat faces that reflect the light. Rocks with granular texture usually fracture between individual grains because the 'cement' holding them together is often weaker than the grains themselves.

The following pages give examples of each type of texture with a description of the main rock types that display these textures.

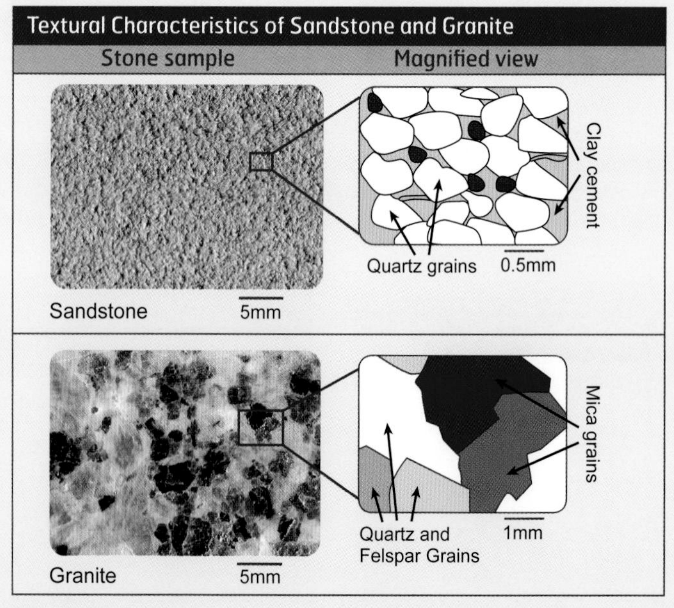

## Crystalline Stone Types

**The main identifying features of crystalline stone types are:**

- Visible crystals of different colours forming an interlocking texture
- Stone tends to be very hard

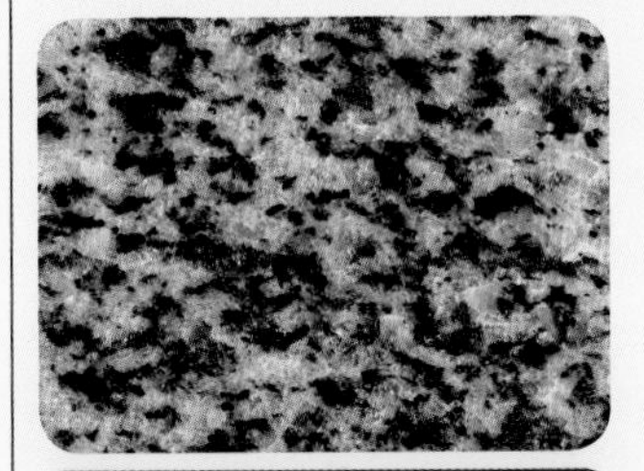

Granite

### Granite

An igneous rock having crystals or grains of visible size; consists mainly of quartz, feldspar, and mica or other coloured minerals.

Gabbro

### Gabbro

Coarse-grained igneous rock predominantly composed of ferromagnesian minerals with crystals visible to the eye; has the same mineral composition as basalt.

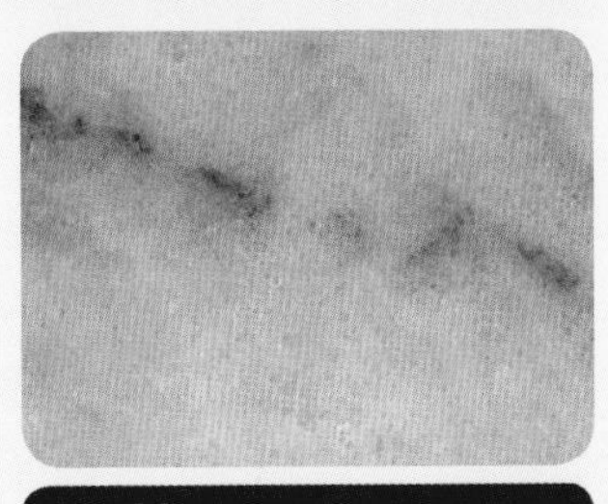

Marble

### Marble

A metamorphic rock formed by alteration of limestone or dolomite, often irregularly coloured by impurities, and used especially in architecture for sculptural elements.

## Granular Stone Types

**The main identifying features of granular stone types are:**

- Individual particles/fossils are visible to the naked eye
- Dull lustre on a broken surface
- Can be any colour, but not usually dark grey or black

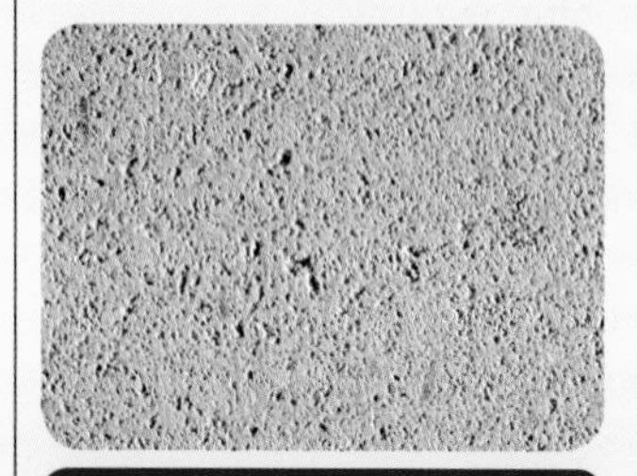

Limestone

### Limestone

Most limestones are formed by the deposition and consolidation of the skeletons of marine invertebrates; a few originate in chemical precipitation from solution.

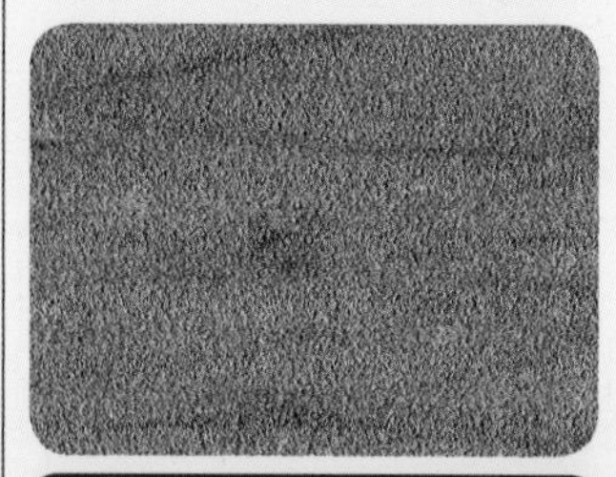

Sandstone

### Sandstone

Sedimentary rock composed of sand-sized grains, naturally cemented by mineral materials. In most sandstone used for building, quartz grains predominate; often used for decorative elements in buildings because it is easy to carve.

## Scratch Test (Mohs Scale)

A 'Scratch Test' (Mohs Scale) can be useful for identifying certain stone types as different minerals have different hardness characteristics. In simple terms 'hard' minerals such as quartz and feldspar cannot be scratched with a steel blade, but calcite, which is the main mineral found in limestone is softer and can be more easily scratched with a penknife blade (see glossary for full description of method).

## Fragmental Stone Types

**The main identifying features of fragmental stone types are:**

- Pebbles or angular fragments embedded in fine-grained granular cement/matrix

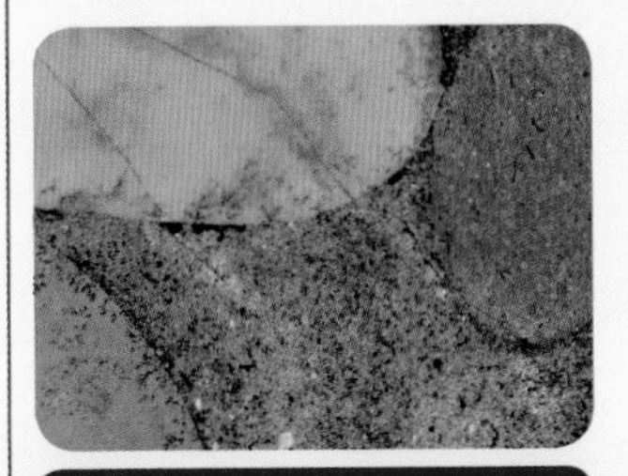

**Conglomerate**

### Conglomerate

A coarse-grained sedimentary rock (cemented gravel) composed largely of pebbles or other rounded particles with a diameter greater than 2mm.

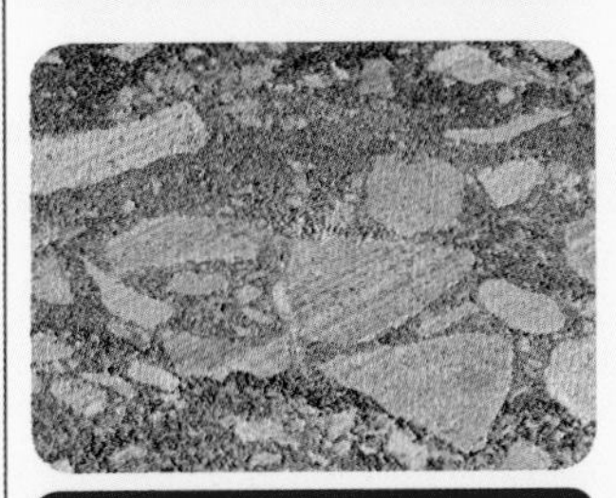

**Breccia**

### Breccia

Coarse sedimentary rock consisting of angular or nearly angular fragments larger than 2mm. Breccia commonly results from processes such as landslides or geologic faulting, in which rocks are fractured.

## Acid Test for Identification of Limestone

A definitive test for limestone is a reaction with dilute hydrochloric acid (HCl). Calcium carbonate, the constituent mineral of limestone, reacts with HCl releasing bubbles of carbon dioxide gas (effervescence) so if the acid fizzes on the surface the rock can be identified as limestone. Lime and cement mortars can also react with the acid.

## Foliated Stone Types

**The main identifying features of foliated stone types are:**

- Alternating dark and light layers that split easily
- Colour: grey-green

Gneiss

### Gneiss

A banded or foliated coarse-grained metamorphic rock usually with alternating dark and light bands of minerals. Gneiss has a similar composition to granite.

Schist

### Schist

Any of various medium to coarse-grained metamorphic rocks composed of laminated, often flaky parallel layers of chiefly micaceous minerals.

### Fine-grained rocks

Grains or crystals less than 0.25mm in size are difficult to see with the naked eye making it hard to identify the rock. Consequently fine-grained rocks are difficult to categorise and even experienced geologists find identification challenging particularly when the rocks have been removed from their geological context.

The flow chart shown (opposite) presents a simplified 'structured enquiry' as one approach to identification of the main fine-grained rock types common to Northern Ireland. Although not fool-proof, this simple process of elimination, together with a little knowledge of the local geology, can help in the recognition of the most common fine-grained building stones in Northern Ireland.

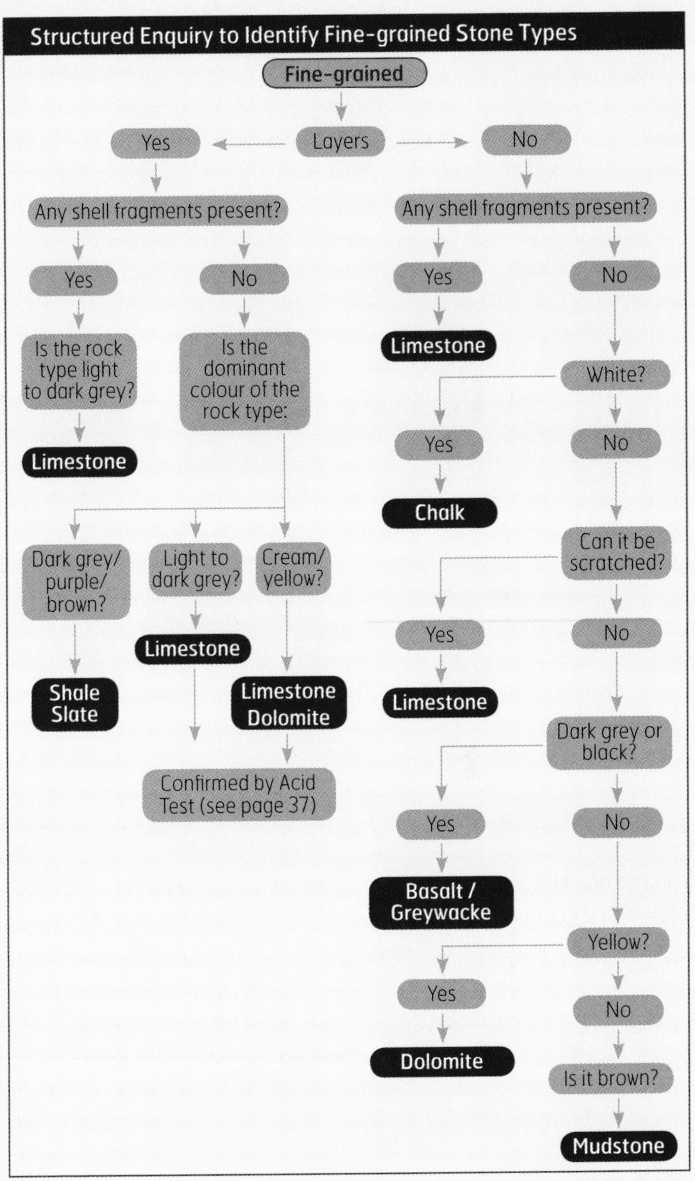
Structured Enquiry to Identify Fine-grained Stone Types
Fine-grained
Layers
Yes
No
Any shell fragments present?
Yes
No
Is the rock type light to dark grey?
Limestone
Is the dominant colour of the rock type:
Dark grey/ purple/ brown?
Shale Slate
Light to dark grey?
Limestone
Cream/ yellow?
Limestone Dolomite
Confirmed by Acid Test (see page 37)
Any shell fragments present?
Yes
Limestone
No
White?
Yes
Chalk
No
Can it be scratched?
Yes
Limestone
No
Dark grey or black?
Yes
Basalt / Greywacke
No
Yellow?
Yes
Dolomite
No
Is it brown?
Mudstone

## Fine-Grained Stone Types

**The main identifying features of fine-grained stone types are:**

- Most particles/fossils are not visible to the naked eye
- Stone generally has a dull lustre on a broken surface
- Can be any colour

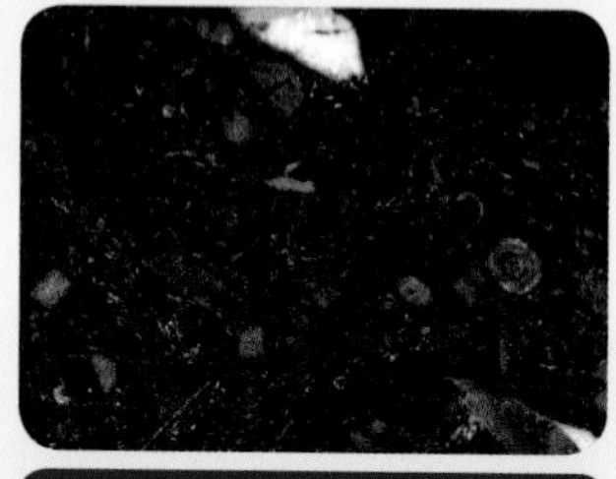

Limestone

### Limestone

Sedimentary rock wholly or in large part composed of calcium carbonate. It is ordinarily white but may be coloured by impurities, iron oxide making it brown, yellow, or red and carbon making it blue, black, or grey.

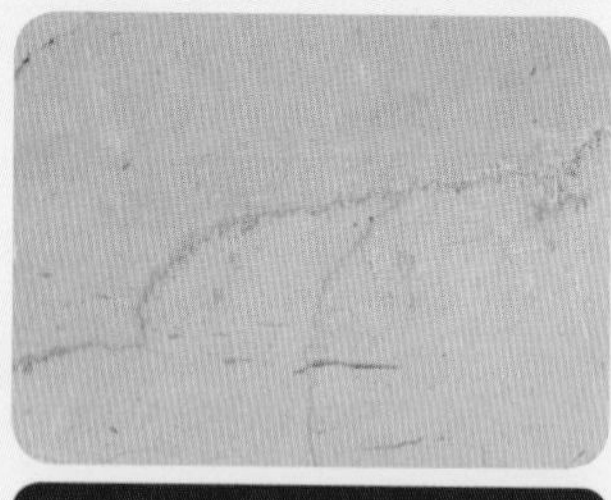

Chalk

### Chalk

Chalk is a uniformly fine-grained, typically light-coloured marine limestone primarily composed of the remains of calcareous nanofossils and microfossils.

Dolomite

### Dolomite

Type of limestone, the carbonate fraction of which is dominated by the mineral dolomite (calcium magnesium carbonate).

## Fine-Grained Stone Types continued

Slate

### Slate

A hard, brittle metamorphic rock consisting mainly of clay minerals, characterized by good cleavage along parallel planes; used extensively as dimension stone in thin sheets for flooring, roofing, panels (both decorative and electrical), and chalkboard, and in granular form as surfacing on composition roofing.

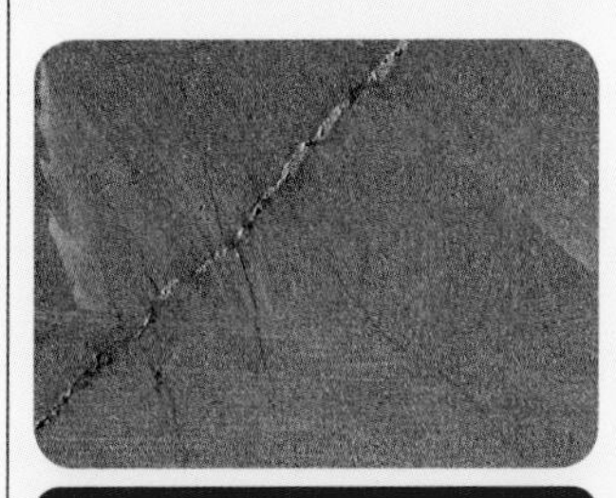

Greywacke

### Greywacke

A dark-coloured sandstone comprising mineral and rock fragments, poorly-sorted and bound together with clay cement.

Basalt

### Basalt

A fine-grained igneous (volcanic) rock (solidified lava) that is characteristically dark grey in colour.

## Rock types in Northern Ireland

The diversity of the bedrock geology of Northern Ireland and the rest of the island of Ireland is shown in the maps opposite and overleaf which have been adapted from information provided by the Geological Survey of Northern Ireland (GSNI) and the Geological Survey of Ireland (GSI). These maps are followed by a diagram showing a simplified overview of the geological succession for Northern Ireland and associated stone most frequently encountered in buildings.

For reasons of cost and availability, the stone used in buildings tended to be sourced from the local area. However, more prestigious structures such as cathedrals, town halls and large urban shops and offices used imported stone especially for decorative elements such as columns and sculptures. Consequently, many of Northern Ireland's landmark buildings contain geology with a more international and exotic flavour.

In the following Chapter, examples of the most commonly occurring local and imported building stones are described with a brief overview of their main characteristics and examples of buildings in which they have been used. More information about the sample buildings identified in the following pages are included in the building inventory in Appendix C. Space limitations preclude inclusion of all stone types and for a comprehensive list of these and the associated historic buildings and monuments, the reader is referred to The Natural Stone Database for Northern Ireland at: **www.stonedatabase.com**

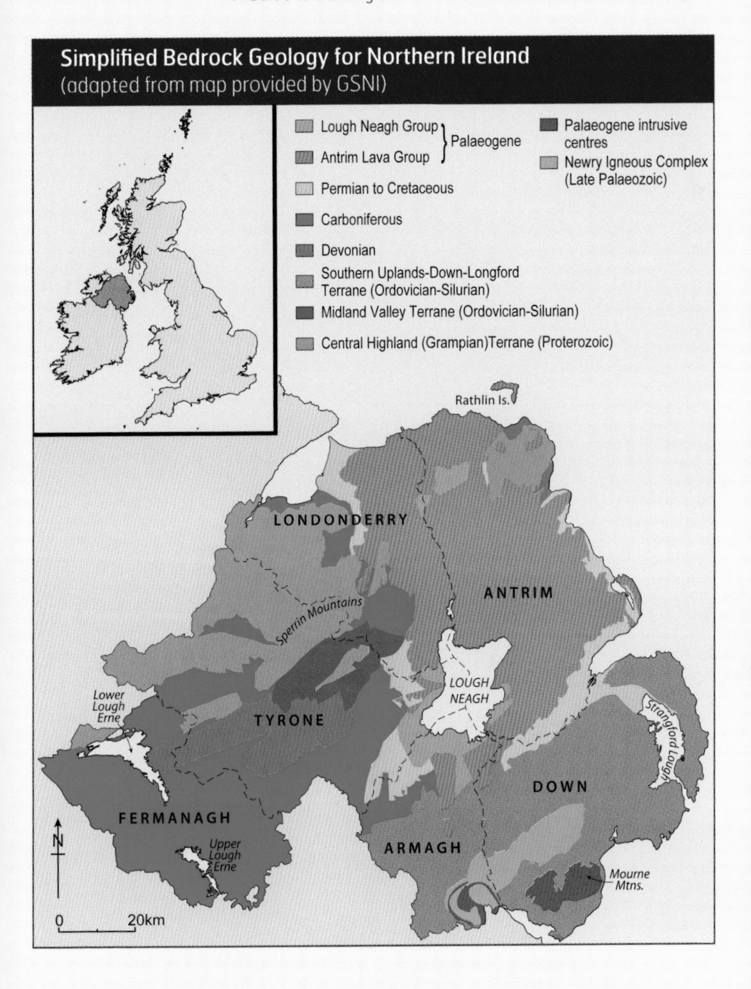


**Simplified Bedrock Geology for Northern Ireland**
(adapted from map provided by GSNI)

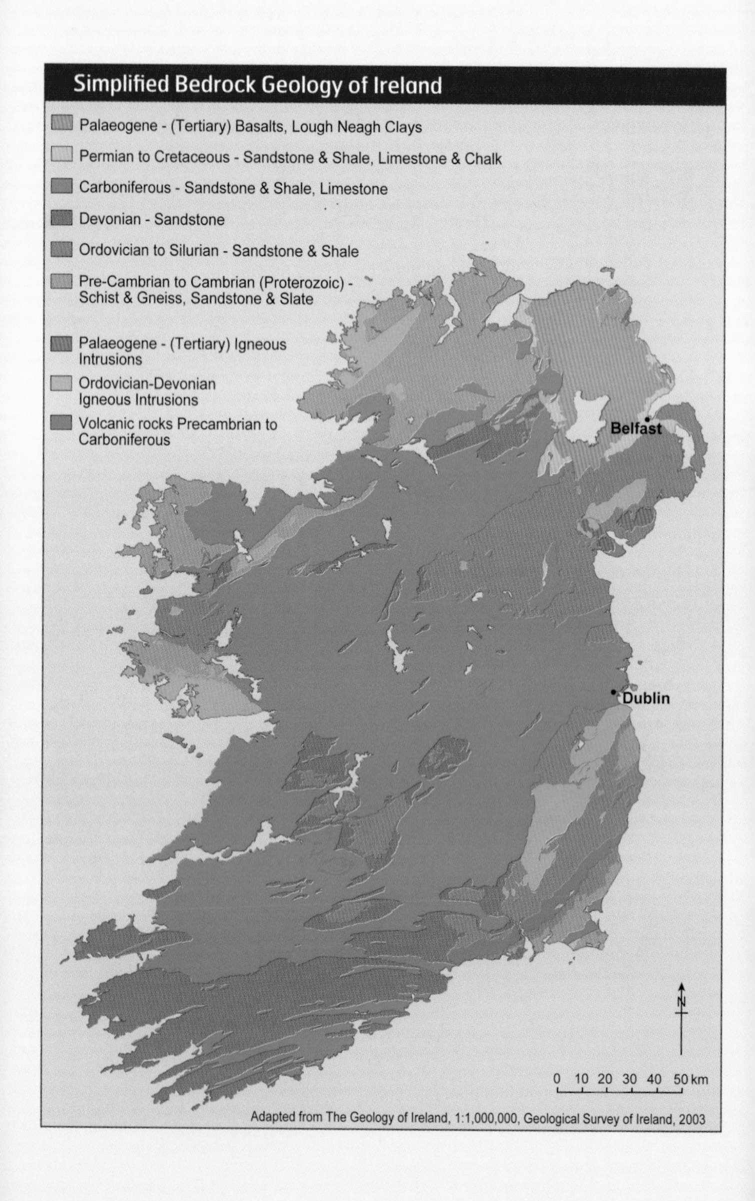
Simplified Bedrock Geology of Ireland
Palaeogene - (Tertiary) Basalts, Lough Neagh Clays
Permian to Cretaceous - Sandstone & Shale, Limestone & Chalk
Carboniferous - Sandstone & Shale, Limestone
Devonian - Sandstone
Ordovician to Silurian - Sandstone & Shale
Pre-Cambrian to Cambrian (Proterozoic) - Schist & Gneiss, Sandstone & Slate
Palaeogene - (Tertiary) Igneous Intrusions
Ordovician-Devonian Igneous Intrusions
Volcanic rocks Precambrian to Carboniferous
Belfast
Dublin
N
0 10 20 30 40 50 km
Adapted from The Geology of Ireland, 1:1,000,000, Geological Survey of Ireland, 2003

## Simplified Geological Succession for Northern Ireland

| Era | Geological Period | Age (millions of years ago) | General Distribution in Northern Ireland | Examples of Local and Imported Stone Types |
|---|---|---|---|---|
| Cenozoic | Palaeogene (Tertiary) | 65 | Counties Antrim & Londonderry, Mourne Mountains, County Down | Antrim Basalt, Mourne Granite, Tardee Rhyolite. Cararra Marble (Italy) |
| Mesozoic | Cretaceous | 140 | County Antrim coastline, Limavady, Moira & Moneymore | Ulster White Limestone |
| | Jurassic | 200 | County Antrim | **Limestones:** Portland, Doulting & Bath Stone (England) |
| | Triassic | 250 | Newtownards, Dundonald, Whiteabbey, Dunmurray & Cookstown | **Sandstones:** Cookstown, Dundonald and Scrabo. Corsehill (Scotland) Cove & St Bees (England) |
| Palaeozoic | Permian | 290 | Belfast Lough (Cultra, Holywood) | Drumarg Conglomerate and Cultra Limestone. Locharbriggs Sandstone (Scotland) Larvikite (Norway) |
| | Carboniferous | 360 | Counties Antrim, Armagh, Down, Fermanagh, Londonderry & Tyrone | **Sandstones:** Ballycastle, Barony Glen, Donegal, Dungannon and Fermanagh. Giffnock and Binny (Scotland) Dukes, Dunhouse & Stanton Moor (England) **Limestones:** Armagh, Castle Espie, Fermanagh, Tyrone & Kilkenny. Cornish Granite (England) |
| | Devonian | 420 | Counties Antrim & Tyrone | Newry Granodiorite and Cushendun Conglomerate. Peterhead Granite (Scotland) Shap Granite (England) |
| | Silurian | 440 | Counties Armagh & Down | Greywacke, Leinster Granite (Wicklow) Slate (Wales) |
| | Ordovician | 490 | Counties Londonderry & Tyrone | Aberdeen Granite (Scotland) |
| | Cambrian | 570 | No outcrops in N. Ireland | |
| Proterozoic | Dalradian (Precambrian) | | Counties Londonderry, Tyrone & North-east Antrim | Derry Schist Balmoral Granite (Finland) |

Boa Island figures, Boa Island, County Fermanagh

Patricia Warke and Joanne Curran

# Building Stones of Northern Ireland

## Introduction

Stones used in construction throughout Northern Ireland represent many geological time periods that span more than 500 million years of recent Earth history.

For the most part, these local and imported stones sit unnoticed in our buildings contributing to the character of our urban and rural landscapes and carrying within them a wealth of information about conditions in the geological past.

Although the main stone types used in construction have historically tended to reflect the local geology of an area, many imported stone types have supplemented this range. Space precludes description of all of these and therefore, in the following pages only the most commonly encountered local and imported varieties are described.

In the following pages the different stone types have been grouped according to their mode of formation i.e. sedimentary, igneous and metamorphic. Sedimentary stone types are the largest and most complex group because of their widespread use throughout Northern Ireland and examples of local and imported sandstone, local and imported limestone and conglomerates are provided. The igneous group, which includes local and imported granite and basalt follows this and, although this is a comparatively smaller group it contains some visually spectacular stone types that are prized for their decorative qualities. Finally, the metamorphic group is the smallest group including stone types such as schist, slate and marble.

While slate is used widely for roofing, schist and marble are

Statue of Queen Victoria in Carrara Marble, grounds of City Hall, Belfast

less common. Marble in particular is almost exclusively used for decorative features such as columns and panels and more obviously for commemorative sculptures and monuments.

A general description and brief history of each type of stone is provided along with summary information of its typical colour and textural characteristics with information on other relevant features. Examples of buildings in which the stone can be seen are given and much more detail about the buildings cited is provided in the building inventory in Appendix C.

## Local Sandstone

Sandstone outcrops throughout Northern Ireland with deposits mainly from the Triassic, Carboniferous and Silurian Periods. Triassic sandstones formed between 200 to 250 million years ago when Ireland was much closer to the equator. Under the prevailing desert conditions, flood events deposited sand and silt to produce the sandstones and mudstones seen today. Due to these climatic conditions Permo-Triassic sandstones exhibit a wide range of colours from red and pink to buff and white.

Carboniferous sandstones outcrop in Counties Fermanagh, Tyrone and Londonderry. They were deposited some 290 to 350 million years ago when Ireland was dominated by alluvial plains, coastal deltas and shallow tropical seas. These sandstones vary in terms of colour (buff to grey), texture and sedimentary structures. They are often found interbedded with limestone and the two stone types are often used together in buildings with limestone as rubble stonework and sandstone as quoins, dressings and carved detail.

Greywacke is the oldest example of Northern Irish sandstone deposited some 440 million years ago during the Silurian.

A cornucopia carved as a stone panel in Ballycastle Sandstone, Holy Trinity Church, Ballycastle

**Triassic**
- Sherwood Sandstone
- Cookstown Sandstone
- Dundonald Sandstone
- Scrabo Sandstone

**Carboniferous**
- Ballycastle Sandstone
- Barony Glen Sandstone
- Donegal Sandstone
- Dungannon Sandstone
- Fermanagh Sandstone

**Silurian**
- Greywacke

## Sherwood Sandstone

**Sherwood**
- Cookstown Sandstone
- Dundonald Sandstone
- Scrabo Sandstone

Local Triassic sandstones are included in the Sherwood Sandstone Group and the best known of these include Scrabo Sandstone which outcrops in the Newtownards and Dundonald areas in County Down and Cookstown Sandstone from County Tyrone.

The Sherwood Sandstones were formed between 200 to 250 million years ago under desert-like conditions and have been widely used as building stone throughout Northern Ireland. The distinction between Scrabo Sandstone and Cookstown Sandstone is related to the effects of post-deposition igneous intrusions which occurred in the County Down area some 60 million years ago and which greatly altered Scrabo Sandstone but did not effect Cookstown Sandstone in County Tyrone.

The metamorphism arising from intrusion of magma resulted in alteration of the chemical and physical characteristics of Scrabo Sandstone with the creation of accessory minerals such as talc and a modification of colour giving rise to paler grey varieties of this building stone. The extent of these changes varies with proximity of the sandstone to heating associated with the magma intrusions.

Scrabo Sandstone, used in Newtownards Priory, County Down

## Cookstown Sandstone

Cookstown Sandstone outcrops in County Tyrone and is one of the main members of the Sherwood Sandstone Group. Like Scrabo, Cookstown Sandstone formed during the Triassic under the same desert-like conditions but unlike Scrabo, Cookstown Sandstone has not been subjected to the effects of metamorphic alteration associated with igneous intrusion. As a result, Cookstown Sandstone does not exhibit the same wide range of mineralogical variability as Scrabo Sandstone. Cookstown Sandstone is used as a building stone mainly in the Cookstown area with occasional examples of use elsewhere such as on one part of the Union Theological College, Belfast.

### Colour and texture

Cookstown Sandstone ranges from buff to pink through to orange or red in colour and contains clay lenses and defined bedding structures.

Cookstown Sandstone weathers by scaling, flaking and granular disintegration

St Laurence's Church, Cookstown, County Tyrone

**Colour Range**
- Buff
- Pink to red

**Texture**
- Granular
- Fine to medium-grained

**Features**
- Colour variability
- Calcite cementing
- Occasional clay lenses visible
- Prone to delamination when weathered

**Lookalikes**
- Barony Glen Sandstone
- Scrabo Sandstone

**Quarry Sources**
- Ballymully Quarry, Moneymore (inactive)
- Drapersfield Quarry, Drapersfield (inactive)

**Buildings**
- Former Provincial Bank of Ireland, Belfast
- Loy St. Methodist Church, Cookstown
- Trinity RC Church, Cookstown

# Dundonald Sandstone

Dundonald Sandstone is a Triassic stone and a member of the Sherwood Sandstone Group that formed between 200 to 250 million years ago. Unlike other local Triassic Sandstones, Dundonald Sandstone was deposited under aeolian or wind-blown conditions. It has mainly been used as a dressing stone in buildings throughout County Down.

**Colour Range**
- Red
- Orange

**Texture**
- Granular
- Medium-grained

**Features**
- Bedding
- Cross-bedding
- Delamination of stone faces when weathered

**Lookalikes**
- Locharbriggs Sandstone
- St Bees Sandstone
- Cove Sandstone

**Quarry Sources**
- Quarry Corner, Dundonald

**Buildings**
- St Mark's C of I Church, Belfast
- Gordon House, Belfast
- St Patrick's RC Church, Belfast

## Colour and texture

Dundonald Sandstone is medium-grained and red to orange in colour because individual grains are coated with iron oxide. It contains well-defined bedding structures that tend to be preferentially exploited by weathering agents such as frost and salt.

Dundonald Sandstone used for dressings on a Scrabo Sandstone building

Dundonald Sandstone is prone to weathering-related granular disintegration and scaling

## Scrabo Sandstone

The most widely used Triassic sandstone within Northern Ireland is Scrabo Sandstone, a member of the Sherwood Sandstone Group. This stone outcrops in the Dundonald and Newtownards areas of County Down. Exposed quarry faces are still visible in the South Quarry at Scrabo and features such as dune-bedding, ripple marks and mudcracks with the preserved footprints of Triassic reptiles and scorpions can be seen. Scrabo Sandstone has been quarried since the Anglo-Norman period, being attractive to stonemasons because of its variety of colours and ease of working.

### Colour and texture

The colour of Scrabo Sandstone can range from yellow to orange and deep red to paler grey and pink hues. The stone contains laminations of clay and silt which can be contorted with the former also occurring as lenses or 'clots' throughout the stone.

High clay content makes Scrabo Sandstone prone to delamination especially in polluted urban environments

Scrabo Sandstone on Stormont Castle, Belfast

**Colour Range**
- Pale grey
- Yellow to orange
- Pink to red

**Texture**
- Granular
- Fine to medium-grained

**Features**
- Colour variability
- Bedding
- Laminations
- Clay lenses
- Delamination of stone faces when weathered

**Lookalikes**
- Cookstown Sandstone
- Binny Sandstone

**Quarry Sources**
- Scrabo Tower Quarry, Newtownards (N'Ards), (inactive)
- Ballycullen Quarry, N'Ards (inactive)
- Ballyalton Quarry, N'Ards (recent)

**Buildings**
- Albert Memorial Clock Tower, Belfast
- Sinclair Seamen's Church, Belfast
- Stormont Castle, Belfast

## Ballycastle Sandstone

A small pocket of Carboniferous Sandstone deposited some 290 to 350 million years ago outcrops near Ballycastle in County Antrim and is used in buildings throughout County Antrim and occasionally in Belfast. The most common type of Ballycastle Sandstone used for building is the Ballyvoy Sandstone Formation (Millstone Grit) which is exposed at the cliffs between Ballycastle and Fair Head (County Antrim) where the sandstone units are interbedded with Carboniferous coal seams.

**Colour Range**
- White to grey
- Pink
- Pale yellow

**Texture**
- Granular
- Fine to coarse-grained

**Features**
- Colour variability
- Bedding
- Laminations

**Lookalikes**
- Barony Glen Sandstone

**Quarry Sources**
- North Star Quarry, Ballycastle (inactive)
- White Mine Quarry, Ballycastle (inactive)

**Buildings**
- Bonamargy Friary, Ballycastle
- Holy Trinity Church, Ballycastle
- Mussenden Temple, Downhill

### Colour and texture

Ballycastle Sandstone is bedded and varies in colour from pink and grey to white with a fine to coarse-grained texture. In urban environments this sandstone typically decays through scaling and granular disintegration.

Ballycastle Sandstone at Bonamargy Friary

Ashlar Ballycastle Sandstone at Holy Trinity Church, Ballycastle, County Antrim

## Barony Glen Sandstone

Barony Glen Sandstone (commonly called Dungiven Sandstone in historical literature) is from the Carboniferous Sandstone and Conglomerate Formation of the Roe Valley Group which formed around 350 million years ago. This group crops out on the west side of White Mountain and Mullaghmore and along the south side of Lough Foyle.

### Colour and texture

Barony Glen Sandstone is extremely variable with regard to both colour and texture. Colours include buff, white, yellow and pink and although individual blocks may be uniform in colour and texture others may exhibit a variety of hues and textural features such as bedding and the inclusion of pebbles and beds of coarser material.

Barony Glen Sandstone on the front façade of the Harbour Commissioner's Office, Londonderry

Surface detail of Barony Glen Sandstone at Dungiven Priory

**Colour Range**
- White
- Pale yellow
- Pink to red

**Texture**
- Granular
- Fine to coarse-grained

**Features**
- Bedding
- Laminations
- Colour variability
- Occasional pebbles or pebble beds

**Lookalikes**
- Ballycastle Sandstone

**Quarry Sources**
- Dungiven Quarry, Dungiven (inactive)
- Dunmurry Quarry, Moneyneany (inactive)

**Buildings**
- Allied Irish Bank, Strabane
- St Eugene's RC Church, Moneyneany
- Ulster Bank, Magherafelt

Donegal Sandstone

**Colour Range**
- Orange to brown
- Buff to yellow

**Texture**
- Granular
- Fine to medium-grained

**Features**
- Orange colouration
- Bedding
- Laminations
- Prone to surface delamination when weathered
- Variable colour when weathered

**Lookalikes**
- Occasionally Giffnock Sandstone

**Quarry Sources**
- Mountcharles Quarry, Co. Donegal

**Buildings**
- Ulster Bank, Lurgan
- Star Factory, Londonderry

## Donegal Sandstone

Carboniferous Sandstone also outcrops in County Donegal and includes the Mountcharles Sandstone of the Mullaghmore Sandstone Formation. Although Donegal Sandstone as the name suggests, outcrops in County Donegal, geology does not adhere to political boundaries with this stone comprising part of a Carboniferious Sandstone deposit that extends into Northern Ireland. Donegal Sandstone was used in the construction of buildings in Northern Ireland such as Clonard Church, Falls Road in Belfast and the Star Factory in Londonderry.

### Colour and texture

Donegal Sandstone is a fine to medium-grained stone and has a very distinctive colour being yellow to rusty orange. This colouration reflects the oxidation of iron within the sandstone during weathering.

Donegal Sandstone on the Star Factory, Londonderry

Weathered Donegal Sandstone on the Star Factory

## Dungannon Sandstone

Dungannon Sandstone is a Carboniferous Sandstone from the Millstone Grit series. It crops out around the town of Dungannon, County Tyrone and was used widely as a building stone in this area in the 19th century. Dungannon Sandstone is usually seen on buildings as quarry-faced stonework with ashlar quoins and as carved detail on window surrounds and doorways.

### Colour and texture

Dungannon Sandstone is fine to medium-grained and ranges in colour from cream to white through grey to yellow. In non-polluted environments it is relatively durable, weathering only gradually by granular disintegration. In polluted urban settings it can rapidly soil and undergo significant breakdown through scaling / delamination especially when the hardened outer stone surface is breached.

Detail of weathered Dungannon Sandstone showing effects of scaling and two-tone grey to yellow colour

Dungannon Sandstone used as dressing stone on St Matthew's Church, Scarva

**Colour Range**
- Grey
- Pale yellow

**Texture**
- Granular
- Fine to medium-grained

**Features**
- Two-tone grey to yellow colouration
- Bedding
- Laminations
- Prone to surface delamination when weathered

**Lookalikes**
- Occasionally Ballycastle Sandstone

**Quarry Sources**
- Gortnaglush Quarry, Dungannon (inactive)

**Buildings**
- Allied Irish Bank, Dungannon
- Headline Building, Belfast
- St Anne's Parish Church, Dungannon

Fermanagh Sandstone

# Fermanagh Sandstone

Carboniferous Sandstones from County Fermanagh are all part of the Tyrone Group which include Ballyness, Topped Mountain and Carnmore Sandstones. These sandstones have been widely used in buildings throughout the county.

**Colour Range**
- Buff
- Grey
- Pink to purple

**Texture**
- Granular
- Medium to coarse-grained

**Features**
- Iron spots or streaks
- Occasional pebbles

**Lookalikes**
- Dungannon Sandstone

**Quarry Sources**
- Eshbralley Quarry, Lisnaskea
- Carnmore Quarry, Roslea

**Buildings**
- Belle Isle House, Lisbellaw
- Armagh Manor, Lisnaskea
- Cooneen Parish Church, Cooneen

## Colour and texture

Fermanagh Carboniferous Sandstones exhibit a wide variety of colours and textures from the greyish fawn, medium to coarse-grained pebbly Carnmore Sandstone to the pink to purplish Ballyness Sandstone with its white quartz pebble clasts. Fermanagh Sandstones are all relatively durable although they are prone to iron staining / leakage as a result of weathering.

Fermanagh Sandstone on Cooneen Parish Church, County Fermanagh

Iron staining on surface of Fermanagh Sandstone on Cooneen Parish Church

## Greywacke

Greywacke is described as an immature sandstone because it consists of poorly sorted, angular, sand to gravel-sized particles. Greywacke formed during the Silurian some 440 million years ago and has been used as a building stone in Northern Ireland for many centuries and is also widely used as road stone and aggregate.

### Colour and texture

Greywacke is characterised by its grey colour and hardness. It can often contain veins of quartz and when it has a high iron content it can appear orange to red in colour. Greywacke is extremely durable and weathers little over time although it is prone to the development of fault-line fractures and very occasionally delamination.

Greywacke wall, Down Cathedral, Downpatrick

Down Cathedral, Downpatrick

**Colour Range**
- Grey
- Orange to red

**Texture**
- Granular
- Fine-grained (matrix)

**Features**
- Very hard
- White quartz veins may occur
- Can be iron stained

**Lookalikes**
- Antrim Basalt
- Fermanagh Limestone

**Quarry Sources**
- Carrowdore Quarry, Carrowdore
- Craigantlet Quarry, Newtownards

**Buildings**
- Ballydugan Flour Mill, Downpatrick
- Bangor Abbey, Bangor
- St Patrick's RC Church, Banbridge

| Scottish Triassic |
|---|
| • Corsehill Sandstone<br>• Cove Sandstone |
| **Scottish Permian** |
| • Locharbriggs Sandstone |
| **Scottish Carboniferous** |
| • Binny Sandstone<br>• Giffnock Sandstone (includes Glasgow Blonde) |
| **English Triassic** |
| • St Bees Sandstone |
| **English Carboniferous** |
| • Dukes Sandstone<br>• Dunhouse Sandstone<br>• Stanton Moor Sandstone |

## Imported Sandstone

In the late 19th and early 20th centuries sandstone was imported in large quantities from Scotland and England to supplement local sandstones during a time of major urban expansion and population growth. In the latter half of the 20th century closure of many local sandstone quarries resulted in a greater reliance on imported sandstones.

### Scottish sandstones

Giffnock and Binny Sandstones are two of the main imported Scottish Carboniferous Sandstones. Both sandstones have similar structural, mineralogical and textural properties to our local Carboniferous sandstones but exhibit slightly different weathering behaviour. Other commonly used Scottish sandstones include Corsehill and Locharbriggs which are Triassic and Permian in age respectively.

### English sandstones

Numerous English sandstones have been used historically but some of the most popular varieties are Stanton Moor, Dunhouse and Dukes Sandstones. All are similar in appearance to our local sandstones and are thus widely used in stone replacement and new-builds.

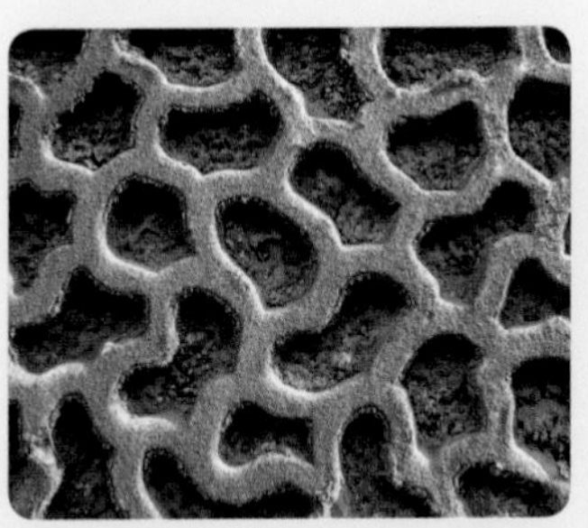

Carved Giffnock Sandstone

## Corsehill Sandstone

Corsehill Sandstone is part of the New Red Scottish Triassic Sandstone group formed some 250 million years ago. It was a popular building stone in the 19th and early 20th centuries and is still used today.

### Colour and texture

Corsehill Sandstone is fine to medium-grained and composed of a mixture of cemented mineral grains including quartz, feldspars, mica and iron-rich minerals such as haematite. All of these mineral grains are coated in reddened, iron-rich clays. This sandstone also contains clearly defined bedding / lamination structures where clay minerals are concentrated. Although Corsehill Sandstone is quite durable and tends to weather gradually by granular disintegration it is prone to delamination if face-bedded.

Corsehill Sandstone on Nelson Memorial Church, Belfast

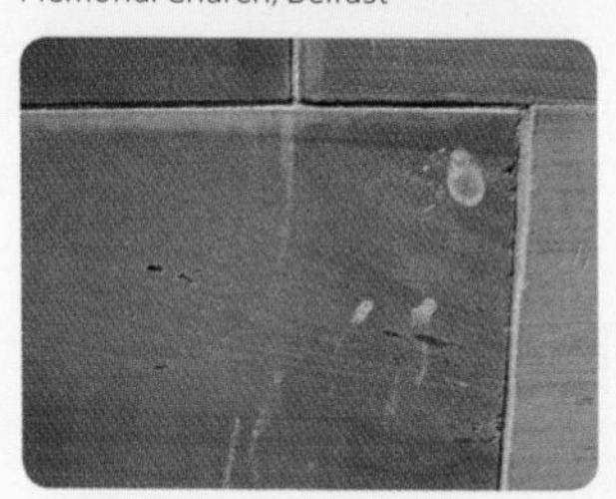

Corsehill Sandstone blockwork

**Colour Range**
- Red to brown

**Texture**
- Granular
- Fine to medium-grained

**Features**
- Bedding
- Laminations
- Prone to surface delamination on weathering

**Lookalikes**
- Locharbriggs Sandstone
- St Bees Sandstone

**Quarry Sources**
- Annan Quarry, Dumfriesshire, Scotland

**Buildings**
- 11-15 Donegall Square North, Belfast
- Northern Bank, Enniskillen
- Ulster Reform Club, Belfast

# Cove Sandstone

Cove Sandstone is a member of the New Red Sandstone group formed during the Triassic some 250 million years ago. It is a Scottish sandstone and has been quarried and used widely as a building stone since the late 1800s.

**Colour Range**
- Red to brown

**Texture**
- Granular
- Fine-grained

**Features**
- Laminations
- Bedding

**Lookalikes**
- Occasionally Dundonald Sandstone
- Locharbriggs Sandstone
- St Bees Sandstone
- Corsehill Sandstone

**Quarry Sources**
- Cove Quarry, near Lockerbie, Dumfries

**Buildings**
- St Matthew's RC Church, Belfast (decorative stonework)

## Colour and texture

Cove Sandstone is fine-grained and red to brown in colour with bedding-related variations in colour. Cove is a relatively durable sandstone although it is susceptible to the effects of salt and frost weathering through granular disintegration.

Surface detail of Cove Sandstone

Cove Sandstone window detail

## Locharbriggs Sandstone

Locharbriggs (or Dumfries) Sandstone was formed during the early Permian some 250 to 290 million years ago when Scotland was close to the equator and desert-like conditions prevailed. It was a popular building stone in the 19th and early 20th centuries and is still commonly used today.

### Colour and texture

Locharbriggs Sandstone is fine to medium-grained and composed of well-sorted, sub-to well-rounded quartz grains coated in iron oxide and cemented by silica. The iron oxide gives Locharbriggs its distinctive red colour. It also contains clearly-defined bedding / lamination structures where clay minerals are concentrated. Locharbriggs Sandstone is durable and tends to weather gradually by granular disintegration. However, if it is face-bedded it is prone to delamination.

Locharbriggs Sandstone on Belfast Central Library, Belfast

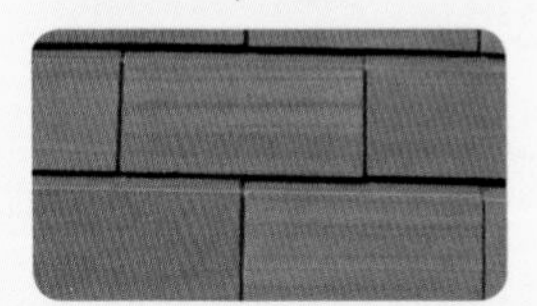

Locharbriggs Sandstone blockwork

**Colour Range**

- Red to brown

**Texture**

- Granular
- Fine to medium-grained

**Features**

- Bedding
- Laminations
- Prone to surface delamination on weathering

**Lookalikes**

- Corsehill Sandstone
- Occasionally Dundonald Sandstone
- St Bees Sandstone
- Cove Sandstone

**Quarry Sources**

- Locharbriggs Quarry, Dumfries

**Buildings**

- Scottish Mutual Building, Belfast
- Belfast Central Library, Belfast
- Bank Buildings, Castle Place, Belfast

# Binny Sandstone

Binny Sandstone is one of only a few sandstones imported from the Edinburgh area. It is a Carboniferous Sandstone (part of the West Lothian Oil Shale Formation) with a very distinctive mineralogy because it contains bitumen and iron carbonate minerals.

## Colour and texture

Binny Sandstone is fine to medium-grained and in its fresh state is grey or buff in appearance. However, because of its mineralogy, darker rusty brown / black streaks may commonly be seen. Binny Sandstone tends to soil rapidly in urban environments because of the presence of bitumen and even after cleaning its colour will change from grey to orange or light brown. Consequently, when matching for replacement stone this surface colour change should be taken into account.

**Colour Range**
- Buff
- Grey
- Orange to brown

**Texture**
- Granular
- Fine to medium-grained

**Features**
- Bedding
- Laminations
- Occasional black patches
- Delamination of thin surface layer when weathered

**Lookalikes**
- Scrabo Sandstone

**Quarry Sources**
- Binny Quarry, near Edinburgh (inactive)
- Humbie Quarry, West Lothian (inactive)
- Straiton Quarry near Edinburgh (inactive)

**Buildings**
- Brownlow House, Lurgan
- Christ Church, Belfast
- Greg Mausoleum, Knockbreda Churchyard

Binny Sandstone on Brownlow House, Lurgan, County Armagh

Binny Sandstone with grey coloured fresh stone exposed by loss of weathered brown surface layers

## Giffnock Sandstone

Giffnock Sandstone (includes Glasgow Blonde Sandstone) is a Carboniferous Sandstone from the Glasgow area. During the Carboniferous Scotland was located close to the equator and experienced tropical conditions. In the Midland Valley Region sands, silts and muds were deposited under deltaic conditions and it is from these that Giffnock Sandstone eventually formed. Giffnock is described as a 'freestone' because of its textural uniformity and as such is often seen as dressings and carved detail on buildings.

### Colour and texture

Giffnock Sandstone is fine to medium-grained and when fresh is buff coloured with specks of darker mineral grains visible. Exposure results in oxidation of iron minerals in the stone surface forming a hardened rust to brown outer layer. If this layer is breached, decay of the underlying sandstone may proceed quite rapidly.

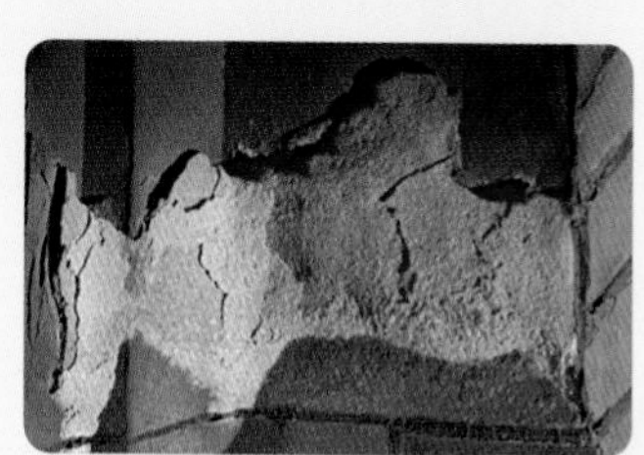

Breaching of the hardened iron-rich surface layer of Giffnock Sandstone

Giffnock Sandstone on the Ewart's Building, Belfast

**Colour Range**

- Buff to light brown
- Orange brown
- Buff (Glasgow Blonde)

**Texture**

- Granular
- Fine to medium-grained

**Features**

- Bedding
- Laminations
- Prone to formation of hardened iron-rich surface layer

**Lookalikes**

- Occasionally, Donegal Sandstone

**Quarry Sources**

- Giffnock Quarry, near Glasgow (inactive)
- Braidbar Quarry, near Glasgow (inactive)
- Cowcaddens Quarry – Glasgow Blonde, near Glasgow (inactive)

**Buildings**

- Bangor Castle Town Hall, Bangor
- Custom House, Belfast
- Former Court House, Coleraine

# St Bees Sandstone

St Bees Sandstone has been quarried in Cumbria since medieval times and is from the New Red Group of Sandstones that formed during the Triassic some 250 million years ago. It is still actively quarried and is used throughout the United Kingdom for stone replacement and in new-builds.

**Colour Range**
- Red to brown

**Texture**
- Granular
- Fine-grained

**Features**
- Laminations and bedding

**Lookalikes**
- Dundonald Sandstone
- Locharbriggs Sandstone

**Quarry Sources**
- Birkhams Quarry, St Bees, Cumbria

**Buildings**
- St Patrick's RC Church, Newtownards

## Colour and texture

St Bees Sandstone has a uniform texture and is fine-grained and a dull red in colour. It is a durable sandstone but can be susceptible to the weathering effects of salt and frost.

St Bees Sandstone used as a replacement dressing stone

St Bees Sandstone window detail

# Dukes Sandstone

Dukes Sandstone is an English Carboniferous Sandstone of the Millstone Grit Series which was widely used as a building stone in England since the 19th century and probably before this time. Dukes Sandstone is still actively quarried and has been used for repair or replacement work and in new-builds across Northern Ireland.

## Colour and texture

Dukes Sandstone is a medium-grained sandstone with clearly defined bedding and lamination features. It is buff to pink in colour and is a durable sandstone that typically weathers gradually through granular disintegration.

Dukes Sandstone was used as a replacement stone in restoration of the Albert Memorial Clock Tower, Belfast

Detail of Dukes Sandstone showing dark brown coloured laminations

**Colour Range**
- Buff to pink

**Texture**
- Granular
- Medium-grained

**Features**
- Bedding
- Laminations
- Dark brown markings

**Lookalikes**
- Scrabo Sandstone
- Stanton Moor Sandstone (Pink)

**Quarry Sources**
- Dukes Quarry, Whatstandwell Derbyshire

**Buildings**
- St Matthew's RC Church, Belfast
- Albert Memorial Clock Tower, Belfast

## Dunhouse Sandstone

Dunhouse Sandstone is from England, a member of the Millstone Grit Sandstone Group and is of Carboniferous age having formed some 290 to 350 million years ago. It is still actively quarried near Darlington in County Durham where it has been extracted since the early 1900s. It is a popular stone widely used throughout the United Kingdom for stone replacement and in new-builds.

### Colour and texture

Dunhouse Sandstone has a uniform texture and is a fine-grained, slightly micaeceous, non-calcareous sandstone. It can be grey or buff in colour and is a relatively durable stone type.

**Colour Range**
- Grey
- Buff

**Texture**
- Granular
- Fine-grained

**Features**
- Occasional fine-grained iron spots that weather to rust / brown

**Lookalikes**
- Scrabo Sandstone
- Stanton Moor Sandstone
- Giffnock Sandstone

**Quarry Sources**
- Darlington Quarry, Co. Durham

**Buildings**
- Custom House, Belfast (replacement blocks)

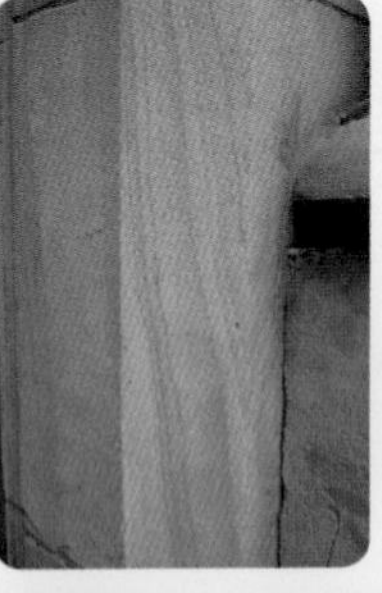

Weathering related iron release can occasionally result in brown staining

Dunhouse Sandstone used as dressing stone

## Stanton Moor Sandstone

Stanton Moor Sandstone is an English Carboniferous Sandstone of the Millstone Grit Series which was widely used as a building stone in England and is still actively quarried. It is a popular sandstone and has been used for repair /replacement work (for example, Albert Memorial Clock Tower, Belfast) and in new-builds (for example, Victoria Square development, Belfast) throughout Northern Ireland.

### Colour and texture

Stanton Moor Sandstone is a fine to medium-grained stone with clearly defined bedding and lamination structures. It is buff to pink or grey in colour and is a relatively durable sandstone that typically weathers gradually through granular disintegration although delamination can occur.

Stanton Moor Sandstone used in replacement stringcourse

Stanton Moor Sandstone used in restoration of part of the Union Theological College, Belfast

**Colour Range**
- Buff
- Pink
- Grey

**Texture**
- Granular
- Fine to medium-grained

**Features**
- Bedding
- Laminations
- Colour variability
- Prone to surface delamination when weathered

**Lookalikes**
- Dunhouse Sandstone
- Dukes Sandstone

**Quarry Sources**
- Dale View Quarry, Derbyshire

**Buildings**
- Union Theological College, Belfast
- Albert Memorial Clock Tower, Belfast

Local Limestone

| Cretaceous |
| --- |
| • Ulster White Limestone (Antrim Chalk) |
| **Permian** |
| • Cultra Limestone |
| **Carboniferous** |
| • Armagh Limestone |
| • Castle Espie Limestone |
| • Fermanagh Limestone |
| • Tyrone Limestone |

## Local Limestone

Limestones are sedimentary rocks that are composed of calcium carbonate often containing the detrital remains of shells or skeletons of marine organisms. Because of its calcium carbonate composition, limestone weathers most commonly through chemical dissolution resulting from contact with rainfall that is naturally acidic.

The best known example of Cretaceous Limestone which formed some 65 to 140 million years ago is Antrim Chalk or Ulster White Limestone (County Antrim). This stone is white in colour, very brittle, and contains numerous bands of flint nodules.

Dolomitic Limestone which outcrops at Cultra was deposited during the Permian some 270 million years ago. This limestone was used only locally as dressing stone and is no longer quarried.

The Carboniferous limestones of Northern Ireland formed in shallow warm tropical seas some 290 to 350 million years ago. They outcrop in Counties Fermanagh, Tyrone and Armagh with outliers in County Down. These limestones are typically grey, white or yellow in colour although pink-red examples of Armagh Limestone also occur.

Carved Armagh Limestone head at the main entrance to St Patrick's RC Cathedral in Armagh

## Ulster White Limestone (Antrim Chalk)

Ulster White Limestone is also known as Antrim Chalk and formed during the Cretaceous some 140 million years ago. Ulster White Limestone is very brittle, fractures easily in situ and contains numerous bands of flint nodules. It is generally unsuitable for building but is occasionally seen as quarry-faced stone blocks on buildings along the County Antrim coast and in Moneymore (County Londonderry). Almost all of the original quarries are now inactive.

### Colour and texture

Ulster White Limestone is white or cream in colour, fine-grained and very hard. It may also contain fine suture-like features called stylolites.

Ulster White Limestone used in the Boat House, Rathlin Island, County Antrim

Ulster White Limestone and Antrim Basalt stonework

**Colour Range**
- White
- Cream

**Texture**
- Very fine-grained
- Dense

**Features**
- Flint nodules
- Hard and brittle with extensive fracturing
- Stylolites

**Lookalikes**
- None

**Quarry Sources**
- Carnlough Quarry, Carnough (inactive)
- Belshaw's Quarry, Lisburn (inactive)
- Carmean Limeworks, Moneymore

**Buildings**
- Roark's Kitchen, Ballintoy Harbour
- St Thomas' Church, Rathlin Island
- Boat House, The Station, Rathlin Island

## Cultra Limestone

Cultra Limestone is a less commonly used dolomitic limestone formed in the Permian some 270 million years ago. Historically it was quarried along the shoreline at Cultra, County Down and was used in County Down as dressing stone on Holywood Priory and across Belfast Lough at Carrickfergus Castle, County Antrim.

### Colour and texture

Cultra Limestone is pale yellow to orange in colour and may contain fossils. It is not a durable stone weathering primarily through scaling and flaking which can be so extreme as to lead to the development of significant hollows in the stone.

**Colour Range**
- Pale yellow to orange

**Texture**
- Medium to coarse-grained

**Features**
- Occasional fossils
- Easily weathered through scaling and flaking

**Lookalikes**
- None

**Quarry Sources**
- No known quarry sites

**Buildings**
- Holywood Friary, Holywood
- Carrickfergus Castle, Carrickfergus

Cultra Limestone used as a dressing stone around the entrance gateway to Carrickfergus Castle, County Antrim

Breakdown of Cultra Limestone through scaling and flaking with associated loss of architectural detail

## Armagh Limestone

Armagh Limestone is probably the most well recognised of Northern Ireland's limestones, and the second most commonly used. The majority of its usage is within County Armagh, with a small number of buildings in County Down and Belfast.

### Colour and texture

Armagh Limestone is Carboniferous in age and can be sub-divided into two groups, 'Grey' Limestone which is a fossiliferous homogeneous limestone varying in colour from pale grey to pink or purple and the red-stained limestone known as Armagh Red Marble which takes a good polish and was widely used for interior decorative work. Armagh Limestone is relatively durable showing little decay over time with only mild weathering along stylolites, where fossils are present, and occasionally mortar damage where 'hard' cement pointing has been used.

Armagh Limestone on St Patrick's Cathedral, Armagh

Ashlar Armagh Limestone with a corduroy/ tooled stone finish

**Colour Range**
- Pale grey
- Pink to purple

**Texture**
- Medium to coarse-grained

**Features**
- Presence of fossils
- Stylolites
- Colour variability

**Lookalikes**
- Castle Espie Limestone

**Quarry Sources**
- Ballybrannon Quarry, Armagh (inactive)
- Armagh City Quarry, Armagh
- Carganamuck Quarry, Armagh
- Tynan Quarry, Armagh
- Rock Road Quarry, Armagh (inactive)

**Buildings**
- Armagh Technical Institution, Armagh
- First Presbyterian Church, Armagh
- Courthouse, Armagh

## Castle Espie Limestone

Castle Espie Carboniferous Limestone was quarried outside Comber, County Down and was mainly used for lime production. It is occasionally seen as dressing stone on older buildings and monuments and as headstones in local graveyards. This stone type is only seen in County Down and the only quarry closed in the late 1800s and is now flooded and forms part of Castle Espie Wildfowl and Wetlands Trust Centre.

**Colour Range**
- Red to pink

**Texture**
- Fine to medium-grained

**Features**
- Visible fossils

**Lookalikes**
- Armagh Limestone

**Quarry Sources**
- Castle Espie Quarry, Comber (inactive and flooded)

**Buildings**
- Tullynagill Church ruins, Loughinisland

### Colour and texture

Castle Espie Limestone is distinctively pink to red in colour, often with visible fossils. It is reasonably durable over time, but occasional blocks can exhibit heavy flaking and surface loss.

Carved detail in Castle Espie Limestone on the Gillespie Monument, Comber

Tullynagill Church ruins

## Fermanagh Limestone

There are several different limestone formations in County Fermanagh including Darty, Knockmore and Ballyshannon Limestones. All of these were formed in the Carboniferous some 290 to 360 million years ago. There are many active and inactive quarries across County Fermanagh and this limestone was widely used throughout the county in a range of buildings.

### Colour and texture

Fermanagh Limestone is grey in colour, fine-grained and often fossiliferous. It is a relatively durable stone type but is occasionally prone to surface loss through heavy flaking and scaling.

Fermanagh Limestone used in the Belleek Porcelain Factory, Belleek

Severe scaling and surface loss of a block of Fermanagh Limestone

**Colour Range**

- Pale to dark grey

**Texture**

- Fine-grained

**Features**

- Presence of fossils
- Occasional examples of scaling and flaking

**Lookalikes**

- Armagh Limestone
- Tyrone Limestone
- Greywacke

**Quarry Sources**

- Crieve Hill Quarry, Fivemiletown
- Slushill Quarry, Lisnaskea
- Rockfield Quarry, Lisnaskea
- Knockninney Quarry, Derrylinn
- Carn Quarry, Ederny
- Belcoo Quarry, Belcoo

**Buildings**

- Belleek Porcelain Factory, Belleek
- Enniskillen Castle, Enniskillen
- Town Hall, Enniskillen

**Colour Range**
- Pale to dark grey

**Texture**
- Fine-grained

**Features**
- Presence of fossils
- Occasional examples of scaling and flaking

**Lookalikes**
- Armagh Limestone
- Tyrone Limestone
- Greywacke

**Quarry Sources**
- Drumquin / Dunaree Quarry, Drumquin

**Buildings**
- Ballymagrane Presbyterian Church, Crilly
- Castle Caulfield, Castlecaulfield
- Dyan Corn Mill, Caledon

## Tyrone Limestone

There are several different limestone formations in County Tyrone including Darty, Knockmore and Ballyshannon Limestones. All of these were formed in the Carboniferous some 290 to 360 million years ago. There are many active and inactive quarries across County Tyrone and this limestone was widely used throughout the county in a range of buildings.

### Colour and texture

Tyrone Limestone is grey in colour, fine-grained and often contains fossils. It is a relatively durable stone type but as with Fermanagh Limestone it is occasionally prone to surface loss through heavy flaking and scaling and as with all limestones is susceptible to the effects of chemical dissolution through interaction with acidic rainfall.

Tyrone Limestone used as the primary stone type in Dyan Corn Mill

Surface breakdown and flaking of Tyrone Limestone

## Imported Limestone

Many varieties of limestone have been imported over the years for building in Northern Ireland. The most widely used are Jurassic limestones that formed between 140 to 200 million years ago in warm tropical seas.

Portland limestone is the most extensively used imported limestone in Northern Ireland. It was used predominantly in Belfast on some of the city's most prestigious buildings and is one of the only limestones that is used in all of the six counties, largely due to its extensive usage by the Commonwealth War Graves Commission for war memorials.

Other commonly used imported Jurassic limestones include Doulting Limestone and Bath Stone. Another less widely used imported stone is the Carboniferous Kilkenny Limestone. Due to their light colours and mineralogical characteristics, all of these limestones are prone to surface soiling in polluted urban settings and also to weathering through chemical dissolution by acid rain which gradually dissolves calcium carbonate which is their primary constituent mineral.

Carved head in Limestone

**Jurassic**

- Bath Stone
- Doulting Limestone
- Portland Limestone

**Carboniferous**

- Kilkenny Limestone

## Bath Stone

Bath Stone is an oolitic Jurassic limestone formed some 140 to 200 million years ago. Bath Stone is described as a freestone which means that it can be worked in any direction unlike other stone types which have distinct bedding layers. Bath Stone has been widely used as a building material throughout southern England.

**Colour Range**
- Creamy brown
- Yellow

**Texture**
- Medium-grained

**Features**
- Contains fossils
- Lacks defined bedding

**Lookalikes**
- Occasionally Portland Limestone

**Quarry Sources**
- Stoke Hill Mine, near Bath

**Buildings**
- Castle Ward, Strangford
- The Temple, Temple Water, Castle Ward

### Colour and texture

Bath Stone is described as being a warm cream or honey colour and contains fossils. It is medium-grained, weathers relatively well over time and is prone to the effects of mild dissolution because of its calcareous chemistry.

Bath Stone front of Castle Ward, County Down

Bath Stone capital, Castle Ward, County Down

## Doulting Limestone

Doulting Limestone has been quarried since Roman times in the area around Shepton Mallet in Somerset. It is of middle Jurassic age around 160 to 170 million years old and is composed of fragments of older limestones that have been eroded and redeposited. Doulting stone quarried historically may be oolitic unlike the stone currently extracted which is rarely so.

### Colour and texture

As Doulting Limestone is made up of older fragments of limestone, it has a coarse granular texture and ranges in colour from creamy brown or yellow to grey. It is not a highly durable stone type and like all limestones is particularly susceptible to the effects of chemical dissolution and other physical weathering processes that result in a loss of architectural detail.

Weathered Doulting Limestone mullions, Holy Cross RC Church, Belfast

Doulting Limestone capitals showing loss of architectural detail

**Colour Range**
- Creamy brown
- Yellow
- Grey

**Texture**
- Granular
- Coarse-grained
- Regular and uniform texture

**Features**
- May be oolitic

**Lookalikes**
- None

**Quarry Sources**
- Doulting Stone Quarry, Somerset

**Buildings**
- Holy Cross RC Church, Belfast
- St Anne's Cathedral, Belfast

## Portland Limestone

Portland Limestone is a white oolitic mid-upper Jurassic limestone from the south coast of England, quarried in Portland, South Dorset. It is composed of ooliths (calcium carbonate spheres) and shell fragments. It was widely used in Belfast with some of the most prestigious examples including Belfast City Hall and Parliament House at Stormont.

**Colour Range**
- White to light grey
- Cream

**Texture**
- Granular
- Fine to medium-grained

**Features**
- Cemented rounded spheres (ooids)
- Visible fossil shell fragments

**Lookalikes**
- Occasionally Bath Stone

**Quarry Sources**
- Portland, South Dorset

**Buildings**
- City Hall, Belfast
- Castle Coole, Enniskillen
- Parliament House (Stormont), Belfast

### Colour and texture

Portland Limestone is fine to medium-grained, white to light grey or cream in colour and contains silica-rich fossil shell fragments which are often left protruding from the stone surface as a result of the dissolution of the surrounding calcium carbonate ooliths. Its pale colour also leaves it prone to rapid soiling, particularly in polluted urban environments.

Dissolution and removal of ooliths leave less soluble fossil shell fragments proud of the weathered stone surface

Portland Limestone on City Hall, Belfast

## Kilkenny Limestone

Kilkenny Limestone formed during the Carboniferous some 290 to 360 million years ago and outcrops in the south of Ireland. It is used widely throughout County Kilkenny and elsewhere in Ireland as a building stone for both plain ashlar and decorative stonework. Its use in Northern Ireland is restricted almost entirely to buildings in Belfast and County Down.

### Colour and texture

Kilkenny Limestone is bluish-grey in colour and often contains visible fossils and stylolites. It is a relatively durable stone but can occasionally exhibit differential weathering along stylolites which form lines of weakness in the stone.

Kilkenny Limestone used for dressings on the Chapel of the Good Shepherd Complex, Belfast

Preferential weathering of stylolites in Kilkenny Limestone columns

**Colour Range**
- Bluish-grey

**Texture**
- Granular
- Coarse-grained

**Features**
- Presence of fossils
- Stylolites
- Prone to preferential weathering along planes of weakness (stylolites)

**Lookalikes**
- Armagh Limestone
- Tyrone Limestone

**Quarry Sources**
- Kellymount Quarries, Co. Kilkenny

**Buildings**
- Good Shepherd Complex, Belfast
- St Peter's RC Church, Lurgan

# Conglomerate

Conglomerate is a form of coarse-grained sedimentary rock that is formed from sediment eroded, transported and deposited by rivers. It is typically composed of rounded and sub-rounded pebbles and cobbles (clasts) of various sizes and often various colours set within a matrix of much finer sediment cemented together. When the clasts are more angular in appearance this is described as a breccia.

As clasts can be derived from many different rock types the colour and appearance of conglomerates and breccias can be extremely variable but generally they reflect the local geology of an area.

The variable textural and colour characteristics of cut and polished conglomerate make it a widely used decorative stone although care has to be taken with regard to cleaning especially when there are significant mineralogical differences between individual clasts and between the clasts and the finer matrix material.

**Conglomerates**

- Cushendun Conglomerate (Cross Slieve)
- Drumarg Conglomerate

Angular limestone clasts in a clay matrix

## Cushendun Conglomerate

In County Antrim, Cushendun Conglomerate is part of the Cross Slieve Group and is interbedded with sandstones and mudstones that have been used for building in the local area. These sedimentary rocks were deposited in the early Devonian Period some 390 to 420 million years ago under desert-like conditions where debris was transported during flash floods and deposited on alluvial fans that spread out from upland areas into lowland plains.

### Colour and texture

Cushendun Conglomerate is coarse-grained with visible clasts of pebble and cobble-sized material that mainly consist of grey-coloured quartzite but which can also include fragments of schist or welded tuff. The clasts may be angular to sub-angular in shape forming more of a brecciated deposit.

Detail of Cushendun Conglomerate showing rounded quartzite clast

Cushendun Parish Church, Cushendun

**Colour Range**

- Red to pink
- Grey

**Texture**

- Coarse-grained

**Features**

- Contains pebble and cobble sized clasts of quartzite, schist or tuff

**Lookalikes**

- None

**Quarry Sources**

- Cushendall West Quarry, Cushendall

**Buildings**

- Cushendun Parish Church, Cushendun
- Cushendall Presbyterian Church, Layde, Cushendall

## Drumarg Conglomerate

The Drumarg Conglomerate Formation is thought to have formed during the Permian some 250 to 290 million years ago.
Due to the rarity of Permian outcrops in Northern Ireland Rock Road Quarry is both an important geological site and is also of significant cultural value because of its strong architectural links with the City of Armagh where Drumarg Conglomerate was widely used in many prestigious buildings.

### Colour and texture

Drumarg Conglomerate consists of sub-angular and sub-rounded fragments (clasts) of Carboniferous Limestone, around 20mm in diameter, suspended within a red-brown medium-grained sandstone matrix. Many of the grey coloured limestone clasts have been stained pink around the edges through contact with the sandstone.

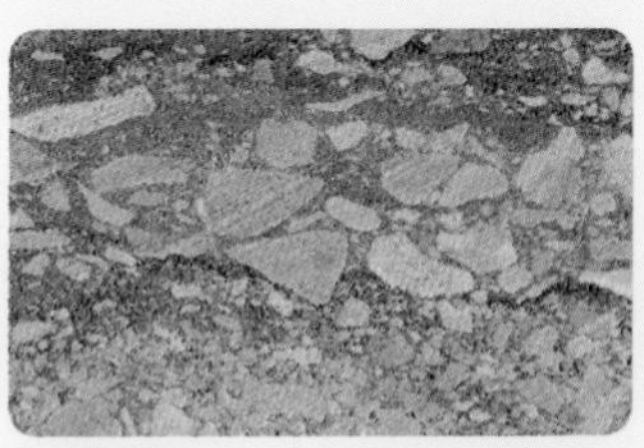

Detail of Drumarg Conglomerate showing limestone clasts within the red sandstone matrix

Drumarg Conglomerate used for the tower and plinth of St Patrick's Cathedral, Armagh

**Colour Range**

- Red to pink
- Red to brown

**Texture**

- Medium to coarse-grained

**Features**

- Contains pebble and cobble sized clasts of limestone which may show fossils

**Lookalikes**

- None

**Quarry Sources**

- Red Barn Quarry, Armagh (now built over)
- Rock Road Quarry, Armagh (inactive)

**Buildings**

- Armagh Gaol, Armagh
- Armagh Observatory, Armagh
- St John's C of I Church, Lisnadill

## Granite

Granite is an intrusive igneous rock. It is described as being 'massive' because of its lack of internal structures such as bedding. Granite is typically a dense, durable stone type that has been widely used as a building material within Northern Ireland. As it is an intrusive igneous rock, it cools slowly beneath the Earth's surface allowing large mineral grains to develop giving it a medium to coarse-grained texture. The main minerals that occur in granite are quartz, feldspar and mica, but the relative proportions of these can vary greatly.

### Local granite

Most local granites were intruded during the early Tertiary (Palaeogene) some 55 to 65 million years ago. The two most widely used in construction are Mourne Granite and Newry Granodiorite both of which outcrop in County Down.

### Imported granite

Many granites from outside Northern Ireland were imported because of their distinctive colour and have been widely used for decorative detail on buildings and memorials.

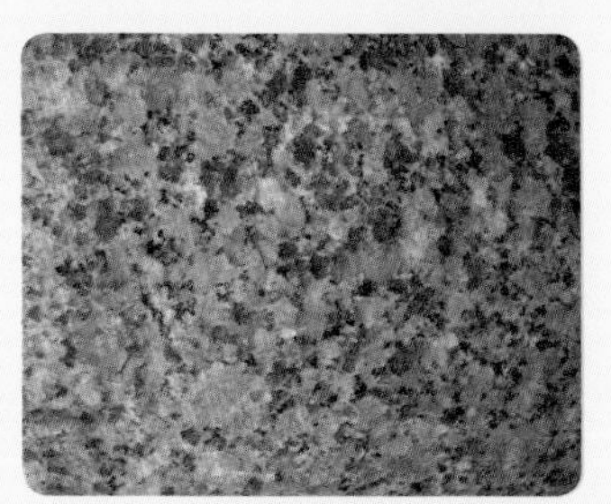

Interlocking feldspar, quartz and biotite crystals in Peterhead Granite

**Local Granite**

- Mourne Granite
- Newry Granodiorite
- Tardee Rhyolite

**Imported Granite**

- Aberdeen Granite
- Balmoral Granite
- Cornish Granite
- Larvikite
- Leinster Granite
- Peterhead Granite
- Shap Granite

# Mourne Granite

Mourne Granite has been extensively used in buildings throughout County Down and as kerb stones in Belfast. The granite outcrops over an area of about 150 $km^2$ in the south of County Down with several sub-types of the stone showing slight differences in colour and grain size reflecting variations in relative proportions of the primary constituent minerals of feldspar, quartz and mica.

## Colour and texture

Mourne Granite is a grey to pink coloured stone. It is coarse-grained and durable generally weathering only slowly by granular disintegration with a tendency to slight rust brown discolouration due to weathering release and alteration of iron from biotite mica mineral grains.

**Colour Range**

- Grey to pink

**Texture**

- Coarse-grained
- Crystalline

**Features**

- Tightly interlocking crystals
- Occasional cavities lined with quartz crystals

**Lookalikes**

- Leinster Granite

**Quarry Sources**

- Bloody Bridge Quarry, near Newcastle (inactive)
- Thomas' Mountain Quarry, near Newcastle
- Hare's Gap Quarry, near Newcastle (inactive)

**Buildings**

- Kilhorne C of I Church, Annalong
- St Patrick's Memorial Church, Saul
- St Colman's RC Church, Kilkeel

Mourne Granite in Saul Church, Downpatrick, County Down

Detail of Mourne Granite blockwork

## Newry Granodiorite

Newry Granodiorite is a granite-type stone of Devonian age formed some 360 to 420 million years ago. This stone has been widely used on buildings in the Newry area and elsewhere throughout Northern Ireland. The key feature of this stone is the inclusion of xenoliths which are fragments of pre-existing rock visible within the rock mass.

### Colour and texture

Newry Granodiorite is coarse-grained and dark grey in colour. Occasional xenoliths can be seen as grey / black patches in an otherwise texturally uniform stone type. Newry Granodiorite is an extremely durable stone type showing only minimal weathering-related alteration or deterioration.

Xenolith in Newry Granodiorite stonework

Newry Granodiorite with Mourne Granite dressings on Castlewellan Castle, County Down

**Colour Range**
- Dark grey

**Texture**
- Coarse-grained
- Crystalline

**Features**
- Xenoliths

**Lookalikes**
- Aberdeen Granite

**Quarry Sources**
- Ballymagreehan Quarry, near Castlewellan
- Croreagh Quarry, near Newry

**Buildings**
- St Brigid's RC Church, Glassdrumman, Newry
- Ulster Bank, Castlewellan
- Drumgooland Parish Church, Ballyward

## Tardree Rhyolite

Tardree Rhyolite is not strictly a granite but is included in this group because it has a similar chemical composition to granite, although it has different textural characteristics and formed in a different way. Tardree Rhyolite formed during the early Tertiary some 60 million years ago but, unlike granite, its formation was associated with extrusive igneous activity during a lull in the formation of the Antrim Basalts. Tardree Rhyolite has been used for building stone and dressing detail.

**Colour Range**
- Light grey to grey

**Texture**
- Fine to coarse-grained
- Crystalline

**Features**
- Large quartz and feldspar crystals set in a fine-grained matrix

**Lookalikes**
- None

**Quarry Sources**
- Tardree Mountain Quarry, Kells
- Sandy Braes Quarry, Kells

**Buildings**
- Stephenson Mausoleum, Kilbride Churchyard, Doagh
- Clotworthy House, Castle Grounds, Antrim

### Colour and texture

Tardree Rhyolite is light grey or grey in colour with a very fine to coarse-grained texture reflecting the presence of large crystals of quartz and feldspar set in a very fine consolidated ash-like matrix.

Detail of Tardree Rhyolite dressing

Tardree Rhyolite used as dressing stone on Clotworthy House, County Antrim

## Aberdeen Granite

Aberdeen Granite formed during the Ordovician Period some 440 to 490 million years ago. It comes from the Aberdeen area in Scotland where is was extensively quarried in the 18th and 19th centuries. It has been widely used in the local area for construction with Aberdeen being known as the 'Granite City' and also further afield in the Houses of Parliament, Westminster and Waterloo Bridge, in London.

### Colour and texture

Aberdeen Granite is a durable, medium to coarse-grained stone that is pale grey or silver grey in colour.

War Memorial, Queen's University Belfast

Surface detail of Aberdeen Granite

**Colour Range**
- Pale grey
- Silver grey

**Texture**
- Medium to coarse-grained
- Crystalline

**Features**
- None

**Lookalikes**
- Newry Granodiorite

**Quarry Sources**
- Rubislaw Quarry, Aberdeen, (inactive)
- Kemnay Quarry, Aberdeenshire,

**Buildings**
- Lurgan War Memorial, Lurgan
- War Memorial, Queen's University, Belfast

Balmoral Granite

# Balmoral Granite

Balmoral Granite or Finlandia Red is an ancient rock type that formed during the Pre-Cambrian more than 540 million years ago. It comes from southwest Finland and has been imported because of its distinctive colour and is used for decorative stonework on buildings and for memorial structures.

**Colour Range**
- Pink
- Red

**Texture**
- Fine to coarse-grained
- Crystalline

**Features**
- Xenoliths

**Lookalikes**
- Peterhead Granite

**Quarry Sources**
- Vehmaa and Taivassalo Quarries, Southwest Finland

**Buildings**
- Anderson and McAuley Building, Royal Avenue, Belfast

## Colour and texture

Balmoral Red occurs in both fine and coarse-grained varieties. It is a hard, durable stone with a strong red to pink colour and may contain occasional xenoliths. The distinctive colour of this granite is primarily due to the well-developed feldspar crystals.

Balmoral Granite used on the street level façade of the Anderson and McAuley Building, Belfast

Detail of Balmoral Granite

## Cornish Granite

Cornish Granite is Carboniferous to early Permian in age and formed around 290 million years ago. It is still quarried in several locations in Cornwall with the best known being De Lank Quarry, Bodmin Moor. Cornish Granite has been widely used as a building stone since Neolithic times with more modern examples of usage including the British Museum, Tower Bridge and the Diana Memorial Fountain in Hyde Park, London.

### Colour and texture

Cornish Granite is very durable with a variable colour ranging from silver to grey and orange to brown depending on the source location. Generally it is coarse-grained and contains biotite and megacrysts of orthoclase feldspar.

Cornish Granite Titanic Memorial, City Hall grounds, Belfast

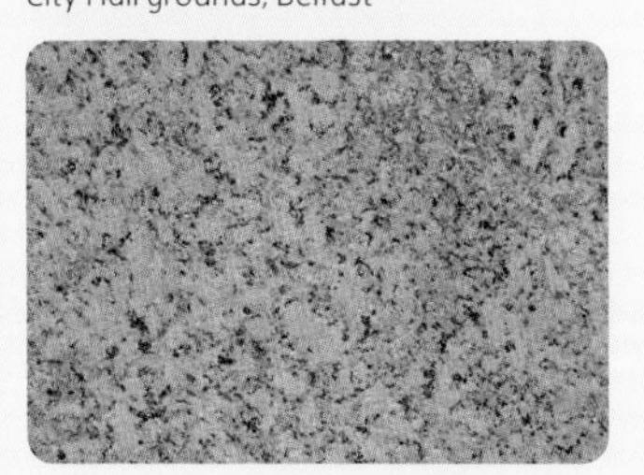

Surface detail of Cornish Granite

**Colour Range**
- Silver to grey
- Red to brown
- Orange

**Texture**
- Coarse-grained
- Crystalline

**Features**
- White tabular megacrysts of feldspar

**Lookalikes**
- Leinster Granite

**Quarry Sources**
- De Lank Quarry, Bodmin Moor, Cornwall

**Buildings**
- Titanic Memorial, City Hall grounds, Belfast (plinth)
- Boer War Memorial, Omagh

**Colour Range**
- Light grey
- Dark grey
- Bluish grey

**Texture**
- Coarse-grained
- Crystalline

**Features**
- Blue sheen when polished

**Lookalikes**
- None

**Quarry Sources**
- Nielsen Quarries, Larvik, Norway
- Storass Quarry, Larvik, Norway

**Buildings**
- Scottish Mutual Building, Belfast (entrance columns)

## Larvikite

Larvikite is Permian in age having formed some 280 million years ago and is still actively quarried in the Larvik area of Norway. Larvikite is known by many different names including Birds Eye Granite, Norwegian Pearl Granite, Blue Norwegian Moonstone and Royal Blue Pearl. Larvikite is technically not a granite but an igneous rock known as syenite which is mostly composed of anorthoclase with olivine and apatite and is generally titanium rich. It is a very attractive decorative stone when polished and is used widely as facing stone and for worktops and plaques.

### Colour and texture

Larvikite is coarse-grained and occurs as dark and light grey varieties both with a blue sheen when polished.

Larvikite used for decorative stonework on the Scottish Mutual Building, Belfast

Polished Larvikite columns

## Leinster Granite

Leinster Granite formed during the Silurian some 440 million years ago. In addition to feldspar and quartz, it is rich in muscovite mica (a reflective mineral grain seen on the stone surface) which weathers relatively easily, thus reducing the durability of this granite. Leinster Granite was predominantly used in the Republic of Ireland especially in the Dublin area although there are examples of its use in Northern Ireland. It is quarried in Counties Wicklow and Carlow.

### Colour and texture

Leinster Granite is light grey in colour and coarse-grained with individual mineral grains clearly visible on the surface. Leinster Granite is prone to the effects of chemical and physical weathering of muscovite mica and feldspar resulting in surface loss through granular disintegration and scaling.

Leinster Granite on the façade of the Northern Whig Building, Belfast

Leinster Granite blockwork

**Colour Range**
- Light grey to grey

**Texture**
- Coarse-grained
- Crystalline

**Features**
- Feldspar and mica crystals are clearly visible
- Brown staining due to iron release from mica as a result of weathering

**Lookalikes**
- Cornish Granite
- Mourne Granite

**Quarry Sources**
- Dalkey Quarry, Dublin (inactive)
- Ryanstone, Blessington, Co. Wicklow

**Buildings**
- Northern Whig Building, Belfast

## Peterhead Granite

Peterhead Granite is similar in appearance to Balmoral Granite and formed during the Devonian some 360 to 420 million years ago. It comes from Peterhead in Scotland where it was extensively quarried in the 18th and 19th centuries. Historically it was widely used in the Peterhead area and further afield for buildings and for decorative stone features and memorial structures, and is still used today.

### Colour and texture

Peterhead Granite is a durable, coarse-grained stone that is pink to grey in colour and may occasionally contain xenoliths.

**Colour Range**
- Pink to red
- Grey

**Texture**
- Coarse-grained
- Crystalline

**Features**
- Occasional xenoliths

**Lookalikes**
- Balmoral Granite

**Quarry Sources**
- Stirling Hill Quarry, Peterhead, Scotland

**Buildings**
- Headline Building, Belfast (columns)
- Clonard Church, Clonard Monastery, Belfast (columns)

Columns of Peterhead Granite on the Headline Building, Belfast

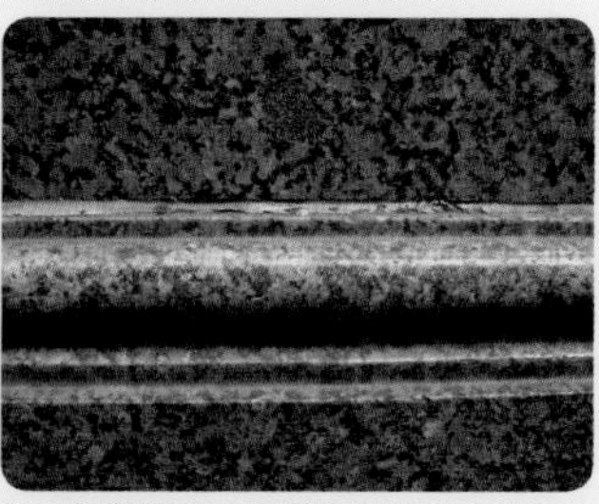

Detail of Peterhead Granite

## Shap Granite

Shap Granite is Devonian in age having formed some 360 to 420 million years ago and is still periodically quarried near Shap in Cumbria. It is a very distinctive granite used for decorative stonework throughout the United Kingdom.

### Colour and texture

Shap Granite is rich in feldspar, mica and quartz and has very distinctive large porphyritic crystals of pink orthoclase feldspar which can be up to 5 or 6cm in length. Very occasionally xenoliths are also present. Two varieties of Shap Granite exist, Dark Shap which is brown to red with black and grey colouration, and Light Shap which is mainly pink and grey in colour.

Shap Granite used for decorative stonework in the Northern Bank building, Royal Avenue, Belfast

Surface detail of polished Shap Granite

**Colour Range**
- Brown to red
- Pink to grey

**Texture**
- Coarse-grained
- Crystalline

**Features**
- Large tabular pink porphyritic megacrysts
- Xenoliths

**Lookalikes**
- None

**Quarry Sources**
- Shap Pink Quarry, Shap Fell, Cumbria

**Buildings**
- Northern Bank Building, Royal Ave, Belfast

Basalt

- Antrim Basalt

Basalt

## Basalt

Basalt is an extrusive volcanic rock that tends to be fine-grained because the rapid cooling of magma as it reaches the Earth's surface prevents the formation of large mineral grains. There are many different types of basalt and it is a rock type that occurs commonly around the world either from recently active volcanoes or preserved within a landscape where volcanic activity no longer takes place.

Basalt is dark grey or grey to green in colour and is very fine-grained with individual grains being invisible to the naked eye. The main constituent minerals are feldspar, pyroxene and olivine. Depending on viscosity and mineralogy and the environmental conditions under which it is extruded, lava can take on different forms on solidification. One of the most exceptional examples of this are the columnar basalts which occur on the Isle of Staffa in the Inner Hebrides, Scotland and at the Giant's Causeway in County Antrim, Northern Ireland. Both of these formed during the early Palaeogene Period (Tertiary) some 55 to 65 million years ago.

Columnar basalt at the Giant's Causeway, County Antrim

## Antrim Basalt

Antrim Basalt is volcanic rock that was extruded in several different phases during the early Palaeogene Period (Tertiary) some 60 to 65 million years ago. It formed an extensive plateau that forms most of County Antrim but which also extends beyond this into County Londonderry. Its most famous surface expression is at the Giant's Causeway World Heritage Site. Antrim Basalt is used as quarry-faced blocks and commonly for dry-stone walling throughout Northern Ireland.

### Colour and texture

Antrim Basalt varies in colour from black to dark grey or grey to green and is fine-grained with individual grains being invisible to the naked eye. It is a durable stone type that is relatively resistant to weathering although surface discolouration associated with oxidation of iron-rich minerals commonly occurs.

Antrim Basalt used in Aghanloo Church, Limavady, County Londonderry

Detail of coursed rubble Antrim Basalt wall showing variable stone colour

**Colour Range**
- Black
- Dark grey
- Grey to green
- Grey to brown

**Texture**
- Fine-grained

**Features**
- Fractures and irregular joints are common
- Occasionally, columnar jointing

**Lookalikes**
- Greywacke

**Quarry Sources**
- Little Deer Park Basalt Quarry, Glenarm
- Glebe Rock Quarry, near Aghadowey
- Bradey's Quarry, Kilrea

**Buildings**
- Aghanloo C of I Church, Limavady
- Billy C of I Church, Bushmills
- Carrickfergus Castle, Carrickfergus

Metamorphic Rock

**Metamorphics**
- Derry Schist
- Marble
- Slate

## Metamorphic Rock

Metamorphic rock is formed as a result of the alteration of a pre-existing rock type because of exposure to the effects of great heat and pressure. Exposure to heat and pressure causes major changes in the physical and mineralogical characteristics of the original rock type which may have been of igneous or sedimentary origin. Metamorphic rocks retain the basic chemical characteristics of the original rock type but the mineralogical structures are generally changed.

As any rock type can be subject to the effects of metamorphism, there are many varieties of metamorphic rock but they all fall into one of two sub-groups, foliated and non-foliated. Foliation describes layering within metamorphic rocks that results from the application of stresses from heat and pressure along one dimensional plane that deforms and preferentially reorientates minerals. Three of the most common metamorphic rocks are Schist, Slate and Marble, with both Schist and Slate being examples of foliated metamorphic rocks and Marble being a non-foliated example.

Close up view of layers in Derry Schist

## Derry Schist

In Northern Ireland Schists mainly occur in County Londonderry as part of the Londonderry Formation although there are small pockets in Counties Antrim and Tyrone. These are very old rocks formed over 500 million years ago. Most of these Schists originated from sediments of clays and muds altered by metamorphic processes to form strongly foliated stone. Derry Schist is rich in the mineral chlorite and is therefore described as a Chlorite Schist. These Schists have been used for rubble stonework throughout the County Londonderry area.

### Colour and texture

Derry Schist is fine-grained and grey to green in colour with well-defined schistose partings that provide lines of structural weakness that tend to be preferentially exploited by weathering agents such as frost and salt.

Foliated Derry Schist

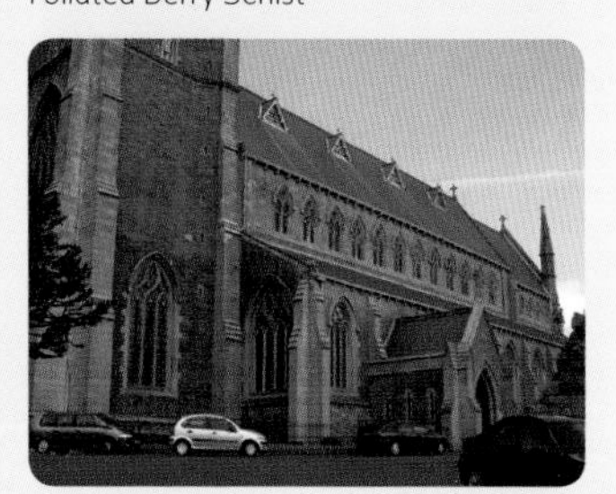

Derry Schist used as the primary stone type on St Eugene's Cathedral, Londonderry

**Colour Range**
- Grey to green

**Texture**
- Fine-grained

**Features**
- Schistose partings
- Foliated

**Lookalikes**
- None

**Quarry Sources**
- Prehen Quarry, off Prehen Park, Londonderry
- Kittybane Quarry, Dunhugh, Londonderry

**Buildings**
- C of I Church, Ballyquin Road, Limavady
- City Walls, Londonderry
- Rock Bakery, Londonderry

# Marble

Marble is limestone metamorphosed by the effects of great heat and pressure. It is a non-foliated metamorphic rock and retains the predominantly calcite mineralogy of the original limestone. The majority of marbles used in buildings within Northern Ireland are imported such as Carrara and Sicilian Marbles from Italy and Savoy Serpentine Marble from Germany. Our most significant closest source occurs in Connemara in the Republic of Ireland. Marble is widely used for statues, monuments and decorative stonework.

**Colour Range**
- White
- Grey
- Red
- Black

**Texture**
- Fine-grained

**Features**
- Variable colours
- Presence of veins and swirls
- Occasional fossils

**Lookalikes**
- None

**Quarry Sources**
- The Black Quarry, Co. Kilkenny
- Carrara Quarries, Apuan Alps, Italy
- Connemara Quarry, Clifden, Co. Galway

**Buildings**
- Victoria Monument, City Hall grounds, Belfast
- Titanic Memorial, City Hall grounds, Belfast

## Colour and texture

Due to mineral impurities, marble occurs in a wide range of colours including white or grey (Carrara Marble), green (Connemara Marble), red (Rouge de Rance) and black (Kilkenny Marble). Mineral impurities can also result in the presence of swirls and veins.

Carrara Marble used for the statue of Queen Victoria outside Belfast City Hall

Veined Savoy Serpentine Marble used in decorative panel stonework at the entrance of the Scottish Provident Building, Belfast

## Slate

Although some slate was quarried in County Londonderry and on the Rosemount Estate in County Down, the majority has been imported with the most common varieties being Welsh or Penrhyn Slate (Bangor Blue) and Westmoreland Slate from the Lake District area. Slate is metamorphosed shale sediments and splits easily into sheets of stone making it ideal as a roofing material.

### Colour and texture

Slate is fine-grained and occurs in a range of colours from light grey through to dark grey and purple. As a roofing material it is relatively resistant to weathering and long-lasting.

Slate used for roof and cladding on Maud's Cottages, Cushendun, County Antrim

Abandoned quarry face in the disused Rosemount Slate Quarry, County Down

**Colour Range**
- Grey
- Dark grey
- Purple

**Texture**
- Fine-grained

**Features**
- Foliated

**Lookalikes**
- None

**Quarry Sources**
- Rosemount Slate Quarry, Greyabbey (inactive)
- Penrhyn Quarry, North Wales

**Buildings**
- Maud's Cottages, Cushendun (roof)

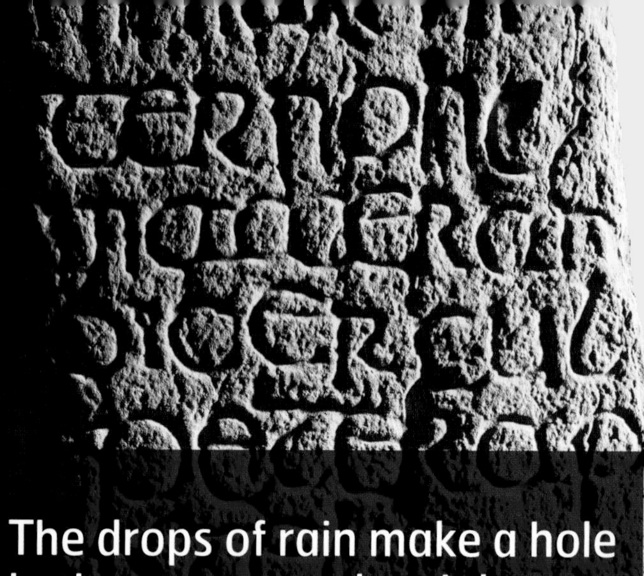

# The drops of rain make a hole in the stone, not by violence, but by often falling

Lucretius (circa 99BC–55BC)

Killnasaggart Pillar Stone, County Armagh

Bernard J. Smith

# Diagnosing Decay: The Nature of Stone Weathering

Most architects plan, most owners expect and most builders hope that the stones they are putting into a building will last forever. Unfortunately, as soon as stone is taken out of the ground it begins to change.

Sometimes these changes can be useful where, for example, certain varieties of limestone can be very soft in their natural state and must be left in the open to cure or harden before being used. However, in most cases exposure at the Earth's surface results in progressive alteration and breakdown as stone adjusts to fluctuating environmental conditions. Normally these adjustments take the form of chemical alteration and/or physical breakdown through the action of weathering processes, ultimately producing loose grains and dissolved material that is carried away by wind, water and gravity.

Stone in a building is exposed to both natural patterns of weathering and additional sets of urban conditions and factors that interact in complex and often unpredictable ways to produce new patterns and rates of decay. Buildings in a polluted coastal town are exposed to both the aggressive conditions linked to the action of marine salts, and the actions of other salts associated with atmospheric pollution. Often these combinations result in an increased rate of decay. In addition, stone has a long memory consisting of structural and chemical legacies from all that has previously happened to it, going right back to before it was even quarried. These legacies can take many forms ranging from networks of

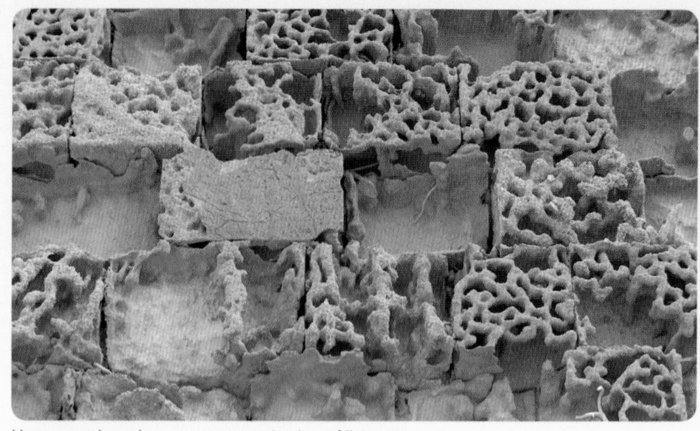

Honeycomb and cavernous weathering of limestone by salts in a coastal environment

micro-fractures caused by the quarrying process and previous weathering, to the presence of pollutants and their by-products such as salts that have become incorporated into the stone fabric. Such legacies can explain why stone continues to decay even after pollution levels have been reduced. Moreover, it means that every stone in a building has its own unique history. Thus, when new blocks of the same stone are inserted during building conservation, it is unlikely that they will ever match the appearance of the surrounding stone because they will not have been exposed to the same historical conditions. Consequently, it is sometimes best not to replace like-with-like, but to choose an alternative that is chemically and physically compatible but which will alter more rapidly to match the original stonework. Due to these complicating issues it is important that expensive decisions related to the specification of new and replacement stone, as well as the cleaning and conservation of old stone, must be underpinned by sound knowledge of its weathering characteristics.

Buildings are complex, dynamic environments that provide numerous possibilities for decay and alteration of stonework. The form that this takes is dependent not just on the present-day environment, but is partly determined by the history of construction and previous environmental conditions and treatments.

## Weathering Processes

In an attempt to make some sense out of the sometimes extremely complex alteration processes that affect stone it is normal to divide weathering processes into three categories although it should be stressed that rarely, if ever, do they operate in isolation.

### Physical weathering

This is the breakdown of stone either into smaller stone fragments, individual constituent grains or, in extreme cases fragmented grains. Often this breakdown is associated with the prior formation of a network of fractures and micro-fractures that can allow the penetration of moisture and dissolved material such as salts into the stone, which can facilitate chemical alteration.

### Chemical weathering

This involves chemical alteration of one or more of the constituents that make up a stone and the removal of some of the by-products in solution. Most chemical changes are accompanied by physical disruption and the exploitation of pre-existing fracture networks.

### Biological weathering

This is the most contentious and least understood of the weathering processes. Biological mechanisms can be chemical, physical or, a combination of the two. At its least subtle it is not uncommon to see plants growing out of neglected and abandoned buildings with their roots physically dislodging stonework. More insidious is the biochemical dissolution and weathering that occurs as organic acids from plant roots break down minerals to release nutrients. Also effective in this regard are the microscopic algae and bacteria that typically colonise all stone.

The type of weathering that occurs generally results from controls exerted by the geological characteristics of stone and the nature of the environment it finds itself in.

## Geological Controls on Weathering (Stone Characteristics)

### Dilatation

Most geological properties influence weathering passively but dilatation, or pressure release expansion is an exception to this. Prior to quarrying all stone exists under variable amounts of compression loading but when this is removed stone expands. In doing so a variety of fractures can be opened up that can both weaken its structure and provide pathways through which moisture can enter. The most obvious of these fractures are the large-scale joint systems that can be seen in quarry faces.

However, in terms of weathering, the most important changes caused by pressure release occur at a much smaller scale, where intricate networks of micro-fractures develop that can later facilitate stone breakdown as they are exploited by weathering processes.

**Geological controls on chemical weathering**

A major control on the susceptibility of stone to chemical weathering is its chemical and mineralogical composition. For example, stones such as limestone, rich in calcium and magnesium carbonate, are prone to solution by acidic rainfall. Reactions between components of the stone and acid rainfall can form soluble salts such as calcium sulphate, which is arguably the main cause of physical weathering of stone in polluted environments.

In general, the susceptibility of stone to chemical weathering depends mainly on its initial mineral complexity. Stone formed at high temperatures and pressures within and below the Earth's crust such as granite are more likely to contain complex minerals and mineral combinations that are out of balance with the highly variable and complex environments encountered at the Earth's surface. The natural response of these minerals is to change through weathering into simpler mineral forms and substances.

In contrast, stone formed at or near the Earth's surface from the stable residue of previous weathering such as sandstone tends to be more resistant to chemical alteration. The exception to this is where stable constituents such as quartz grains are held together by less stable 'cement'. This is the case in some calcium-rich sandstone, where a limited amount of chemical weathering targeted at the calcareous cement can result in a disproportionate amount of breakdown.

**Geological controls on physical weathering**

Geological controls on physical weathering are more straightforward in comparison with those that govern chemical and biochemical weathering. The most obvious control is that exerted by the physical strength of the stone and its ability to resist an applied force. Beyond

Selective weathering of a block with slight differences in its geological makeup

Load-induced crack in sandstone lintel

the generalisation that stronger stones will be more resistant to weathering, distinction has to be made in terms of the way in which the force is applied with some stones having a high compressive strength while others have a high tensile strength.

Porosity and the associated property of permeability (the extent to which the pores are connected to one another) exert major controls on weathering through controlling uptake of moisture, its movement through stone and ultimately its loss through evaporation. Pore size influences the uptake of any salts that might be contained within moisture and also appears to influence the disruptive effect of crystallising salts with greater susceptibility shown by stone with a high proportion of small pores less than 5 microns in diameter. However, porosity is not a fixed characteristic as it can change overtime in response to weathering. For example, pores can become filled and the connections between them blocked with salt. Conversely, as a stone weathers fractures develop that create a 'secondary porosity'. These fractures are important not just because they provide additional pathways for moisture, salts and weathering products to migrate through the stone, but because they lower the overall strength of the stone and provide potential failure planes. The development of near-surface micro-fractures will also affect a stone's surface hardness. Such brittle stones can also be prone to fracturing when rapidly heated or cooled and demonstrate the importance of the thermal properties of stones in determining their susceptibility to a range of weathering processes.

Soiling differences in stone window dressing related to aspect/micro-climate

Capillary rise of groundwater

## Environmental Controls on Weathering

It is tempting to think of environmental controls on weathering as comprising factors such as average annual rainfall and average annual temperature. However, most weathering processes are driven by change and respond not to average conditions but to extreme events. A clear example of this is frost weathering, for which the most meaningful statistic is not the average low temperature, but how often temperatures fall below freezing and the intensity and duration of the frost. Similarly, the wetting patterns of stone are not determined by average rainfall, but by how often it rains, how long for and the total amount in each storm. After that, the most important environmental factors are localised conditions or micro-climate experienced at the surface of the stone.

Micro-climate can be very different from the macro-climate of the region or even the meso-climate around a building. For example, under clear daytime skies stone surface temperatures, and those of the layer of air immediately above it can be significantly higher than average air temperature because of stone's ability to absorb and store solar energy. Consequently, the direction that stone faces (its aspect) has a major influence on the micro-climate it experiences. For example, in northern latitudes south-facing surfaces are heated for much of the day and dry out more quickly and thoroughly than, north-facing surfaces. Aspect is also important in relation to the prevailing wind direction, in that driven rain blowing on to a surface is particularly effective at wetting stone. At the other end of the spectrum, areas sheltered from rain are likely to see preferential surface accumulation of dust and soot as well as any salts they might contain, leading to the patchy growth of unsightly black gypsum crusts.

### Moisture controls on weathering

The most severe decay of stone in buildings is commonly associated with water damage, normally where failed gutters, pipes or roofs have allowed water to saturate and flow over and through stonework. Alternatively the absence of an effective damp course can allow groundwater to move upwards through stone by capillary rise, bringing with it potentially damaging salts in solution. Whilst such patterns of damage are not strictly weathering phenomena they highlight the ability and significance of moisture for shortening the lifespan of stone used in construction. Aside from failures in rainwater goods and damp proofing, the effects of moisture tend to be more subtle.

**Solution**: The weathering process most commonly associated with water is that of solution. This occurs because rainwater is naturally acidified by its reaction with carbon dioxide in the atmosphere to form a very weak carbonic acid. This process is exacerbated in polluted environments by reactions with other gases such as sulphur dioxide to produce a weak sulphuric acid rain. Limestone is particularly susceptible to solution. However, solution is not restricted to limestone as most minerals are soluble to some extent under conditions found at the Earth's surface. Solubility is, however, influenced by a variety of additional factors. In the case of silica, for example, crystalline quartz has a low solubility but amorphous (non-crystalline) silica is significantly more soluble under normal conditions. The significance of this is that whilst amorphous silica is not common as a stone-forming mineral it does form the cement that holds many quartz sandstones together and this makes them prone to damage from selective dissolution. The rate of silica solution is also enhanced by other factors such as the salinity of the solution. Thus the presence of salts in water that soaks into stone may further facilitate selective dissolution and weaken the structure of a stone. The salts themselves are also prone to dissolution and can re-crystallise if the solution is later evaporated. Despite the variety of factors that can influence solubility of stone constituents, by far the most important control is a solution's acidity or alkalinity. In general the solubility of most stone-forming minerals tends to increase with increasing acidity, although some, such as silica and aluminium also show enhanced solubility under very alkaline conditions. The precise relationships depend on other controls such as temperature and the degree of oxidation or reduction of the water, as measured by the Eh scale on which positive values indicate an oxidised environment and negative values a reduced or anoxic environment. In terms of weathering processes this particularly affects iron, which is a common element in many stones occurring as either a component of stone-forming minerals, a cement, a coating that colours grains or sometimes as a hard outer coating. Iron can exist as either ferric iron under oxidised conditions or ferrous iron under reduced or saturated conditions. Under normal (neither too acid nor too alkaline) conditions, ferrous iron is relatively mobile and, in saturated stone, can move in solution through stone. If the stone dries out the iron oxidises to become ferric iron and becomes fixed and immobile under all but the most acid or alkaline conditions. In this way iron can be brought from within a stone and precipitated at the surface to change the stone's colour and, in extreme circumstances, to form a hard outer crust. The removal of iron from the stone's interior can weaken it and make it susceptible to rapid erosion if, for example, over-energetic cleaning should breach this crust. The process of iron mobilisation and fixation happens slowly under natural conditions, but can be accelerated in polluted urban environments or through the inappropriate use of acid and alkaline solutions during stone cleaning.

**Hydrolysis**: It is possible for water to react chemically with stone-forming minerals. The most important consequence of hydrolysis for weathering is the conversion of complex primary minerals into simpler, secondary clay minerals with a reduction in the competence of a stone. However, hydrolysis operates very slowly and therefore, except under extreme conditions such as those experienced by buildings in the humid Tropics, it is unlikely that hydrolysis has any major impact before building stones are destroyed by other, more aggressive weathering processes. The exception to this is where stone was altered by hydrolysis prior to inclusion in a building.

Scaling of iron-rich crust

Preferential weathering of clay lenses

If this is the case it could bring with it a legacy of embedded clay minerals and any structural deterioration that was associated with their formation.

**Hydration/dehydration**: Minerals can be affected by the absorption of water molecules into their structure without any chemical reaction occurring. This means that on drying out, water is lost and the mineral returns to its original structure. This is known as hydration/dehydration. In the context of stone weathering, the most important example of hydration/dehydration is that associated with some soluble salts found within stone pores, fractures and joints. As these salts hydrate they expand and exert pressures that can be greater than the strength of many building stones, especially if they have already been weakened by previous weathering. This kind of weathering does not need liquid water to occur as some of the potentially most damaging salts, such as calcium sulphate and sodium sulphate, hydrate in response to the presence of atmospheric humidity. So, unlike salt dissolution/re-crystallisation that requires liquid water and frost weathering that requires both water and freezing temperatures, hydration/dehydration is more commonplace and potentially very frequent.

**Slaking**: Slaking is the breakdown of materials in response to repeated wetting and drying. The precise mechanism responsible is unclear, although it is possible that on drying a thin layer of negatively charged water molecules is left adsorbed to the surfaces of individual grains. Successive wetting and drying could build up the thickness of these layers to the point where they could begin to 'repel' surrounding grains with similar,

Salts accumulating in sheltered honeycombs

Complex pattern of black gypsum crusts conditioned by airflow

negatively charged coatings. Although it is not slaking in the precise sense of the term, wetting and drying can also generate expansion and contraction when certain types of clay mineral are present in a stone. Some clay minerals expand when wet with repeated expansion on wetting and contraction on drying eventually weakening the stone.

**Direct moisture deposition:** As well as rain, moisture can be deposited directly on to stone via frost, dew and from fog/mist. The amounts involved are typically small but the limited quantities of these forms of moisture can have significant impacts on buildings because they can reach areas sheltered from rain. In this way, salts deposited in sheltered zones can be 'activated' through periodic dissolution/re-crystallisation without being washed away.

### Wind as a control on weathering

The significance of wind is its role in facilitating moisture evaporation from stone surfaces. This can help increase the cooling rate of surface layers of stone as well as influencing the extent and location of salt crystallisation. Wind flow patterns over the surface of a building are also very important in determining where airborne dusts are deposited that can then be incorporated into surface crusts. These patterns of airflow can be extremely complex and are reflected in the equally complex distribution of black crusts over many buildings. Finally, wind can carry away the fine debris produced by stone weathering.

### Temperature controls on weathering

**Heating/cooling**: There is a common belief, often linked to popular sayings, that the sun is hot enough to split stone but there is no definitive evidence to support this phenomenon except through the effects of rapid surface heating of stone or thermal shock associated with fire. This results in the outer layer of stone being forced to expand more rapidly than the interior creating stresses that cause the outer layer to fracture and break away from the interior. Aside from such rare extreme events, the most important effect of temperature is associated with frequent low magnitude temperature cycles caused by heating and cooling. These result in stone being subject to numerous small-scale stresses on a daily basis that may eventually contribute to fatigue-related failure.

Until relatively recently, it was assumed that the most important temperature cycles driving weathering were the diurnal ones associated with heating during the day and cooling at night. However, it is now recognised that stone temperatures can fluctuate very rapidly during the day as, for example, surfaces are shaded by clouds or cooled by the wind. These short-term changes, often only 15-30 minutes duration, can set up internal temperature gradients and stresses markedly higher than those driven by diurnal changes. The recognition that these short-term fluctuations, superimposed on diurnal cycles, significantly increases the possibility of fatigue failure has also changed our understanding of which factors might control patterns of weathering observed on a building.

In addition to the amount of solar heating received, the absolute temperatures and rates of temperature change experienced by a stone are controlled by other factors such as its thermal properties. Included amongst these are thermal conductivity and heat storage capacity, which together exert a major influence on sub-surface temperature gradients. Stones with a low thermal conductivity, but high heat storage capacity experience steep temperature gradients and localised stressing because the surface of the stone heats up more rapidly than the absorbed energy can be transmitted into it. The magnitude of these stresses will also be influenced by other properties such as the coefficient of thermal expansion of the stone or how rapidly and by how much the stone expands on heating.

Albedo, or the degree to which a surface absorbs or reflects heat radiation, is the most

Frost damage to limestones – Budapest

obvious property that influences temperature conditions experienced by stone. In general, darker surfaces absorb more radiation and are likely to be hotter than more reflective lighter surfaces. As warmer surfaces probably lose energy more rapidly overnight, they may also experience greater diurnal temperature ranges, steeper rates of heating and cooling and are more likely to dry out thoroughly. This can go a long way towards explaining different susceptibilities to a range of weathering processes between stones of different colour.

It is impossible to isolate temperature change as a cause of stone weathering. Apart from the positive influence that temperature has on the speed of almost all chemical reactions, temperature change is always linked to the operation of other weathering processes.

**Freeze/thaw**: The conditions required for freeze/thaw to generate significant stresses within a stone are more complicated and rare than a simple drop in temperature below 0°C and the freezing of water already in the pores of a stone. For example, the maximum expansion associated with the transition of water into ice actually occurs at -22°C. Although it must be admitted that if this point is actually reached, the pressures generated are more than enough to shatter most stones. As temperatures drop, however, a number of factors combine to inhibit freezing and also to relieve any pressure generated by ice that has formed

Loss of structural Integrity

Loss of cultural heritage

within pores. For example, when ice begins to form within pores the pressure on the remaining water increases. This lowers the freezing point and slows down further freezing. The presence of salts will also lower the freezing point, and in an unsaturated, open-textured stone the pressures generated by freezing and expansion might be partly absorbed by compression of air within the pores and feasibly by displacement and possible expulsion of water via any exposed surface.

Susceptibility to the effects of freeze/thaw is strongly determined by the propensity of a stone (or areas of stone on a building) to prolonged saturation. The pressure generated by freezing water under these saturated conditions is often concentrated within pre-existing cracks and as water continues to migrate towards the ice the cracks are extended by growth at their tips. The key word is, however, pre-existing. Again, it is impossible to isolate the effects of freeze/thaw in terms of its weathering effectiveness. Freeze/thaw may be the final act that breaks the stone, but more often than not failure reflects many years of gradual weakening through the action of a variety of weathering processes.

The more detailed, the more susceptible to decay

## The Consequences of Placing Stone in a Building

Placing stone in a building exposes it to new sets of conditions that do not replace natural weathering processes but combine with them to accentuate rates of decay and sometimes to produce distinctively different decay patterns and products. Broadly speaking the consequences of using stone in construction fall into two categories: those resulting from the physical act of placing the stone in the building and those brought about by exposing stone to often polluted urban conditions.

### Physically placing stone in a building

Placing stone in a building creates a wide range of new physical, chemical and environmental conditions that can alter its response to natural weathering processes. Principal amongst these is the location and geometry of a building, which can influence the degree of exposure to and shelter from sun, rain and wind. The importance of exposure stems from its relationship with patterns of wetting and drying and heating and cooling, which in turn influence factors such as the frequency of salt crystallisation and, ultimately, the speed at which stone weathers.

The most obvious control in this respect is aspect, or the direction stone surfaces face as this controls the physical stresses experienced by stone through repeated expansion and contraction associated with heating and cooling and wetting and drying. The pattern of airflow around a building influences evaporation rates and the deposition of pollution particles on stonework with even relatively minor changes in surface detail having major effects on patterns of soiling.

In addition to these environmental factors, there are chemical and physical stresses exerted by materials surrounding stone, such as mortar, which can constrain individual blocks when they expand as a result of chemical alteration, expansion of internal salts and thermal and moisture cycling. The use of different stone types in combination can also trigger decay where, for example, calcium sulphate (gypsum) salts produced by the reaction of atmospheric sulphur with carbonate stones can wash into adjacent, non-calcareous stonework. Similar contamination of non-calcareous stone can occur from surrounding mortars, whilst the use of 'hard' mortars in combination with weaker stonework can lead to disruption of the stone during expansion, producing a honeycomb or 'boxwork' effect as mortars are left proud of the retreating stone. Finally, the surface dressing of stone influences pollution deposition and patterns of decay. Roughened stonework provides a greater surface area to react with the environment and sheltered hollows in which dust and salts can accumulate protected from rainwash.

**Effects of exposing stone to atmospheric pollution**

A major environmental issue that has been faced by industrialized societies in recent years, and which is now affecting newly industrialized countries, is the problem of acid deposition related to atmospheric pollution. Attention has tended to concentrate on the effects of acidified rainfall upon soils, forests, rivers and lakes with the impact on urban stone receiving less emphasis. Yet, annually across Europe huge sums of money are spent on cleaning and renovating buildings with some irreplaceable monuments being allowed to literally crumble and wash away.

Stone is not absolutely durable and exposure to the weather over many thousands of years brings about its eventual disintegration. The speed of disintegration varies according to stone type and environmental conditions. In polluted urban environments stone decay rates have greatly accelerated, so that its natural lifespan can be reduced from thousands to just tens of years. The main cause of this accelerated decay is thought to be acid rain, or more accurately, acid deposition. Acid deposition occurs as a result of the release of gaseous pollutants into the atmosphere primarily from the burning of coal and oil for domestic and industrial purposes and from vehicle exhausts. These combine in sunlight with atmospheric moisture to form a cocktail of chemicals including sulphuric and nitric acids that are washed out and deposited as classic 'acid rain'. Added to this are pollution particles that fall to the ground as 'dry deposition'. These all combine to create the phenomenon of acid deposition.

Stone decay is largely a local phenomenon concentrated within a few kilometres of pollution sources where dry deposition of pollutants is particularly important. Despite clean air legislation in the United Kingdom, stone decay continues in response to the less visible gaseous components of atmospheric pollution and changes in pollution patterns. The most important of these being the growth in road traffic that has lead to a rise in the local soiling of buildings from the street up. To this must be added the effect of years of accumulated pollution that continues to promote decay long after the original source of pollution has been removed.

Stones such as limestone and marble, which are primarily made up of calcium carbonate are particularly prone to damage by acid rain because two complementary weathering processes can act upon them. The first of these is solution weathering. In polluted environments, rainfall acidity is increased and solution intensified when oxides of sulphur are present in the atmosphere resulting in the formation of a weak sulphuric acid. When this falls on stone containing calcium carbonate a reaction occurs producing calcium sulphate salt (gypsum). Typically most of the gypsum is removed in solution as rainfall runs off the building, but if some of the rainfall soaks into the stone or is held on the surface and subsequently evaporates, gypsum crystallises, contributing to physical disintegration of the stone by salt weathering (see diagram on following page).

Although gypsum is the most common salt produced by acid deposition it is not the only one. The great variety of stone types used in buildings and the chemical complexity of acid deposition means that a wide range of other salts can also be found. Salt weathering is a naturally

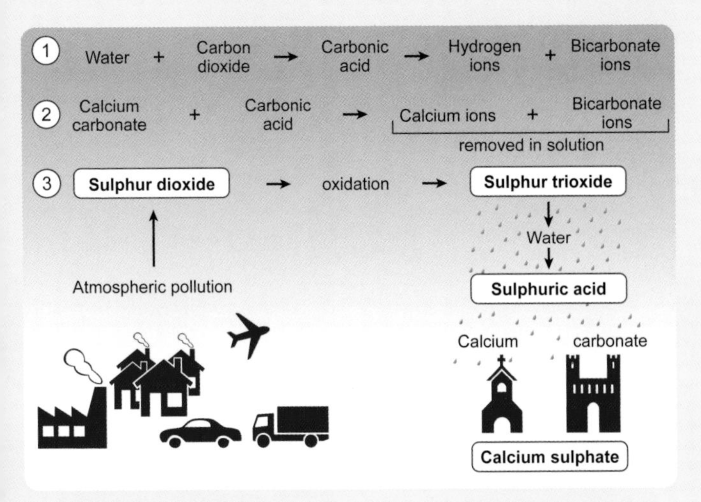


Natural and acid rain solution of limestones to form gypsum

occurring process and its effects are clearly seen on many stone buildings in coastal environments. Salts can also be dissolved by later rain or by percolating water and transferred to other porous building materials and in this way materials, such as granite, non-calcareous sandstones, slate, brick, concrete, mortar, wood and paint that are not readily prone to attack by acid rain can be severely damaged. Because of this ability for all stones to be contaminated, damage from salt weathering can ultimately be more dramatic than material loss through solution.

**Solution damage to buildings:** Solution is the most direct form of urban stone decay and is particularly important because of the extensive use of limestone in many important civic and ecclesiastical buildings. The effects of solution are best seen when it attacks intricate carvings and statues and smoothes and rounds off protuberances and sharp edges. In such cases it is often difficult to assess just how much removal of stone by solution has occurred. Headstones in city graveyards can sometimes help quantify this by providing a fixed point or datum from which measurements can be made. Metal inscriptions

Solution of marble memorial

Cavernous hollows typical of salt weathering

Contour scaling

are particularly helpful in that they can be used to obtain information on rates of surface lowering. Image, top left shows a marble memorial plaque erected in south Belfast in 1872, on which a lead inscription that was originally flush with the stone surface now stands above it allowing calculation of an average annual weathering rate. Unfortunately such measurements cannot show whether this rate has altered over time or in response to changes in rainfall acidity.

**Salt weathering mechanisms:** Salt weathering is probably the most important agent of stone decay in cities. This is because salt crystallisation and associated damage can occur every time a salt-contaminated stone is wetted and dries out. There are several mechanisms by which salt damages stone. When stones are wetted by rain or condensation, salts are dissolved and washed into pore spaces. When drying begins, evaporation causes crystals to grow and press against surrounding grains.

Repeated wetting and drying and the resultant expansion and contraction can eventually lead to physical breakdown.

In addition to crystallisation pressures, some salts such as calcium sulphate (gypsum) react to variations in temperature and relative atmospheric humidity by absorbing or releasing water molecules. This hydration and dehydration causes the salts to expand and contract which can also exert pressures on the surrounding stone. What makes this mechanism important is that the temperature and humidity thresholds may be crossed several times in a day producing numerous expansion and contraction cycles that may eventually lead to the fatigue failure of the stone.

Finally, if pores are filled with salts that have higher coefficients of thermal expansion than the stone, subsequent heating will cause the salts to expand more rapidly and exert pressure on the surrounding stone thereby contributing to breakdown where other mechanisms are also active.

**Recognising salt weathering:** Disruption of stone by salt manifests itself in several ways. A common feature, which usually represents an early stage of breakdown, is contour scaling. An example of this phenomenon is shown in opposite, right. The clearly legible inscription indicates that the blackened stone surface is outwardly sound and that the headstone has stood for many years with no obvious sign of damage. Following this period of apparent stability parts of the surface layer have become detached to reveal a white underlying efflorescence of gypsum crystals.

We cannot say with any certainty why phenomena such as contour scaling occur. One possibility is that on wetting, salts, such as gypsum, migrate in solution to a uniform depth within the stone where some of it crystallises if the stone rapidly dries out. Repetition of this gradually promotes salt accumulation at this depth and eventually causes the stone surface to lift off as a layer or scale. The presence of the gypsum crystals beneath the scale lends some support to this explanation.

It has also been suggested that if stone dries out more slowly, salt solutions are more likely to accumulate at or just below the stone surface. Under these conditions stone is susceptible to breakdown either by granular disaggregation or by the development of thin flakes. It may take many years for salts to accumulate and for stresses to build up within the stone before there are visible signs of decay. However, once the surface is broken decay can accelerate as granular disintegration and multiple flaking attack previously weakened sub-surface stone. This can lead to the development of sizeable pits or hollows – often referred to as 'honeycomb weathering'. Hollows may initially begin by exploiting a point of weakness within the stone – perhaps an area that is more porous or less strongly cemented. Once a small pit is formed it creates its own shaded micro-climate which encourages salt accumulation and moisture retention. The most extreme form of this accelerated weathering is seen where complete blocks of stone rapidly retreat and disappear.

**Biological weathering of building stones:** Although the most obvious evidence of biological weathering is the physical disruption of stone by the roots of plants that are allowed to grow on a building façade, this is a relatively rare phenomenon. Of greater significance for weathering are the mechanisms that operate at the micro-scale. Included in this are cyanobacteria that effectively digest minerals and colonisation by algae and fungae that enhance the dissolution of stone. The effects of this are seen on limestone where algae can be associated with a characteristic pitting of the stone surface. Some algae can live within the stone contributing to internal breakdown provided that enough sunlight can penetrate the overlying layer.

One additional effect of algal and fungal colonisation is that it tends to form a surface film that blocks pores reducing the breathability of stone with any moisture that does penetrate evaporating more slowly thereby keeping the stone wetter for longer and allowing any dissolved salts to penetrate more deeply. This latter point is an illustration of the way in which weathering processes are interconnected and frequently act either in sequence or together to bring about decay.

**Soiling and aesthetic damage to buildings:** As well as contributing to the dissolution, cracking and crumbling of stone buildings in cities, air pollution can detract from their appearance by causing staining and blackening of surfaces. This effect is most noticeable on surfaces that are

Algal growth on sandstone pillar

Soiling by black gypsum crust

not directly exposed to rain. Rain falling on stone surfaces does cause damage, but it also tends to keep the stone in a relatively clean condition. On areas of buildings that are protected from rainwash the dirt and soot particles present in the atmosphere can adhere to stone dirtying its surface and masking architectural detail (see top right).

The most common form of soiling occurs when pollution particles become incorporated into a layer of gypsum that crystallises from the underlying stone, is washed over a non-calcareous stone from an adjacent limestone or mortar joint or is formed by re-precipitation of gypsum from the dust itself. This forms black crusts, which in particularly sheltered locations can develop into thick overgrowths. The shape of the building and the pattern of surface airflow influence patterns of soiling.

Soiling is obvious to building owners and is the main reason why many pay for conservation. However, there is debate over the extent to which black crusts pose a threat to the physical structure of a building. Some suggest that they act as a reservoir of potentially damaging salts that should be removed while others view them as a relatively benign means of holding together otherwise friable stone. What is clear is that the impact of black crusts depends very much on the stone type in question. There is also an unresolved cultural debate over whether buildings should reflect their exposure histories or whether they should be returned to, or near to, their original appearance.

Black crusts are not the only example of surface soiling. For example, many sandstones exhibit staining by iron oxides, which can

Weathering along bedding planes

Water damage

be slowly brought to the surface in solution from within stone and precipitated by evaporation or, in some cases, rapidly mobilized and precipitated by inappropriate chemical cleaning. In both instances this can result in the formation of a hardened surface layer with weakening of the stone below. Initially this hardened layer may protect stone from erosion, but if it is breached the underlying stone can be rapidly lost. As a result, it is important when cleaning such stones that chemicals are not used that will mobilize the iron and that if a crust already exists mechanical cleaning should not break through it.

## Structural controls on building stone decay

Different stone types can respond to similar climatic conditions in quite different ways. This is most obvious where the minerals that make up a stone exhibit different susceptibilities to different chemical weathering processes. However, stone also responds differently to physical weathering processes. In addition to differences related to the type of stone used in a building, weathering can often be seen to act differentially on stone surfaces as a result of irregularities in its structure. This is best illustrated by the effect of bedding planes. Bedding planes are particularly well developed in sandstones and are also found in some limestones. For example, when a block of stone containing bedding planes is positioned in the wall of a building, beds can be orientated in three possible ways: horizontally (normal-bedding), vertically and parallel to vertical joints (joint-bedding) or vertically and parallel to the wall surface (face-bedding). With regard to the first two it is not unusual to see blocks of stone on buildings that display a 'furrowed' appearance due to the preferential weathering of weaker beds (see opposite, left). However, weathering is usually most

Bomb damage to Portland Limestone of Victoria and Albert Museum, London

detrimental when blocks of stone are face-bedded. Stonemasons will always try to avoid this situation, but it can occur due to either poor workmanship or difficulty in establishing the presence or orientation of bedding planes. It creates a problem because the junctions between beds comprise natural weaknesses that are readily exploited by weathering agents with detachment of complete sheets resulting in rapid block retreat.

**Other sources of damage to building stone**

There is no limit to the ingenuity with which humans find ways of intentionally or unintentionally damaging stone. In addition to the problems of inappropriate methods of cleaning these can include:

- Treatment with consolidants that change stone colour and/or block pore spaces and prevent it from 'breathing'
- Inadequate maintenance of rainwater goods
- Re-pointing with hard mortars against which comparatively less rigid stone breaks down
- Inappropriate stone combinations, such as, contamination of quartz sandstones by gypsum washing down from a limestone placed above it
- Fracturing caused by expansive corrosion of metal fixings
- Damage through bombs and gunfire

Human actions can accelerate decay, but even without pollution-induced damage, exterior stonework is still subject to natural weathering processes with stone decay rarely being a reflection of one process operating in isolation but representing many years of accumulated stresses and changes that are a natural response to the external urban environment.

## Symptoms of Urban Stone Decay

In the following section some common manifestations of urban stone decay are shown. However, it is important to note that identifying the causes of these is not straightforward and therefore decay features should be viewed within the context of the building on which they occur with consideration given to the influence of stone type, micro-climatic conditions and the building's history.

### Physical breakdown

**Blistering**: Blistering of Portland Limestone on St Paul's Cathedral, London possibly associated with salt that has gradually accumulated at a shallow depth within the stone. Expansion and contraction due to repeated wetting and drying may have lifted the surface layer away from the underlying stone.

Blistering of Portland Limestone

**Scaling**: Scales often follow the surface detailing of a stone and so are also referred to as 'contour scales'. Scaling is often linked to the accumulation of salt at a frequent wetting depth within the stone and the eventual lifting away of the outer layer. Scales may also form when a hardened outer surface breaks away from underlying weakened stone (see alteration features).

Detail of scaling

**Flaking**: Formation of thin, multiple flakes most commonly associated with rapid surface retreat of salt-laden stone. Flaking may also be associated with exploitation of weakened stone that has been exposed by detachment of a surface scale.

Detail of flaking

**Granular disintegration:** This occurs in granular (for example, sandstone) and crystalline (for example, granite) stones where cement holding the grains together is weakened by solution or where salts crystallise in pores to force individual grains apart. Typically granular disintegration produces debris that is a mixture of salt and individual mineral grains that accumulates beneath stones that are actively decaying.

Granular disintegration

**Honeycomb weathering**: Multiple flaking and granular disintegration are frequently associated with salt accumulation and often occur in humid, shaded areas where salts are protected from solution loss by rain. These features may begin as a patch of stone that is more susceptible to weathering because of different porosity characteristics. However, once the stone starts to weather hollows are created that in turn encourage salt retention resulting in preferential weathering to create a honeycomb appearance.

Honeycomb weathering

**Cavernous weathering (tafoni)**: Larger hollows, sometimes developed from the coalescence of a patch of smaller hollows, can destroy complete blocks of stone. The size of the caverns can be controlled on a building by block dimensions that weather and retreat more rapidly than surrounding stonework. One explanation for their formation concerns breaching of hardened outer crusts on stone with accelerated weathering of the underlying weaker stone.

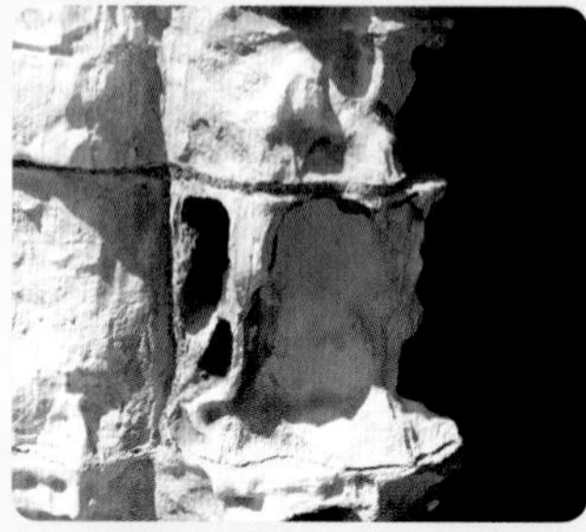
Cavernous weathering

**Cracked stones**: The creation of cracks in stone blocks is not particularly common on buildings. In most instances they can be traced back to poor workmanship or design. Cracking can arise from unequal loading of stone in the building or where metal fixings corrode and expand. Although relatively rare, such damage must be treated seriously as it may indicate more serious structural problems.

Cracked stones

## Chemical breakdown and alteration

**Solution**: On a uniform limestone surface it is sometimes difficult to judge the effects of solution. However, where stone contains fossils such as the shell fragments in this limestone (above right), lowering of the surrounding stone surface by solution leaves these standing proud.

Chemical breakdown and alteration

**Staining**: In this example the products of solution (gypsum) from limestone have washed over and contaminated underlying stonework. This is potentially damaging, as gypsum is a salt that can crystallise within masonry and cause decay. This combination of materials also means that the bricks become subject to salt attack, even though they themselves do not contain calcium and do not react with pollutants to form salts.

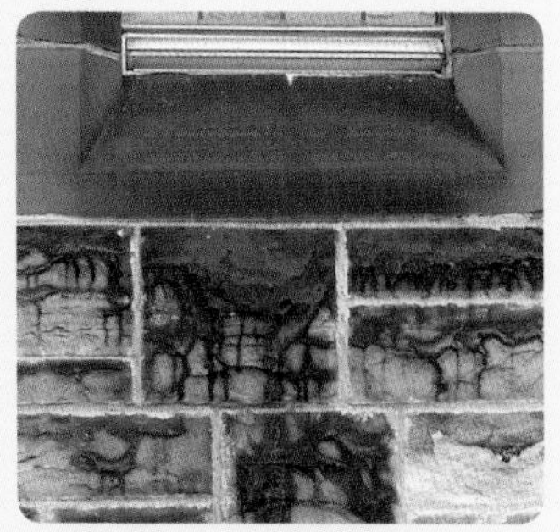
Staining

**Pitting**: In dry environments, or in the sheltered areas of wetter climates, it is common to see the pitting of limestone surfaces. Microscopic examination often shows that the interiors of these pits are colonised by communities of algae, fungi and bacteria. These help to dissolve stone, and in doing so create tiny ecological niches that encourage further colonisation.

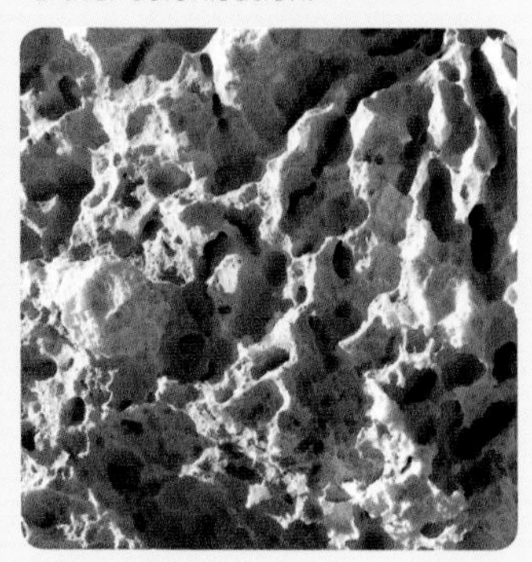
Pitting

**Scalloping/fluting**: As water flows over limestone the patterns of turbulent flow in the thin film of moisture mean that solution rates are uneven and gradually the flow patterns are translated into complex wave-like shapes on the stone surface. Examples of these patterns can be seen below.

Scalloping/fluting in hard limestone

### Alteration and depositional features

**Re-crystallisation**: If a film of rainwater is left on limestone and allowed to evaporate, any dissolved calcium carbonate will be re-precipitated as crystals of calcite leaving a very clean surface that presents a typically sparkling appearance when light is reflected off the fresh crystals. The whiteness of the exposed side of the limestone pillar from St Mark's Basilica, Venice (following page), appears in sharp contrast to the black gypsum crust that has developed on the sheltered area.

Re-crystallisation

**Efflorescence**: Stonework contaminated with salt when wetted and then dried very slowly can result in salts being brought to the stone surface and precipitated by evaporation to produce a white salt efflorescence. Crystallisation of salt at and near the surface can eventually result in granular disintegration of stones that are susceptible to salt weathering.

Efflorescence

**Cryptoflorescence**: This is formed by salts that crystallise within stonework. They are revealed, however, when they cause the detachment and falling away of an overlying surface layer by contour scaling. Salt crystallisation at depth may be related to frequent wetting of stone to a consistent depth with crystallisation of salt at this depth as the stone rapidly dries out.

Cryptoflorescence

**Stone meal**: Granular disintegration of stonework often results in the formation of a crumbly layer of mixed salt and stone debris often seen accumulating below the actively weathering stone. Stone meal accumulating within the interior of a rapidly weathering tafoni is shown below.

Stone meal

**Alteration rind**: Alteration rinds on buildings are most commonly found associated with iron-rich sandstones where the iron that cements the grains and/or is present in accessory minerals goes into solution when the stone is wet and then precipitated at and just below the surface as the stone dries out. The following photo shows an alteration rind formed over *c.* 150 years of exposure on Queen's University in Belfast. The hardened outer layer protects the stone from weathering until it is breached when the underlying weakened stone rapidly deteriorates.

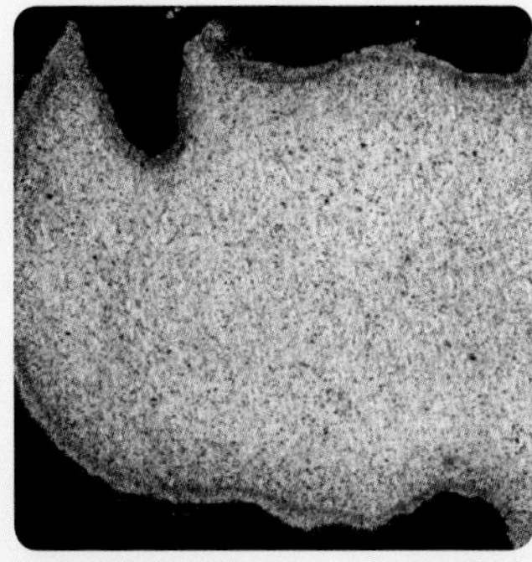

Alteration rind

**Case hardening**: This is a type of alteration rind found principally on limestones, in which a dense surface layer is formed by the outward migration in solution and re-precipitation of calcium carbonate. This does not change the chemistry of the stone but can significantly decrease surface porosity and strengthen the outer layer of stone. This may increase short-term stability but if case hardening has occurred at the expense of weakening sub-surface material, the breaching of the crust can ultimately accelerate decay.

Case hardening

**Iron staining**: Mobilisation of iron during formation of alteration rinds can also result in changing the surface colour of stone. Normally this is a fairly uniform process that contributes to the slow formation of a surface patina indicative of a mature building. Problems occur when there is uneven mobilisation of iron through, for example, stone cleaning by acid, which can result in uneven and unsightly staining by iron brought to the surface (see next page).

Iron staining

**Black crusts**: These form where gypsum (calcium sulphate) crystallises on a stone surface sheltered from direct rainwash in a polluted environment. Incorporation of pollution particles gives the deposit its characteristic blackness. Crusts form best on limestones where calcium carbonate can be rapidly transformed to gypsum in a sulphate-rich atmosphere. However, crusts can also grow on non-calcareous stones where, for example, they become loaded with calcium washed in from adjacent limestones and mortars or blown in as dust particles.

Black crusts

**Grey crusts**: These may represent an early stage in the development of a black gypsum crust or may be a thinner, denser crustal form.

Grey crusts

**Black encrustations**: In extreme cases of high levels of pollution and/or long time periods, black crusts can continue to grow ultimately developing into thick encrustations that both cover and hang from stonework.

Black encrustations

**Flowstone**: Where water percolates through stonework it often does so by following the porous network of mortared joints. When this moisture eventually leaks out of stonework dissolved material is precipitated out sometimes leading to the formation of calcium carbonate deposits resembling the 'flowstones' that form on the walls of limestone caves.

Flowstone-like deposit

### Biological weathering features

**Lichen**: Lichen on stonework develop best under clean air conditions, but their growth may be facilitated by certain pollutants such as nitrogen oxides derived primarily from vehicle pollution. It is thought that lichens may contribute to chemical weathering of underlying stone and to the physical damage of stone by plucking out grains as the lichen dries out and contracts. It is also suggested that lichens indicate surface stability because of the length of time they take to grow

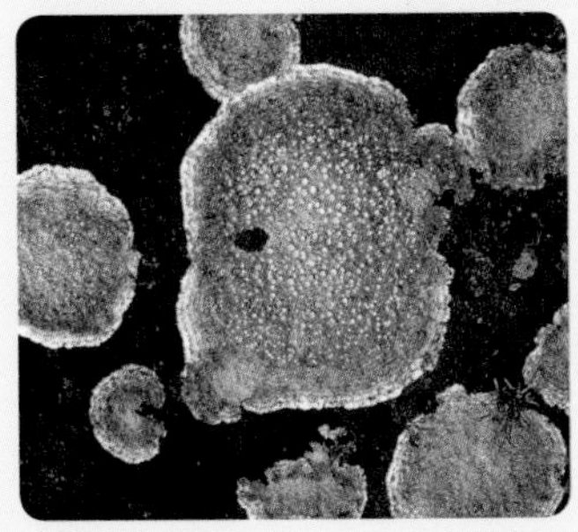

Lichen

**Epilithic algae**: These grow on stone surfaces and can promote the solution of limestones. Algal growth is frequently associated with moisture availability especially where, for example, rainwater is allowed to concentrate and flow down a façade. There is evidence that some forms of chemical cleaning of stone may encourage algal growth by opening up pores and loading stone surfaces with a residue of potential nutrients.

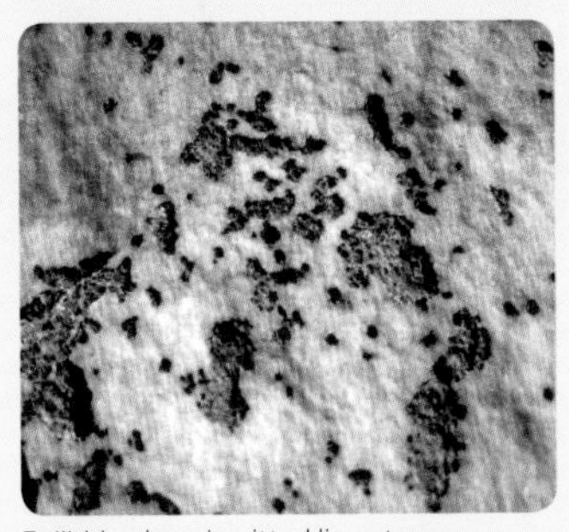

Epilithic algae in pitted limestone

**Endolithic algae**: Algae can live within pores beneath the surface of stone provided enough sunlight can reach them. They often appear as a thin blue-green line just below the surface when the stone is fractured. Within the stone algae can promote processes such as the dissolution of inter-granular cements.

**Vegetation growth**: If building façades are not maintained vegetation will eventually colonise sheltered areas by extending roots into joints and fractures. As the roots grow they can widen these joints and cracks and force stone apart. They may also encourage dampness thus exacerbating other processes such as salt weathering.

Vegetation growth

## Human impacts

**Repair**: Use of a hard cement mortar during re-pointing of relatively soft stone can constrain blocks of stone when they expand and contract in response to heating and cooling and wetting and drying. Repeated compressive stressing of the blocks may eventually result in failure and surface retreat through, in this case, multiple flaking.

Hard mortar repair

**Cleaning**: Overly aggressive power-hosing to remove a cover of epilithic algae from soft, weathered sandstone can result in loss of decorative detail.

Loss of sculptural definition after cleaning

**Corrosion of metal fixings:** Volumetric expansion associated with the corrosion of an iron fixing for a gate in a sandstone wall has caused catastrophic failure of enclosing stone.

Corrosion of metal fixings

**Conflict damage**: The picture below shows bullet damage to a limestone wall in Budapest that was caused during the siege of the city in 1945. Note how black crusts have developed in the sheltered interiors of the bullet holes.

Conflict damage

## Conclusion

Careful observation of the spatial distribution of weathering features developed on stone across a building can provide indications of differences in the severity of conditions the stone is exposed to. For example, groundwater problems may be evident in deterioration of stonework in the lower 1-2m of the building while proximity to a busy road junction may result in one or two façades becoming more soiled than the others. Whilst stone weathering features reflect the action of many different processes acting on different stone types, differences in the nature and extent of their development often reflect the complex micro-environmental conditions created by the building itself and sometimes the effects of human intervention that can unintentionally accelerate decay.

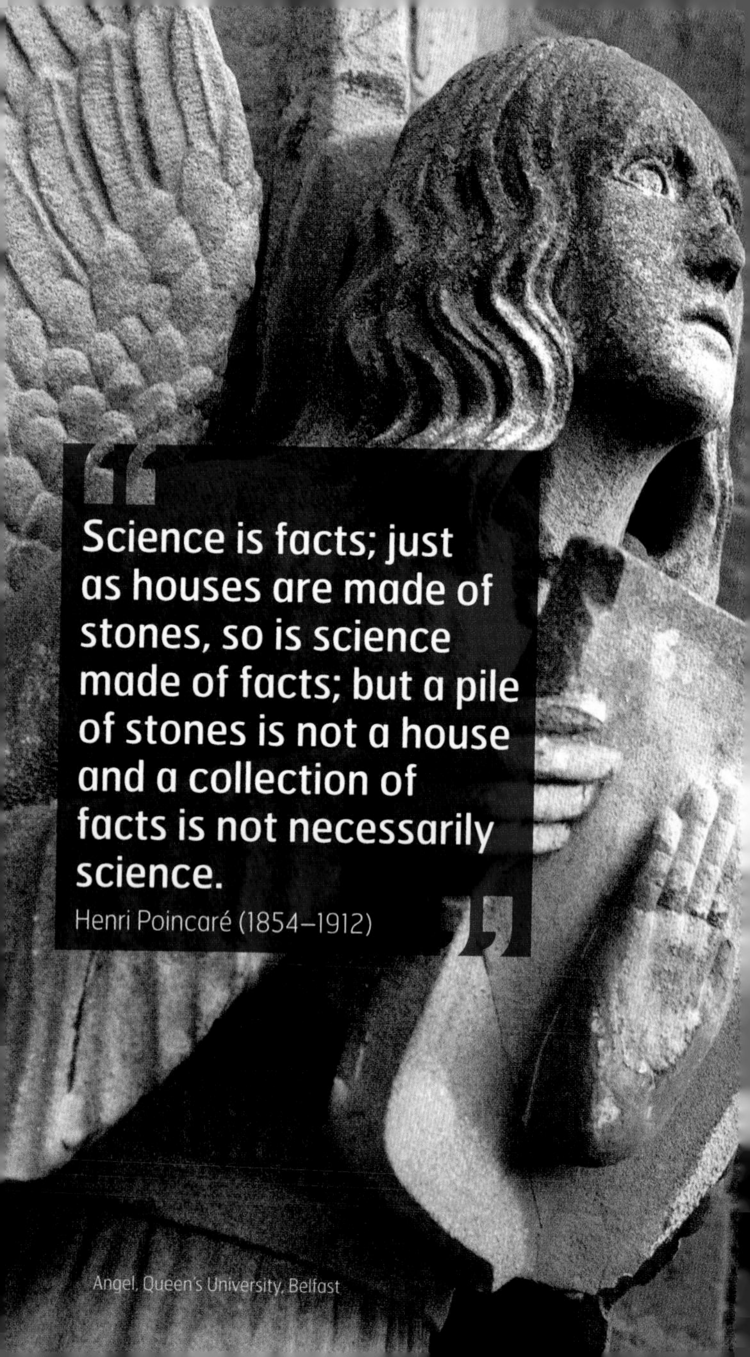


Angel, Queen's University, Belfast

Patricia A. Warke

# Mapping Stone Decay

There are many types of stone built structures ranging from the historically and archaeologically prestigious to those that are less culturally significant. The former are typically of great international importance whilst the latter may be considered valuable in a more local context. However, regardless of their individual merits, together these different structures imbue our city and townscapes with character and bear witness to the cultural and stylistic mores of previous generations.

The internationally important buildings such as the great medieval cathedrals and the wealth of archaeological structures found in countries around the Mediterranean coastline have provided the focus for development of detailed and descriptive schemes for recording stone decay at a block by block and within individual block, level of detail. Due to the degree of detail required, these schemes are costly to apply in terms of both time and manpower and require a high level of expertise. Such schemes are undoubtedly essential components in the development of conservation programmes for internationally significant heritage structures but are definitely not appropriate for those with a 'duty-of-care' for historic buildings who just want a rapid assessment of overall building condition.

Unfortunately, because the focus in assessment scheme development has been on high value structures, buildings at the other end of the significance scale have tended to be treated in a decidedly more *ad hoc* fashion with condition assessment of stonework being reliant on the expertise of the appointed contractor. This non-standardised approach has several disadvantages:

- The quality of expertise depends on training and this may have been gained at the expense of mistakes on other buildings
- There tends to be a lack of a common descriptive terminology with each contractor employing descriptive language for weathering features and stone condition that only *they* fully understand
- Underpinning the above is the lack of a common assessment method that can result in the absence of long-term records of a building against which to compare other buildings and the success or failure of conservation treatments or intervention measures.

Given the above comments, it is obvious that a need exists for development of a recognised standard method for assessing the condition of stonework. The method needs to be relatively simple and rapid to use but sufficiently robust to accommodate different levels of operator expertise. Such a scheme is needed to help safeguard the future of an ever-dwindling stock of comparatively unremarkable historic buildings that nonetheless possess collective significance. The scheme could be used in several ways:

- By individual building owners or those with a 'duty of care' for historic buildings to provide an initial assessment of building condition and as a first-step in identifying problems and the need for intervention
- For a general stock assessment of all historic buildings in a particular urban area by local or national government bodies as a means of creating a database for prioritising and targeting spending on conservation programmes
- By contractors involved in the planning and provision of conservation services whereby the use of such a scheme in initial assessment would provide the first stage of conservation programme planning. It would also provide a base-line record of condition before intervention against which the future condition of the structure could be assessed and the relative success or failure of intervention strategies evaluated.

## Staging System Approach to Condition Assessment of Stonework

Many disciplines have developed condition assessment schemes but there are few that can match the flexibility and rigour of the Staging System developed by medical clinicians to aid in the assessment and treatment planning for cancer patients. This is an internationally recognised and widely applied scheme that provides a shorthand notation for describing the extent of a tumour based on unambiguous categories related to its size, type, degree of local involvement and spread to distant parts of the body.

At first glance the relevance of adapting such a scheme for condition assessment of building stone may seem somewhat tenuous but there are many areas of similarity particularly with regard to diagnosing the severity of deterioration, predicting the extent of intervention required and providing a forecast of 'life expectancy'. The ethos underlying the medical Staging System approach is concerned with producing a relatively rapid measure of the condition of the system as a whole based on assessment of the condition of smaller elements within the system and an understanding of the links between them. In addition, the Staging System approach possesses the following attributes, which are clearly applicable to any stonework evaluation strategy:

- The scheme provides a common assessment method that can be applied to any type of building or monument
- It uses a relatively simple descriptive terminology that facilitates comparisons between assessments done by different personnel at different times
- It facilitates the formulation of a meaningful record of condition before and after treatment
- It allows the success or failure of specific treatments to be evaluated
- The scheme also enables a forecast of outcome to be made with an in-built option to place emphasis on supportive rather than curative treatments.

This latter point is significant for two reasons. First, as a natural response to ageing and long-term exposure stone can undergo varying levels of change in structural and mineralogical characteristics. Such changes are to be expected and may

UAS Staging System grid showing the links between the extent and spread of stone deterioration and the condition stage which in turn gives an indication of the degree of intervention required and an assessment of potential outcome if no remedial treatment is undertaken. (Key to abbreviations in Table 1)

Nature of manifestation and extent of façade involvement →

Outcome: Good → Poor

| Stage | U | A | S |
|---|---|---|---|
| 1 | U0 U1 U2 | A0 | S0 |
| 2 | U1 U2 | A1 | S0 |
| 3 | U1 U2 U3 | A2 A3 | S0 |
| 4 | U1 U2 U3 | S1 | S1 |

pose no immediate threat to the integrity of the structure, with only minimal, targeted intervention and on-going monitoring being the best management option. Second, if deterioration is severe and widespread, the historical or architectural value of the building may not justify the economics of full-scale restoration with effort being more realistically aimed at supportive intervention to keep the building structurally safe but not necessarily resulting in an extension of the 'life expectancy' of the stonework.

## Stage Assessment Method

The Staging System comprises three categories that describe in general terms the extent of deterioration of stonework (see above):

- **Unit (U)** - this refers to the condition of individual stone blocks
- **Area (A)** - this category provides a measure of the involvement of adjoining blocks
- **Spread (S)** - this refers to the extent of visible deterioration across an individual façade.

Each of these categories are divided into different sub-categories **(Table 1)** based on a relative measure of the extent of visible deterioration. When these sub-category values are combined they enable one of the four condition stages to be assigned to the building façade as shown above. The higher the numerical value of the stage identified, the worse the condition of the façade in question and the greater the extent of remedial

Table 1 **Unit, Area and Spread Sub-category Divisions**

| Category | Sub-Category | Description |
|---|---|---|
| **UNIT** | **U0** | No deterioration detectable |
| | **U1** | Surface alteration with minimal evidence of surface breakdown detected affecting only parts of individual blocks |
| | **U2** | Surface alteration and/or obvious surface breakdown involving whole blocks but less than 50% of the whole façade |
| | **U3** | Well-established surface breakdown with loss of original stone surfaces affecting more than 50% of the façade |
| **AREA** | **A0** | No involvement of surrounding blocks detectable |
| | **A1** | Some positive involvement of surrounding/connecting blocks |
| | **A2** | Positive involvement of surrounding/connecting blocks affecting up to 25% of the façade |
| | **A3** | Extensive localised involvement of connecting blocks and beyond affecting 25–50% of the façade |
| **SPREAD** | **S0** | Deterioration is restricted to specific sections of the façade – for example, adjacent to broken rainwater goods |
| | **S1** | Positive deterioration affecting distant unconnected portions of the façade involving more than 50% of the total surface area |

intervention required **(Table 2)**. As previously outlined, in the staging system approach there is in-built recognition that once Stage 4 has been reached there is the option, if funds are limited, to shift emphasis from curative to supportive treatment strategies especially if the cost of intervention outweighs the architectural and historic value of the structure.

A recording sheet should be completed for each façade and the predominant stage value for

| Table 2 **Summary Guidelines for Each Condition Stage** | |
|---|---|
| **STAGE** | **Extent of intervention required** |
| 1 | A façade in this condition would require only localised remedial treatment concentrating on individual stone blocks. A staging classification of 1 may also indicate that no active intervention is required with only periodic reassessment of the façade advised. |
| 2 | Section specific remedial action would be required in this case but the extent of intervention should be relatively limited because of the lack of distant involvement within the façade boundaries. |
| 3 | Significant intervention will be required with up to 50% of the total façade surface showing evidence of deterioration. Although the extent of deterioration is severe, appropriate conservation treatment should prolong the life expectancy of the structure. |
| 4 | Serious deterioration affecting more than 50% of the total façade surface with extensive stone decay detected across the façade. On a Stage 4 category of façade, considerable intervention will be required to restore the stonework. If the structure is of limited historic and/or architectural merit then consideration should be given to the provision of supportive rather than restorative treatment. |

all façades used as an overall condition assessment for the building as a whole. The reliability of the stage assignment can be increased through the collection of stone samples for laboratory analysis. The more samples collected and the greater the variety of analyses employed will increase the certainty of the final stage assignment (**Table 3**).

For example, the presence of obvious surface deterioration of stonework can lead to assumptions regarding the cause of the decay and the depth of stonework affected which may not be accurate and lead to selection of inappropriate intervention treatment. This was clearly demonstrated on a building constructed of clay-rich sandstone that was showing extensive evidence of surface breakdown through flaking, scaling and granular disintegration. The initial intention was to dress the stone blocks back by some 25mm to remove the outer decayed material but subsequent analysis of stone

Table 3 **Summary of Analytical Techniques and Sampling Strategy for Different Certainty Levels**

| Certainty Factors | List of potential analytical techniques | Extent of stone sampling |
|---|---|---|
| CF1 | Visual assessment only | None |
| CF2 | Visual assessment, Ion Chromatography, Atomic Absorption Spectroscopy, X-ray Diffraction | Sampling limited to surface material from blocks showing evidence of deterioration |
| CF3 | Visual assessment, Ion Chromatography, Atomic Absorption Spectroscopy, X-ray Diffraction, Thin-sectioning, Scanning Electron Microscopy, Coring of stonework | Widespread sampling of stone surface and subsurface material from across the whole façade from both intact stone and stone exhibiting evidence of surface deterioration |

cores showed that the salts that were driving this surface breakdown were present in high concentrations deep within the sandstone blocks. Consequently, removing the outer 25mm of stone would have provided only a short-term answer with flaking and scaling becoming re-established within a few months as deep salt deposits were activated. This analytical interpretation of laboratory data was substantiated by a test panel of dressed-back stone on the building. Analysis of stone samples can also help avoid the unnecessary replacement of stone that, apart from some superficial deterioration, is in reasonably good condition.

The stage assignment procedure is outlined in the following sequence of steps, the key components of which are outlined on the site recording sheets shown in the following pages.

| Building Record Sheet | |
|---|---|
| **Building Name** | |
| **Address** | |
| **Townland** | |
| **Architect** | |
| **Building Function** | |
| **Date of Construction** | |
| **Historic Building Record** | |
| **Listing** | |
| **Grid Reference (IG)** | |
| **Date of Survey** | |
| **Exterior Description and Notes**<br><br>Photograph of Building | |
| **Stone Types** | |
| Primary | |
| Secondary | |
| Other | |
| **Construction Type** | |
| **Sample Codes** | |
| **Location of Samples** | |

## Façade Condition Assessment Form

| Name of Building:<br><br>Grid Reference: | | Pointing (L or C)* % | Mortar Repair % | Stone Replacement Type % | Clean/Treatment | Fracturing % | Stone Decay % | Soiling Biological or Pollution % | RW** Goods | Stage & UAS Scores |
|---|---|---|---|---|---|---|---|---|---|---|
| NORTH | | | | | | | | | | |
| EAST | | | | | | | | | | |
| SOUTH | | | | | | | | | | |
| WEST | | | | | | | | | | |
| RESULTS<br>[Certainty Factor: ] | | | | | | | | | | STAGE ? |

* L= Lime; C= Cement; ** RW= Rainwater goods (these were assessed as being in either Good, OK or Poor Condition).

## The Assessment Process

### Step 1

Complete as many of the general background questions on the 'Building Record Sheet' for the building as possible. This section requires a general description of the building with some indication of its age, the architect (if known) and any other relevant information such as, any record of previous conservation treatment and when this took place. It is useful to accompany this section with a general photographic record of the main architectural features and structural components and possibly some images of the immediate environs such as proximity to roads, other buildings etc. In this section stone types used in construction should be identified and a note made of any samples taken.

### Step 2

Using the 'Façade Condition Assessment Form', select the first façade for assessment ie: North facing, South facing etc. Identify a section of the façade that is roughly representative of the condition of the rest of the façade. The size of the section selected should be in proportion to the total size of the façade in question. If there appears to be complex patterns of deterioration across the façade and it is not possible to select a representative section, then the whole façade will need to be assessed. Make a note of any known previous conservation interventions and/or any obvious repairs to the façade (for example, insertion of replacement stone blocks, application of cement render repairs etc.). If any repairs are obvious then a photographic record should be made of these.

### Step 3

Record the main stone type used in construction and any secondary stone types used for architectural detailing such as string-courses, corbelling, quoins etc. Often a general identification such as sandstone, granite etc. will be sufficient at this stage in the process. In some cases it may not be possible to identify the stone type and in such instances, it is recommended that with permission from the building owner, a surface or drilled core sample of stone should be taken for specialist identification. Another important part of this step in the process is the identification and recording of any factors that may predispose stone to deterioration. Examples of common predisposing factors are:

- Poorly maintained rainwater goods that allow water to flow over the stone surface thus

Plant growth and broken drain pipes

'Hard' mortar and flaking sandstone

Salt-driven sandstone breakdown

'Greening' of sandstone façade

encouraging biological growth, surface staining, potential degradation of mortars and deep moisture penetration of stonework. Poorly maintained rainwater goods tend to have localised effects on a building and can facilitate biological activity (top left)

- Inappropriate pointing or mortar replacement with hard cement mortar can have a particularly widespread adverse impact on 'soft' stones such as sandstone as it prevents the natural expansion of stone associated with heating or wetting. This constraint typically results in flaking and scaling around the edges of blocks (top right). The presence of 'hard' mortar in association with deterioration of stone is a good indication that the mortar may need to be replaced. However, it is important to note that not all stone types are adversely affected by 'hard' mortars.

**Step 4**

Carry out the visual assessment of stone condition within the

Soiling of limestone

Limestone washed by rain

Fracturing of stone due to corrosion of embedded metalwork

selected section of the façade. The criteria used in visual assessment are quite limited and generalised with a reliance on assessing whether they are present or absent and if present, to what extent through an estimation of the percentage area of the façade affected. The criteria included on the recording sheet are:

- Evidence of obvious surface stone decay through scaling, flaking and granular disintegration (ie; whether there is loose material on block surfaces that can be easily dislodged) (previous page, bottom left)
- Presence and extent of biological colonisation (for example, algae, lichens, moss etc.) – if individual plant forms are not visible a general surface 'greening' of stone indicates the presence of algae (previous page bottom right)
- Presence and extent of surface staining and/or soiling. Soiling may be widespread affecting most of the façade caused, for example by proximity to a busy road junction and the associated vehicle exhaust emissions that have discoloured the façade of this Portland limestone building (top left). Soiling may also be related to some more localised factor where, for example, sections of the façade are sheltered from direct rainwash (top centre)
- Presence of any other signs of stone alteration or deterioration such as fracturing of blocks (top right). Such features may be associated with failure of an individual stone block due to corrosion of metalwork or may indicate more serious structural problems.

Table 4 **Example of Stage Assignment Where Individual Building Façades Display Different Stage Characteristics**

| Façade description | UAS notations | Stage classification |
|---|---|---|
| North-facing | U1, A2, S0 | 3 |
| East-facing | U2, A2, S0 | 3 |
| South-facing | U3, S1 | 4 |
| West-facing | U1, A3, S0 | 3 |
| **Overall Stage Assigned** | | **3** |

**Step 5**
On the basis of the visual assessment a sub-category from each of the main **U, A** and **S** categories should be assigned to the façade in question. For example, a sandstone façade showing evidence of surface deterioration of individual blocks and some entire blocks with deterioration affecting some adjoining blocks but no extensive involvement of the whole façade will fall into the U2, A1 and S0 sub-categories. When checked on the staging assessment grid these notations give the façade in question a Stage 2 classification with a certainty factor of CF1 because the stage assignment was based solely on a visual assessment.

**Step 6**
The above sequence should be repeated for each façade with the predominant stage value being used to represent the condition of the building as a whole (**Table 4**). If the building referred to in Table 4 had two façades being classified as Stage 3 and the other two as Stage 4 then an overall Stage 4 classification should be assigned to the building. It is unusual to encounter a building where there is a significant disparity between the condition of different façades but it can happen where, for example one façade has been protected from exposure to atmospheric pollution by the presence of another building (see next page). If the sheltering building is subsequently demolished the newly exposed façade will present a very different

Differences in façade condition

appearance and condition to the rest of the structure. In such cases the predominant higher stage value should be recorded as being representative of the building as a whole. Some differences between the condition of separate façades is to be expected and may be related to aspect with the 'weather' side of the building often showing more evidence of deterioration.

Assignment of the correct 'Stage' is extremely important, for example, under-staging a building can result in the need for intervention being under-emphasized. Conversely, over-staging can result in a rush to intervention that may not be immediately necessary. If an assessment is borderline between two stages then the higher value stage should automatically be assigned.

The completed assessment and stage assignment provides an important record of the condition of the building. Even if the stage assigned indicates that no immediate intervention is required, a regular regime of monitoring should be initiated with a reassessment of the building carried out every two to five years depending on results from the initial assessment.

Billy Parish Church. A Gothic style chapel built in 1815

Basalt blocks, showing no evidence of deterioration

## Stage Classification Examples

As an aid to stage classification, examples of buildings in the four different stage categories, are shown in the following section.

### Stage 1 Classification

**Example: Billy Parish Church, County Antrim.**

A façade in this condition should require only localised remedial treatment concentrating on individual stone blocks. A staging classification of '1' may also indicate that no immediate intervention is required with only periodic reassessment of the façade being advised.

| Building Record Sheet | |
|---|---|
| **Building Name** | Billy Parish Church |
| **Address** | 1 Cabragh Road, Glebe, Bushmills, BT57 8UH |
| **Townland** | Glebe |
| **Architect** | Not known |
| **Building Function** | Church |
| **Date of Construction** | 1815 |
| **Historic Building Record** | HB05/07/001 |
| **Listing** | B+ |
| **Grid Reference (IG)** | 295829 438235 |
| **Date of Survey** | 11/01/06 |
| **Exterior Description and Notes**  | Gothic style nave fronted by a three stage square tower with battlements, corner pinnacles and arched windows with hood moulds. Pitched slate roof. Later addition of apse style chancel in 1890. Yellow sandstone used on original window dressing with red sandstone courses. The building was recently cleaned, repointed with lime mortar and fitted with new rainwater goods. |
| **Stone Types** | |
| Primary | Basalt |
| Secondary | Ballycastle Sandstone |
| Other | English Carboniferous Sandstone |
| **Construction Type** | Rough coursed rubble |
| **Sample Codes** | AM/C/BILLY1 |
| **Location of Samples** | Window Surround |

## Façade Condition Assessment Form

| | **Name of Building:** Billy Parish Church<br>**Grid Reference:** 295829 438235 | Pointing (L or C)* % | Mortar Repair % | Stone Replacement Type % | Clean/Treatment | Fracturing % | Stone Decay% | Soiling Biological or Pollution% | RW** Goods | Stage & UAS Scores |
|---|---|---|---|---|---|---|---|---|---|---|
| NORTH | **Soiling**: limited<br>**Decay**: basalt in good order. Sandstone: courses eroded, weathering and flaking under window | 100 L | 0-2 | 0 | yes | 0 | 2-10 | 0-2 | Good | 1 **U**2 **A**0 **S**0 |
| EAST | **Soiling**: limited, mainly sandstone dressing – green patches of biological growth<br>**Decay**: basalt in good order. Sandstone: surface granular disintegration under door archway. Heavy flaking under window arches, occasional flaking under courses | 100 L | 0-2 | 0 | yes | 0 | 2-10 | 2-10 | Good | 1 **U**2 **A**0 **S**0 |
| SOUTH | **Soiling**: limited, mainly chancel, sandstone and courses<br>**Decay**: basalt in good order. Sandstone: surface granular disintegration on window. Replacement corner stone of lower course and door entrance | 100 L | 0-2 | 0-2 | yes | 0 | 2-10 | 2-10 | Good | 1 **U**2 **A**0 **S**0 |
| WEST | **Tower Soiling**: clean, patches of bio on pinnacles<br>**Decay**: basalt in good order. Sandstone: surface weathering and granular disintegration, older blocks weathered. Replacement blocks on courses & window | 100 L | 0-2 | 0-2 | yes | 0 | 0-2 | 0-2 | Good | 1 **U**2 **A**0 **S**0 |
| | **RESULTS**<br>**Certainty Factor: CF2** | 100 L | 0-2 | 0-2 | yes | 0 | 2-10 | 2-10 | Good | **STAGE 1** |

* L= Lime; C= Cement; ** RW= Rainwater goods (these were assessed as being in either Good, OK or Poor Condition).

Stormont Castle, a Scottish Baronial style castle built in 1830

## Stage 2 Classification

### Example: Stormont Castle, Belfast.

Section specific remedial action would be required in this case but the extent of intervention should be relatively limited because the areas showing decay are isolated.

Much of the sandstone decay observed appears to be related to the type of mortar used which may require intervention in the future.

Deterioration of block corners

| Building Record Sheet | |
|---|---|
| **Building Name** | Stormont Castle |
| **Address** | Stormont Estate, Upper Newtownards Road, Belfast |
| **Townland** | Ballymiscaw |
| **Architect** | Thomas Turner (LA); Stone Contractor |
| | (Restoration): McConnell and Sons |
| **Building Function** | Offices/Administrative |
| **Date of Construction** | 1830, enlarged 1858, works: 1920s, recently: 2001 |
| **Historic Building Record** | HB26/13/014 |
| **Listing** | B+ |
| **Grid Reference (IG)** | 340292 374768 |
| **Date of Survey** | 18/07/07 |
| **Exterior Description and Notes**  | Scottish Baronial style castle. The main face is three storeys and eight bays wide. The centre of the main face has a two storey canted bay window with remaining windows with square-topped sashes and bartizans at either end of the façade. There is a tall tower at the East end with a large door surround, topped with a balustrade. |
| **Stone Types** | |
| Primary | Scrabo Sandstone (Ballyalton) |
| Secondary | Stanton Moor Replacement |
| Other | |
| **Construction Type** | Uncoursed rock-faced |
| **Sample Codes** | |
| **Location of Samples** | |

## Façade Condition Assessment Form

**Name of Building:** Stormont Castle

**Grid Reference:** 340292 374768

FAÇADE DESCRIPTIONS

| Façade | Description | Pointing (L or C)* % | Mortar Repair % | Stone Replacement Type % | Clean/Treatment | Fracturing % | Stone Decay % | Soiling Biological or Pollution % | RW** Goods | Stage & UAS Scores |
|---|---|---|---|---|---|---|---|---|---|---|
| NORTH | **Modern Extension (not assessed)** | | | | | | | | | |
| EAST | **Soiling**: mild black soiling across face, green biological growth in sheltered areas<br>**Decay**: mostly mortar damage, flaking and scaling around edges, some pitting, whole block faces | 100 C? | 0-2 | 0-2 | yes | 0-2 | 30-50 | 10-30 | OK | 2 **U**2 **A**1 **S**0 |
| SOUTH | **Soiling**: mild black soiling across face, white and yellow lichen on lower string-course<br>**Decay**: mortar damage causing flaking and scaling, whole block faces, occasional pitting and differential weathering | 100 C? | 0-2 | 0-2 | yes | 0-2 | 30-50 | 10-30 | OK | 2 **U**2 **A**1 **S**0 |
| WEST | **Soiling**: mild black soiling across face, heavier and green biological growth on string-course and detail | 100 C? | 0-2 | 0-2 | yes | 0-2 | 30-50 | 10-30 | OK | 2 **U**2 **A**1 **S**0 |
| | **RESULTS**<br>**Certainty Factor: CF1** | 100 C? | 0-2 | 0-2 | yes | 0-2 | 30-50 | 10-30 | OK | **STAGE 2** |

* L= Lime; C= Cement; ** RW= Rainwater goods (these were assessed as being in either Good, OK or Poor Condition).

Front of Star Factory, Londonderry

## Stage 3 Classification

### Example: Star Factory, County Londonderry

Significant intervention will be required on façades with this stage classification with up to 50% of the total façade surface showing evidence of significant deterioration. Two of the three façades assessed were identified as being at Stage 3 with the other identified at Stage 2. An overall assignment of Stage 3 was made. Despite the extent of deterioration, appropriate conservation treatment should prolong the life expectancy of the building.

Scaling and flaking of sandstone window dressing

Flaking of sandstone associated with hard cement mortar pointing

| Building Record Sheet | |
|---|---|
| **Building Name** | Star Factory, Londonderry |
| **Address** | 79E Foyle Road |
| **Townland** | Londonderry |
| **Architect** | Daniel Conroy |
| **Building Function** | Factory |
| **Date of Construction** | 1889 |
| **Historic Building Record** | HB01/17/004 |
| **Listing** | B+ |
| **Grid Reference (IG)** | 243089 415887 |
| **Date of Survey** | 01/08/07 |
| **Exterior Description and Notes**  | Five storey, ten bay former factory. Rounded arch windows on ground floor and large central archway with 'Star Factory' above. Windows on other floors are segmented arches with keystones. Clock at centre of 4th floor with stone surround, keystone and balustrade. Rest of 4th floor is metal sheeted apart from sides |
| **Stone Types** | |
| Primary | Donegal Sandstone (Mullaghmore) |
| Secondary | English Carboniferous Sandstone |
| Other | |
| **Construction Type** | Coursed quarry faced |
| **Sample Codes** | LY330 |
| **Location of Samples** | |

## Façade Condition Assessment Form

**Name of Building:** Star Factory, Londonderry

**Grid Reference:** 243089 415887

FAÇADE DESCRIPTIONS

| | Description | Pointing (L or C)* % | Mortar Repair % | Stone Replacement Type % | Clean/Treatment | Fracturing % | Stone Decay % | Soiling Biological or Pollution % | RW** Goods | Stage & UAS Scores |
|---|---|---|---|---|---|---|---|---|---|---|
| NORTH | **Rendered (not assessed)** | | | | | | | | | |
| EAST | **Soiling**: heavier soiling on this façade with mild black and green especially at the base. Occasionally moss with heavy black soiling on stringcourse and cills<br>**Decay**: Sandstone in a very bad condition, flaking over much of the façade with granular disintegration, scaling bedding plane weathering and occasional honeycombing. Some replacement at northern end | 100 C | 0-2 | 0-2 | Yes | 0-2 | >50 | 30-50 | OK | 3 **U**3 **A**3 **S**0 |
| SOUTH | **Soiling**: rust staining down part of face (corrosion-related) with some greening on clock and cills<br>**Decay**: worse on this face with granular disintegration, pitting, flaking and honeycombing of ashlar stone | 100 C | 0-2 | 0-2 | Yes | 0-2 | >50 | 10-30 | OK | 3 **U**3 **A**3 **S**0 |
| WEST | **Soiling**: patchy black soiling especially under windows and cills<br>**Decay**: Sandstone in better condition with some pitting, flaking and occasional hollow development. Evidence of some block replacement | 100 C | 0-2 | 0-2 | Yes | 0-2 | <50 | 30-50 | OK | 2 **U**2 **A**1 **S**0 |
| | **RESULTS**<br>**Certainty Factor: CF2** | 100 C | 0-2 | 0-2 | Yes | 0-2 | >50 | 30-50 | OK | STAGE 3 |

* L= Lime; C= Cement; ** RW= Rainwater goods (these were assessed as being in either Good, OK or Poor Condition).

Larne Town Hall

**Stage 4 Classification**

**Example: Larne Town Hall, County Antrim**

Serious deterioration affecting more than 50% of the total façade surface with stone decay detected on unconnected, distant portions of the façade. On a stage 4 category of façade, considerable intervention will be required to restore the stonework. If the structure is of limited historic and/or architectural merit and if funds are limited then consideration may be given to the provision of supportive or selective rather than full restorative treatment.

Widespread surface deterioration of stonework with loss of architectural detail

| Building Record Sheet | |
|---|---|
| **Building Name** | Larne Town Hall |
| **Address** | Upper Cross Street, Larne, BT40 1SZ |
| **Townland** | Town Parks |
| **Architect** | Alexander Tate, Samuel P. Close. |
| **Building Function** | Town Hall |
| **Date of Construction** | 1868 |
| **Historic Building Record** | HB06/12/002 |
| **Listing** | B+ |
| **Grid Reference (IG)** | 340039 402601 |
| **Date of Survey** | 23/08/05 |
| **Exterior Description and Notes** | Italianate style Town Hall (two storey, eleven bays) with a central square tower and clock. Pitched slate roof with gabled upper windows. Main stone type is Scrabo Sandstone with string-course detailing in red sandstone and slate columns on windows and at the entrance. |
| **Stone Types** | |
| Primary | Scrabo Sandstone |
| Secondary | Slate Columns |
| Other | |
| **Construction Type** | Random coursed, rock-faced |
| **Sample Codes** | AM/B/TH1, AM/B/TH2, AM/B/TH3 |
| **Location of Samples** | |

## Façade Condition Assessment Form

**Name of Building:** Larne Town Hall

**Grid Reference:** 340039 402601

| FAÇADE DESCRIPTIONS | | Pointing (L or C)* % | Mortar Repair % | Stone Replacement Type % | Clean/Treatment | Fracturing % | Stone Decay % | Soiling Biological or Pollution % | RW** Goods | Stage & UAS Scores |
|---|---|---|---|---|---|---|---|---|---|---|
| NORTH | **Soiling**: Some vegetation at roof level, some biological growth<br><br>**Decay**: Scaling and flaking across face. Loss of some faces of stone | 100 C | 0-2 | 0 | No | 0 | >50 | 10-30 | OK | 4<br>**U**3<br>**A**2<br>**S**1 |
| EAST | **Adjoining Building (not assessed)** | | | | | | | | | |
| SOUTH | **Soiling**: Heavy in corners, cills, and lower face<br><br>**Decay**: Heavy scaling and flaking across face. Cracks in slate columns | 100 C | 0-2 | 0 | No | 0-2 | >50 | 30-50 | OK | 4<br>**U**3<br>**A**2<br>**S**1 |
| WEST | **Soiling**: Biological growth on cills, courses, and tower, gables heavy. Some vegetation growth on gables and corner, slates clean.<br><br>**Decay**: Heavy scaling, flaking of majority of exposed stone faces. Heavy loss of detail on door carving. Scaling on string courses. Loss of face occasionally open joints. Broken slate columns in doorway | 100 C | 0-2 | 0 | No | 0-2 | >50 | 30-50 | OK | 4<br>**U**3<br>**A**2<br>**S**1 |
| | **RESULTS**<br><br>**Certainty Factor: CF2** | 100 C | 0-2 | 0 | No | 0-2 | >50 | 30-50 | OK | **STAGE 4** |

* L= Lime; C= Cement; ** RW= Rainwater goods (these were assessed as being in either Good, OK or Poor Condition).

## Summary Comments

Condition assessment is an essential first step in development of an appropriate conservation strategy. Even when conservation work is not envisaged, condition assessment is important because it creates a base-line record of building condition against which to monitor future change and to provide early warning of the potential need for any remedial action.

In the care of buildings it is important to recognise that change is a natural characteristic of stone and that most building stone will show some evidence of change following construction as it adjusts to the new conditions of exposure. Such change may affect colour or texture and is generally benign occurring relatively gradually over many decades. However, there is a big difference between such relatively benign gradual change associated with the natural ageing of a building and change that heralds the onset of more serious deterioration. For example, the nature and rate of stone decay may change relatively rapidly in response to a variety of actions such as overly aggressive stone cleaning, poor maintenance of rainwater goods, use of inappropriate re-pointing material, fire damage, increased atmospheric pollution, or a change in groundwater conditions. Recognition that stone has a finite 'life-span' which can be greatly shortened by either well-intentioned but inappropriate intervention or long-term neglect, is an important first step to good building management.

The importance of having a formal record of the building condition cannot be too greatly emphasized. It is only with such a record that it is possible to evaluate long-term stone response and identify sections 'at risk' on a building from accelerated deterioration with all the associated implications of this for the rest of the structure. The staging system approach is a first-step in formulating a standardised method of building stone condition assessment that is relatively rapid and straightforward to use. Aside from its value as a preliminary assessment tool for building owners, the main value of this scheme lies in its use in the creation of a base-line assessment of historic building stock within a town, city or region. Such inventories are essential in targeting the ever-diminishing funds available for conservation and for establishing a database of structures, the condition of which may not have been formally recorded or monitored.

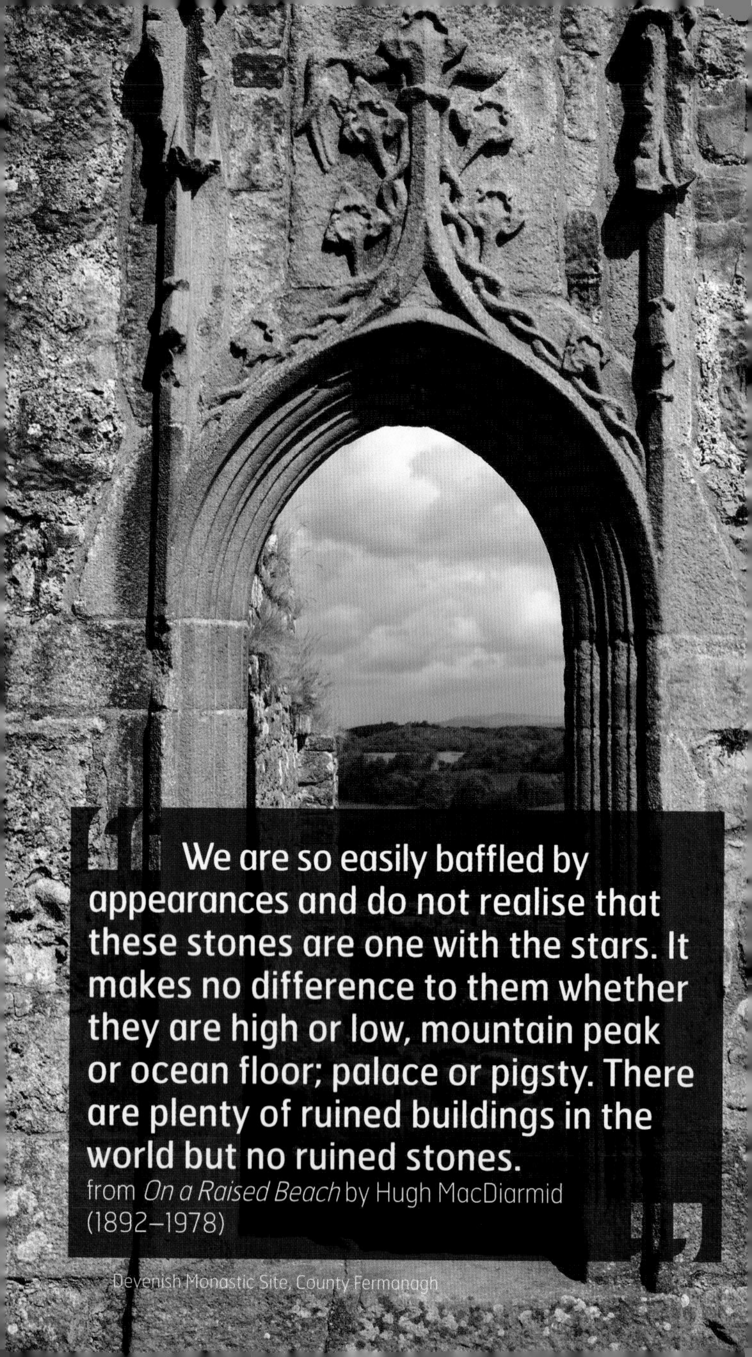


Devenish Monastic Site, County Fermanagh

Joanne Curran, John Savage and Dawson Stelfox

# Repair Strategies for Stone

## Overview

Every repair project will present different combinations of physical and environmental factors. There is no 'one size fits all' solution but a carefully thought out repair strategy made up specifically for each case is required.

However, there are some universal principles that should be applied to every conservation based project, and against which any repair strategy should be tested before being applied:

- The historical importance of the building or structure should be established at the start of a project so that its significance can be preserved or enhanced
- There should be comprehensive recording by drawings, photographs and written notes, before, during and after the works
- There should be a full survey and analysis of the problems before deciding on repair and restoration works
- A policy of minimal intervention should be applied to all decisions on repair or replacement of historic fabric – so that only repairs that are absolutely necessary to secure the physical or structural integrity of the building are carried out with maximum retention of historic material. Prioritisation of repairs is essential
- There should be 'clarity' about the extent of repair or restoration work. For most masonry buildings this will be achieved by careful recording, with new work aimed at seamlessly blending in to the original. However, in the case of scheduled monuments the aim is normally to visibly distinguish between original work and repairs by for example, making

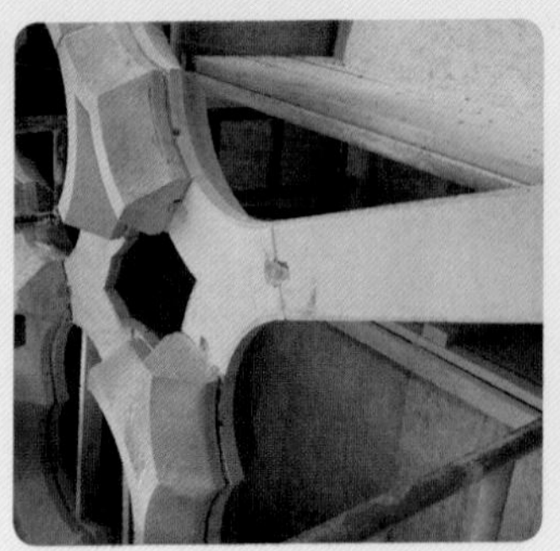
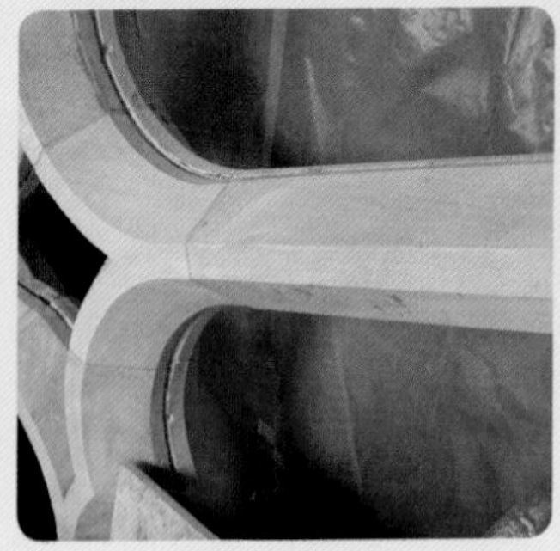

Repair to sandstone tracery with removal of defective stone and replacement with new sandstone chosen to match the original (see also page 174)

a deliberate distinction between new and old materials or a separating layer so that there is no conjecture

- The 'holy grail' of reversibility should underpin all conservation work. In other words, whatever we do now should, if future needs arise, be able to be reversed with no overall loss of historic fabric or significance. In practice, as you might imagine, this is difficult to achieve
- Repair goes hand-in-hand with maintenance so all repair strategies should be prepared with future maintenance programmes in mind.

Exemplary stone repair, like most aspects of conservation, is not the preserve of any one profession or trade, but rather the product of collaboration between disciplines such as architects, archaeologists, geologists, analysts, stone masons, structural engineers, surveyors, historians, maintenance officers and habitat ecologists, depending on the nature of a project. It is essential at the start of each project that the appropriate team is assembled to properly address all the relevant issues. To do this, requires broad knowledge and experience, and this normally falls within the remit of the Conservation Architect whose role it is to know enough about all of the issues so that he or she can manage, guide and coordinate the overall team. Knowledge in aspects of architecture, hard practical experience of construction methods and craft skills is crucial to ensure that the theoretical analysis and desired outcome of the repair strategy are translated into realistic and practical methodologies, specifications and schedules. The appointment of the professional team is probably the most crucial

Acknowledgement of conservation works

Membrane distinguishing area of stone work rebuilt during monument restoration

decision the client will take in the course of a repair or restoration project as trust in their advice is central to a successful, cost effective and high quality result. Appointments can be made in many ways and there are advantages and disadvantages associated with each, as detailed in **Table 1** overleaf.

**Accreditation**

It is clear that the ability to properly survey, assess and specify repairs and conservation of historic stonework requires a combination of experience and expertise, within a general understanding of the philosophy of conservation practice. Increasingly, historic building conservation is recognized as a specialism within the construction professions, though it is also important that there is sufficient expertise within the general profession to know when and how to get specialist help when it is required. Unfortunately, most college training of architects, engineers and surveyors focuses on new construction rather than adaptations and repairs, despite the fact that around half of the construction industry is involved in refurbishment, repair, maintenance and conservation. There is therefore an important role for post-graduate qualifications.

Most of the professional bodies representing architects, engineers and surveyors are at present collaborating on a coordinated process for accreditation in conservation expertise. This is broadly based on a training website developed by the groups to be found under **www.understandingconservation.org.** Each professional body has its own accreditation system and details of these can be found in Appendix B.

| Table 1 **Factors to Consider When Appointing a Professional Team** | |
|---|---|
| **Approach** | **Suitable for** |
| Appointment by recommendation of individual professionals or a team with a lead consultant. | Private owners<br>(No public money involved) |
| Using accreditation schemes and/or directories. | Private owners<br>Companies<br>(No public money involved) |
| Select list drawn up using recommendations, accreditation schemes and directories, followed by appointment process involving a quality submission and fee proposal and possibly an interview. | Private owners<br>Companies<br>Churches<br>Community / Charitable groups |
| Public advertisement with criteria listed to prepare shortlist, followed by appointment process involving a quality submission and fee proposal. | Public money involved<br>Companies<br>Churches<br>Community / Charitable groups<br>Government |
| Framework agreements: appointment as above but for multiple projects. | Government bodies<br>Large institutions |
| Design competition. | Government<br>Major community projects |

| Advantages | Disadvantages |
| --- | --- |
| Quick, easy, process based on a personal recommendation or in viewing their other work. | Difficult to be certain you are making the right choice or getting value for money. |
| More objective than above, using for example, RIBA or RIAI conservation accreditation schemes or UAHS / Irish Georgian Society directories. | No 'competitive' process to ensure value for money. |
| A verifiable process to justify decisions and help ensure quality of appointment and value for money. | Brief development and scoring criteria needs careful preparation. |
| Open, public, process to arrive at a justifiable decision based on objective scoring. | More expensive process than above requiring even higher levels of brief development and scoring criteria. |
| Useful where client is carrying out a series of similar projects, creating appointment efficiency and a build up of relationships and corporate knowledge. | A certain inflexibility. No two conservation projects are likely to be identical and team selection should reflect needs of each job. |
| For significant and complex projects where a high design quality is required to realize the full potential of a project. | Expensive process for all concerned. RSUA/RIBA/RIAI can provide the organisation to run a fair and open competition. |

Three flying butresses added to the 'Collation Seat' of Grey Abbey in 1908 by the conservation enthusiast William Morris. This 'visible crutch' was preferable to taking down and rebuilding. However, this intervention was strongly criticised for inappropriate style and overpowering effect

The Royal Society of Ulster Architects (RSUA) offers a Certificate and Diploma in Historic Building Conservation. Practicing architects who have gained this post-graduate qualification are listed in the RSUA Handbook and on their website. The scheme, however, is open to all professions, and a number of planners, engineers, surveyors and building control officers, as well as architects, have completed this course in recent years.

The Royal Institution of Chartered Surveyors (RICS) has a Building Conservation Forum which runs an accreditation scheme for surveyors in conservation. The Building Conservation section of the website contains a lot of useful and relevant material on good practice in conservation. There is an active branch of the Institute of Historic Building Conservation (IHBC) in Northern Ireland and, uniquely, this body brings together all those interested in conservation, from all professions, with membership drawn from both public and private sectors.

The trend is towards the statutory and grant-giving bodies requiring professional accreditation of those charged with work to

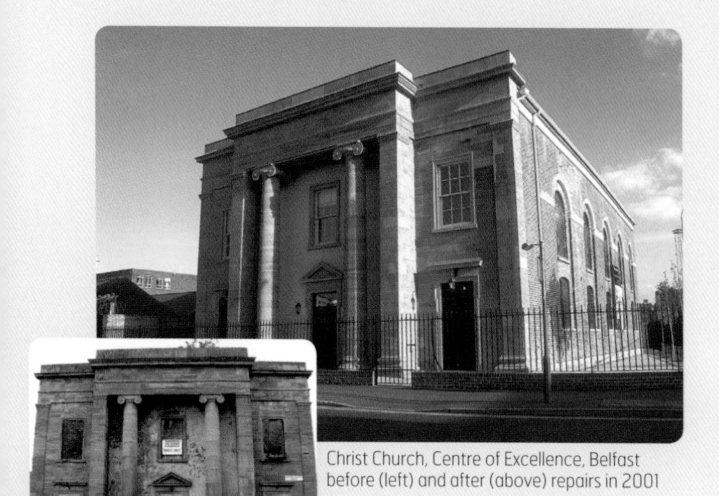

Christ Church, Centre of Excellence, Belfast before (left) and after (above) repairs in 2001

historic buildings, in particular where public money is being sought. In Northern Ireland, the NIEA grant scheme currently requires those responsible to be 'suitably experienced or qualified' but it is expected that this will change to require formal accreditation within the next three to five years. It is therefore in the interests of all those working in historic building conservation to gain accreditation.

**Directories**

The Ulster Architectural Heritage Society (UAHS) Directory of Traditional Building Skills is a very useful source for professionals, contractors and suppliers but it is important to note that this is not an accreditation scheme. This directory can be downloaded from the UAHS website at **www.uahs.co.uk**. Those listed are self selecting, standing on the basis of their named projects, so the onus is on those tasked with appointing specialists to check their credentials.

The Irish Georgian Society (IGS) publish a similar directory – the Traditional Building Skills Register, which can be found on their website at **www.igs.ie**.

Removing section of detached high level brickwork

Unstable stone mullion to dormer window

## Condition Surveys and Reports

As described in the chapter on 'Mapping Stone Decay', there is a simple condition assessment process to provide building owners and those with a 'duty-of-care' for historic stone structures with a means for identifying the overall condition of a building. When a decision has been made to proceed with the implementation of a remedial works programme a much more detailed 'stone by stone' condition survey is an essential first step in project planning.

For successful repair and conservation of stone structures a coordinated and comprehensive assessment of stone fabric carried out by specialists is an essential pre-requisite. There is no pro-forma for a stonework survey as it depends on the detailed form of the structure or building and it is important that any survey and accompanying report should be practical and of use to the building owner. A brief initial report should outline essential repairs and direct the building owner to the next steps, whilst a detailed report should provide information that is transferable and can be used in any future tender documentation. It is also important that the survey considers the building in its entirety, both exterior and interior fabric, to gain an overview of the whole structure. Problems with building fabric are often due to interlinked defects and knowledge of how a building is constructed, the type of roof, leadwork, rainwater disposal, drainage, internal wall and floor construction, can help solve problems with the stone fabric and inform the method of repair.

All Condition Survey and Reports should provide building owners with some level of information on the following:

- A brief history of the building including any significant events (such as a fire) and previous works

Unstable high level stonework

- An overview of the condition of the building fabric
- A record of defects (marked up on drawing or photos)
- Prioritised repairs with recommendations for timescales and feasible packages of repairs
- Research and analysis for the specification of materials and methods for repair
- Budget costs.

**Hoists and harnesses**

Experience shows that surveying stonework from the ground can never provide an accurate picture of fabric condition and leads invariably to costly variations when a repair scheme goes on site. Stone should be inspected closely at all levels and it is essential that the high level stonework is checked to assess stability, movement and nature of mortar joints (see photos above and opposite). Ideally, surveys should be carried out from a Mobile Elevation Work Platform (MEWP) or 'cherry picker' with personnel (driver and surveyors) secured with appropriate harnesses for safety. In some circumstances where vehicle access is restricted or not available, rope access techniques (abseil) will be needed to carry out a survey. Surveying by abseil can only be done by IRATA (Industrial Rope Access Trade Association) qualified personnel.

A Heath and Safety Policy, Risk Assessments and Method Statements should be provided by stone surveyors, together with appropriate Public and Employer's Liability Insurance in place.

Point Cloud data from Digital Laser Scan

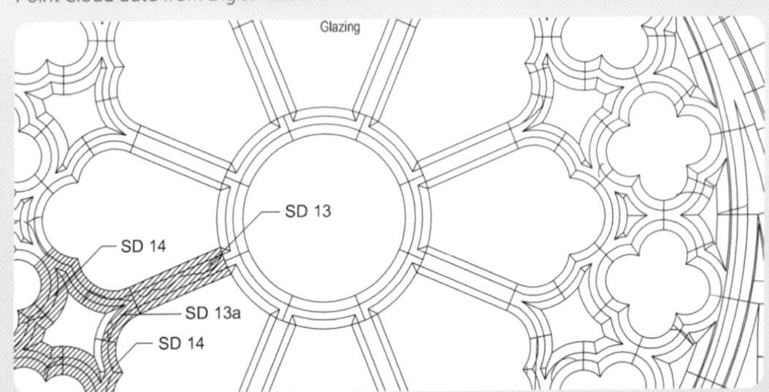

Detail drawn up on Computer Aided Design (CAD) software

**Drawings and photographs**

Ideally, stone defects should be marked up accurately on elevation drawings on which details of the stonework are shown. Alternatively, when drawings are not available, stone defects can be marked up on detailed photographs of the elevations. Increasingly, laser scanning equipment is becoming more widely available, this produces drawings to millimetre accuracy. Laser scanners can capture the 3D geometry of exposed surfaces in minutes in the form of accurate '3D point clouds' and the scanner can be rotated or moved around the site to capture entire façades or landscapes. The 3D point clouds can be exported to CAD and other rendering software (see above). Slices through these data allow the creation of planimetric and elevation drawings. Such 'stone accurate' drawings can be of great benefit as they allow defects to be marked up accurately. The resolution of the scan determines

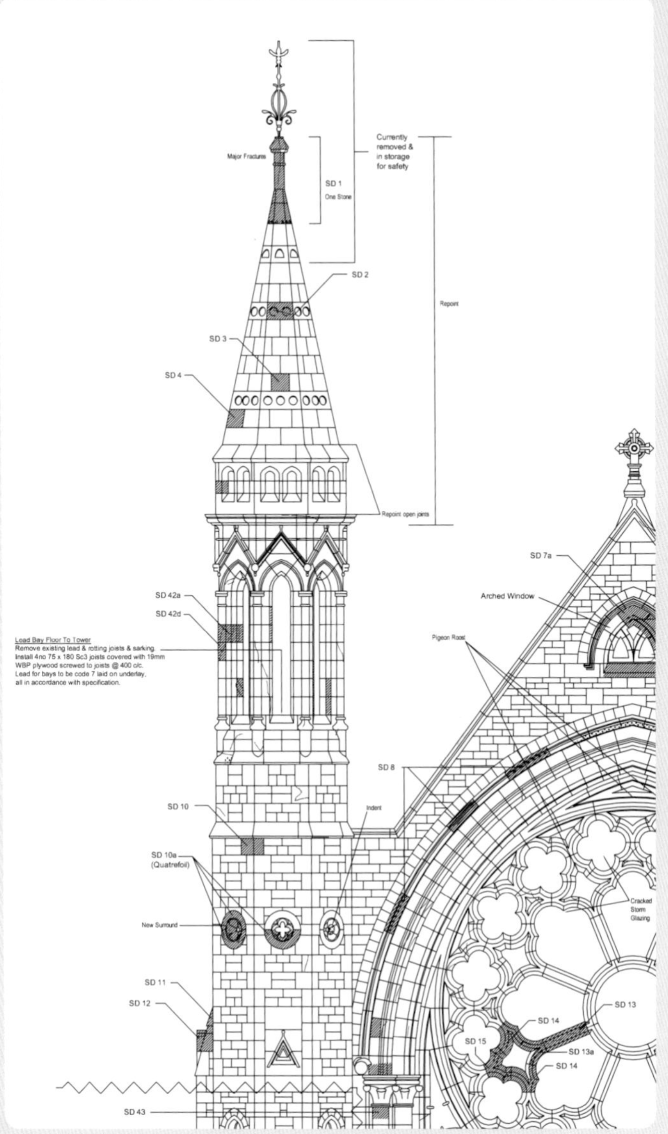


Marked-up drawing following survey

Fracturing of stone due to rusting of embedded metal

Opening of joints and movement of stone due to expansion caused by rusting of embedded metal

the level of detail recorded. For example, intricately carved elements can be scanned at a very high resolution to ensure capture of all detail. Accurate drawings can also be used to extract information for stone sizes, profiles and details when putting together the 'Schedule of Works' for tender documentation.

**Stone by stone**

Regardless of how accurate the drawings are, how detailed the photography or how sophisticated the technology, there is no substitute for thorough eye level and hands-on inspection of each façade by surveyors. This allows an in-depth assessment of the stonework and provides an overview of the condition of the building fabric. Having this first-hand information allows remedial works to be prioritised accurately, informs recommendations for repair and directs the next steps for the building owner.

Close inspection of elevations at all levels can also provide an assessment of 'hidden' defects likely to become a major issue for the future. This is especially true for embedded metal in stonework. Water penetration through open joints and fractures causes corrosion of internal metal elements and the associated expansion can catastrophically fracture stonework. Failure of stone at high level presents a serious health and safety risk. In addition, remedial works associated with these defects can be extremely invasive and expensive often requiring significant quantities of replacement stone.

The extent of corrosion can often be difficult to ascertain unless

## Marking up Stonework Repairs on Photographs

**Key for stone replacement**

Priority 1

Priority 2

Priority 3

a close inspection is carried out. In many cases, rusting can progress within the stonework without any obvious visible signs on the surface. When surface cracking does commence it proceeds rapidly and usually requires immediate action to secure and stabilise stonework. An experienced surveyor with a good knowledge of the construction of the building being inspected will look out for tell-tale signs of corrosion and will provide an assessment of the extent of corrosion and repair needed.

### Recommending stone repairs

There is no 'standard' proforma for recommending repairs to stonework. Repairs to stone fabric depend on the nature of the stone, type of construction, condition of the fabric, previous repairs and use of the building. However, it is often useful to prioritise and give timescales for repairs to allow building owners to 'rank' remedial works according to their importance or urgency.

Stone repairs marked up on photograph

Unstable finial – an example of a Priority 1 repair

**Priority 1: Emergency and urgent repairs**
These are repairs to the most severely deteriorated stonework which are required to address major health and safety issues (such as stones about to dislodge or fracture) or significant water ingress.

**Priority 2: Essential repairs**
Repairs needed to maintain a weather resistant external fabric and maintain structural stability.

**Priority 3: Optimal repairs**
Repairs to replace or repair deteriorated stone elements or carved detail to improve the long-term condition and aesthetics of the building fabric, and put back missing detail to match original where this is judged desirable.

Within the repair prioritisation scheme it is also useful to provide recommended timescales for repairs and put together realistic 'packages' of remedial works. Setting out time-bound and prioritised repairs in realistic packages of work focuses the requirements for conservation and advises the owner objectively on the most efficient use of resources. Such comprehensive 'Schedules of Work' are also essential for successful applications for grant aid from funding bodies.

## Priority Stonework Repairs

### Priority 1: Emergency and urgent repairs

Immediate Health and Safety risk of collapse or significant water ingress

### Priority 2: Essential repairs

Likely water ingress and accelerated stone decay with threat to integrity of building fabric

### Priority 3: Optimal repairs

Loss of architectural detail but no significant short-term fabric integrity issues

Petrological microscope for stone identification

Probe permeability measurement of sandstone

## Stone Testing and Analysis

Numerous research projects, case studies and costly conservation mistakes testify to the fact that historic buildings and monuments cannot be conserved 'by formula'. A crucial link between the condition survey and tender documentation is often a programme of materials testing and analysis. The extent of testing and analysis of existing and replacement masonry materials depends on the nature of the repair programme and the types of materials. However, it is important that all materials are assessed at design and specification stage by a team experienced with stone.
In that way the methods for repair and conservation can be specified accurately, based on scientific rationale.

Despite this need, stone research and analysis is a much under-used resource in historic building conservation. Often it is either omitted completely or considered at too late a stage in a project to be of real benefit. Although it is largely the responsibility of specialist consultants and university research groups, architects and building owners should be aware of the methods available for stone analysis so that the most appropriate techniques can be included at the design stage.

**Table 3** (overleaf) provides a brief summary of some useful analytical methods available in Northern Ireland that range from identifying existing stone on a building or monument to high definition recording of surface features and artificially weathering stone.

## Table 2 Examples of Results from Analytical Techniques

### X-ray diffraction trace identifying salts present in stone sample

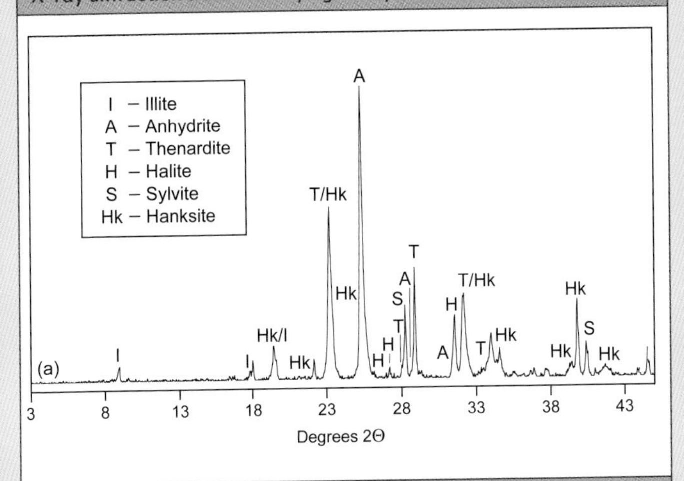


### Atomic absorption spectroscopy (AAS) and ion chromatography (IC) used to identify salt concentration within a core sample from a sandstone block

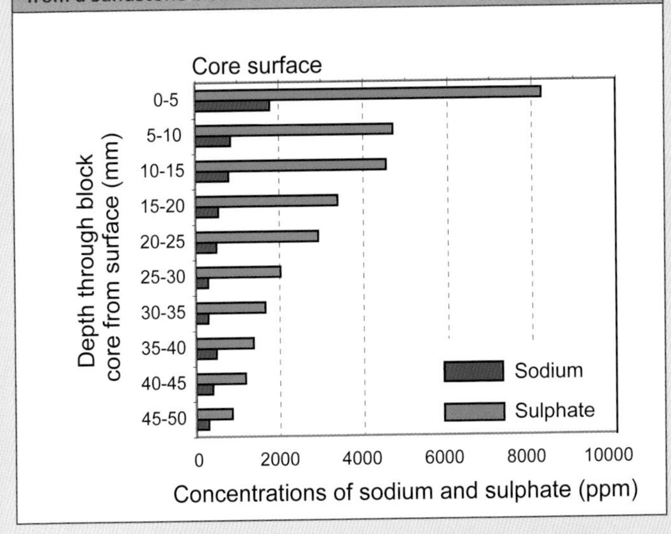

Table 3 **Analytical Techniques for Stone**

| Technique | Purpose |
| --- | --- |
| **Petrography** | Mineral identification using petrological microscope (see pages 180 and 199) |
| **XRD (X-Ray Diffraction)** | Identification of crystalline minerals not visible under petrological microscope. |
| **Salt Analysis (Ion Chromatography) and Atomic Absorption Spectroscopy** | Determination of concentration of salt phases. |
| **Probe Permeability** | Using compressed gas (usually air), the surface permeability of stone is measured. |
| **Simulated Weathering Experiments** | Temperature and humidity cycles in an environmental chamber |
| **Object Scanning – High Definition Laser Scanning** | An initial scan provides base line data with re-scanning providing a measure of surface change over time. |
| **GPR (Ground Penetrating Radar)** | Non-destructive testing of stone using electro-magnetic wave propagation. This allows the structural integrity of the fabric to be assessed and the presence of voids, fractures and planes of weakness to be identified. |
| **Metal Detection** | Enables detection of embedded metal in stone. |

| Result |
| --- |
| Identification of rock type, nature of the stone fabric and porosity. |
| Particularly useful for identification of clay minerals, salts and minor phases (see previous page for examples of salts output). |
| Provides useful information if a core of stone is taken and the salt content analysed with depth through the stone (see **Table 2** on previous page for examples of output). |
| A non-destructive technique that can be performed in situ on a building or in the laboratory. Measurement of surface permeability provides useful information for the absorption potential of stone surfaces. This technique is useful for testing stone treatments as it can be carried out before and after application to provide an indication of 'breathability' of treatments such as water repellents, biocides, etc. |
| Stone samples are exposed to customized temperature and humidity cycles to simulate conditions of exposure in different environments. This technique is useful of assess change of new stone over time and/or the durability characteristics of stone. |
| Accurate scanning can provide a rate of weathering or surface change over time, useful for establishing protocols for conservation of monuments. |
| Provides an assessment of the sub-surface and structural integrity of stone fabric. |
| Locating the extent of embedded metal in stonework enables identification of potential areas at risk of corrosion related fracturing and destabilisation of stone. |

## Decision-making for Stone Conservation and Repair

The aim of stone conservation is to retain as much existing fabric as possible wherever this does not compromise the physical integrity of the building or monument. Choosing when to replace, rebuild, redress, consolidate, treat, clean or leave intact existing stonework are key decisions as they determine the amount of original fabric that is to be retained or replaced and have direct implications for the cost of a scheme. Consequently, it is crucial that these decisions are based on scientific rationale with a sound knowledge and understanding of the masonry materials that are used and not visual inspection alone.

In Northern Ireland, the performance of our building stones is determined by three factors:

- The history and properties of the material itself
- The action of water, salts and other pollutants
- How the stonework is built – from solid wall construction with lime mortar to stone fixed to a steel frame.

These factors influence the way in which stone weathers and decays over time and must be considered when formulating repair schemes.

Conservation or retention of stone fabric can be carried out on a variety of scales: from small scale surface consolidation of intricately carved detail to rebuilding large sections of stonework on a building or monument.

### Shelter coats, chemical consolidants and water repellents

Shelter coats are a weak lime mix either with or without aggregate. Similar to lime washes they are usually applied with a brush and repeated lime washing of specific areas is a way of applying shelter coats. These should be regarded as sacrificial surfaces and are most effective when they can bond well to the surface. As shelter coats are lime-based they are of most use on limestones and some sandstones. They can be coloured to match the stone they are being applied to. They are normally only used today where there is a long-established tradition of use on a particular building.

Coloured shelter coat applied to finial of stone pinnacle

Consolidation of the surface of stone can be an appropriate method of stone conservation particularly for the retention of important historic carved detail. This technique can stabilise a stone surface and decrease the rate of weathering and decay and extend the life of the carving. However, it is an extremely complex issue and consolidants should not be used without thorough testing and an understanding of the chemical processes at work. Consolidants work best if the entire object or carving can be immersed in the chemical as this allows the maximum uptake of the treatment in all directions. When the treatment can only be applied to the surface, there is a risk of moisture within the stone, being trapped behind the consolidated surface causing the outer layers to deteriorate more rapidly. Consolidants inevitably reduce breathability of stone and can therefore cause an undesirable change in water movement through a wall.

Similarly, water repellents, whether marketed as 'breathable' or not, should be treated with great caution and used only in certain circumstances and after site specific testing. All water repellents will reduce breathability, to a greater or lesser extent and this may cause more problems than their application might solve. Specialist advice is required.

### Stitching, dowelling and stainless steel anchors

Stabilising and strengthening stonework using modern materials such as stainless steel can allow retention of stonework that would otherwise have to be taken down and rebuilt or completely replaced. On a small scale this can be simply the stitching of fractured stonework with small stainless steel pins. Larger scale stabilisation includes; strengthening stonework of pinnacles, towers and chimneys where fracturing is due to movement or associated with the corrosion of embedded metal and the pinning of random rubble walls. For these larger works stainless steel anchors in a grout injection system are often used very successfully.

Stainless Steel Anchor Systems (for example, 'Cintec') comprise a steel bar in a mesh fabric sleeve, into which a cementitious grout is injected under pressure. The flexible sleeve of woven polyester restrains the flow and expands, eventually moulding itself into the shape and spaces within the stonework, providing a mechanical as well as chemical bond.

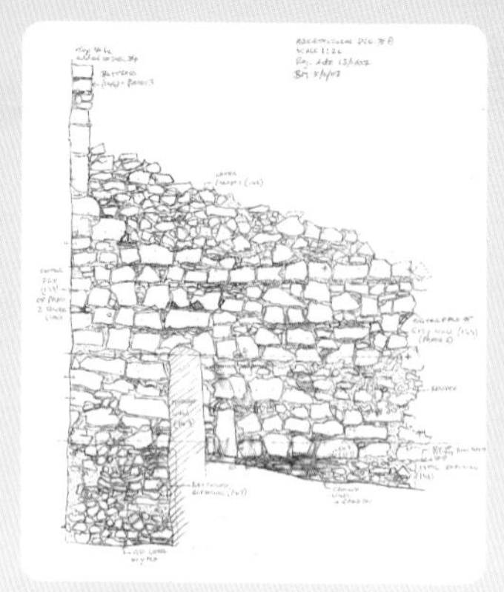

Archaeological recording of stonework detail

**Rebuilding stonework**

Under certain circumstances, usually when a section of the structure is unstable, stonework has to be rebuilt. Where possible the existing stone should be retained and used for rebuilding. This is more common for monuments but occasionally for buildings.

To rebuild stonework to match the existing structure as closely as possible requires skill and patience. The structure should be drawn up accurately with each stone identified. For historic monuments, often the best and most accurate way to do this is to attach polythene to a timber frame and trace over each section of stonework, retaining each plastic sheet for rebuilding. Millimetre accurate drawings produced from laser scanning can also be used. Before dismantling, each stone should be labelled and the outer surface marked.

Stones should be taken down carefully and stored according to the labels, noting the method of construction and taking photos and notes during the process. Rebuilding should, match the original construction as closely as possible, the bedding and pointing mortar analysed and new mortar should always be lime-based with aggregate that matches the original as closely as possible.

For stonework that is missing or collapsed and where there is no record, rebuilding should be carried out to match the existing as closely as possible in construction style. For historic monuments, it is usually the protocol to identify any new sections of stonework to ensure that this new work can be easily identified and is not assumed to be part of the original construction. This can be achieved by different methods such as stainless steel pins set into the mortar joints or by recessing the new stonework. The older practice of inserting a DPC (Damp Proof Course) type material between original and new work is no longer used but can be seen on a number of repaired monuments.

**Deciding between repair and replacement**

The most difficult choices in stonework repair projects are based around deciding which stones can be kept and repaired and which need to be replaced.

Albert Memorial before restoration with severely decayed Scrabo Sandstone, widespread cement render repair of ashlar blocks and absence of the original canopy over the statue of Prince Albert

Albert Memorial following restoration in 2000

Predicting future weathering is an important part of that process.

Our most common local stone, Scrabo Sandstone, weathers in a very variable and unpredictable way. Scrabo decays – often catastrophically – through the combined action of expanding and contracting clays in the stone fabric associated with the action of salts in polluted and/or coastal environments (for example, gypsum, halite). This explains why this sandstone performed so poorly in 19th-century polluted maritime environments, particularly in locations close to the docks in Belfast such as Albert Memorial and Sinclair Seamen's Church. Decisions on replacement are made significantly easier when information on the composition of the stone and how deeply pollutant salts have penetrated is available (see page 181). For example, removing the surface by re-dressing sandstone may be an effective measure on some stone façades and result in retention of a significant proportion of the original fabric. However, for other stone buildings, in which the sandstone contains high levels of salts, cutting back can expose a sub-surface weakened by salt action and cause accelerated decay leading to more problems in the future. This is particularly the case where cement mortar has been used to repair stone in the past. For these stone façades, repair schemes comprising the targeted replacement of severely decayed stones such as replacing elements key to the integrity of

## Decay of Scrabo Sandstone Due to the Action of Salts

Sulphur Dioxide from pollution reacts with calcium from stone or mortar to form Calcium Sulphate (Gypsum) in near-surface zone.

Crystallisation of Gypsum causes damage by exerting pressure on the surrounding grains.

Calcium
Mortar
SULPHUR
Calcium
Mortar

B

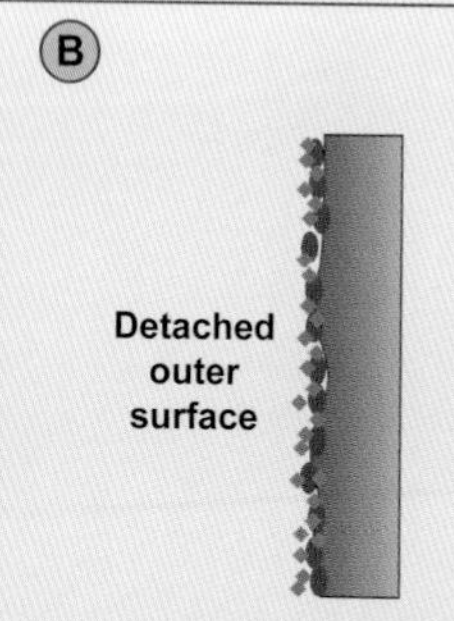


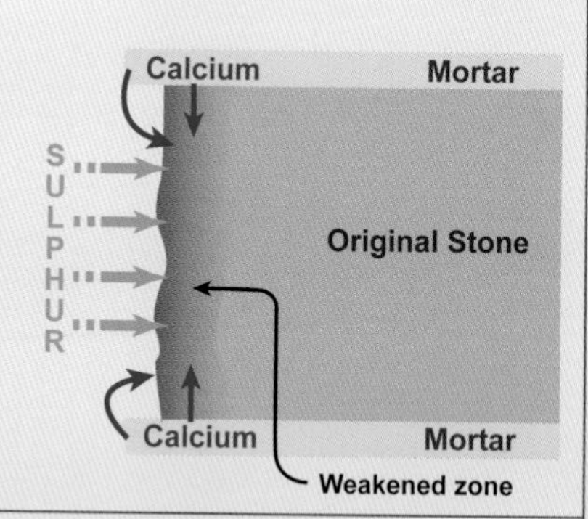


C

Severely weathered sandstone block

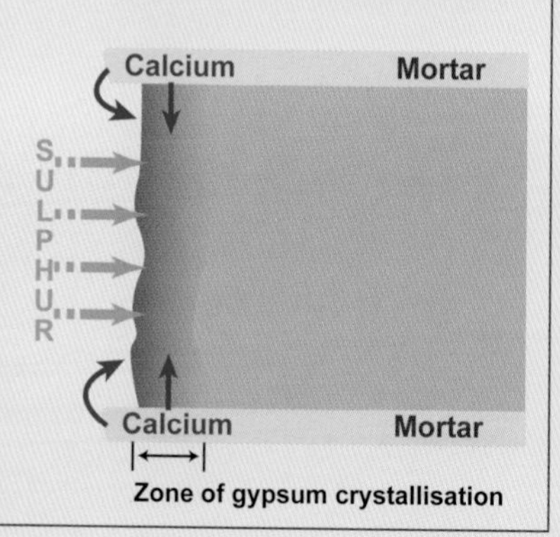

the fabric such as quoins, buttress stones, copings and string courses, whilst leaving the remainder of the stonework with the outer surface intact, may be the most appropriate course of action.

There is also often a case for carrying out 'mortar repairs' to stonework, usually to retain the maximum amount of original fabric and control costs. However, mortar repairs should always be considered as a short-term solution, with around a ten year maximum life. Modern mortar repairs are lime based, weaker and more porous than the stone. Their primary use is filling pockets or shelves where water might collect and accelerate decay. Coloured aggregates can be used to match the colours of the stone but in most cases the mortar repair will weather differently than the surrounding stone over time.

## Weathering of Giffnock Sandstone at Queen's University Belfast

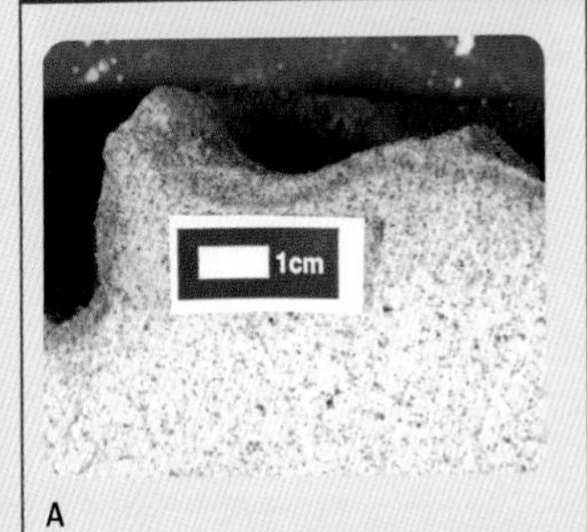

A

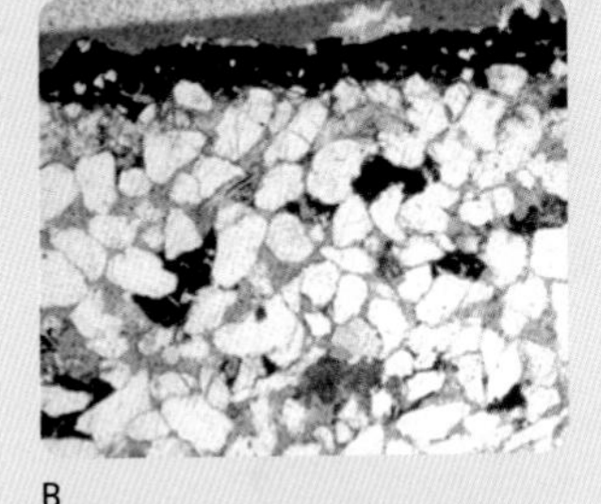
B

**A** shows hardened iron crust as seen by the naked eye;

**B** shows hardened iron crust as seen in thin-section under the microscope;

**C** shows impact of breaching the outer surface with accelerated decay of underlying stone.

C

In Scotland, stone quarrying is enjoying a new lease of life. Cullaloe Quarry, near Burntisland in Fife, had been dormant for fifty years until it was discovered that the quarry's more yellowish-grey sandstone is one of the best replacement stone (physically, chemically and visually) for Craigleith Stone used in much of Edinburgh's New Town

## Selection of Replacement Stone

When the decision is made to replace stone elements it is important to identify the existing building stone and match it as closely as possible. This is usually possible using a combination of geological knowledge of stone samples and historical information. Where feasible, the original stone type should be used in repair schemes. Unfortunately, this is not always possible. For most local building stones in Northern Ireland, the original quarry sources are now inactive or used as a source for aggregate and other quarry products. Nevertheless, it is worth investigating the original quarry source or other related quarries for several reasons:

- Firstly, if a supply of stone is still available expressions of interest to quarry owners demonstrate the existence of a potential market for dimension stone and may prompt continued extraction of stone materials for dimension stone rather than for aggregate alone
- Secondly, the inactive quarry can be sampled to provide material for testing that can be used to compare potential replacement stone.

It may also be worthwhile contacting local stone masons as they often have a stockpile of salvaged local stone which can be ideal for smaller repair projects.

### Replacement stone

If no original or salvaged stone is available, a replacement stone type or types must be selected for the repair scheme. Currently there is no set protocol for choosing replacement stone for repair schemes. In the worst cases, where there is no information on which to base selection, the

## Examples of Inactive Stone Quarries

Remains of the main Dundonald Sandstone Quarry at Quarry Corner, Dundonald, County Down

South Quarry at Scrabo, Newtownards, County Down, now a Nature Reserve

## Examples of Active Stone Quarries

Ballymagrehan Granite Quarry near Castlewellan, County Down

Large blocks of Limestone set aside for processing for building stone from Slushill Quarry, Lisnaskea, County Fermanagh

architect/specifier relies on visual appearance to match with original stone and anecdotal evidence from the quarry with regard to the quality and durability of the stone type. At best, an architect is supplied with stone test data – information obtained from testing to BS EN standards and BRE methods that states whether the stone is 'fit for purpose' as a building material but provides no information to help in matching with the existing stone.

In the following pages common stone property tests are described.

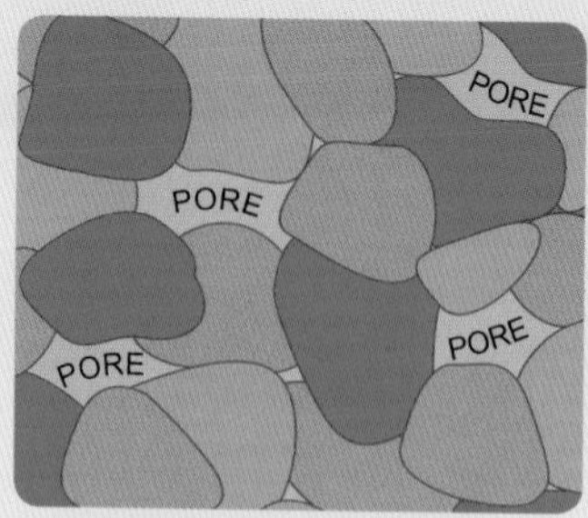

Individual pore spaces in sandstone

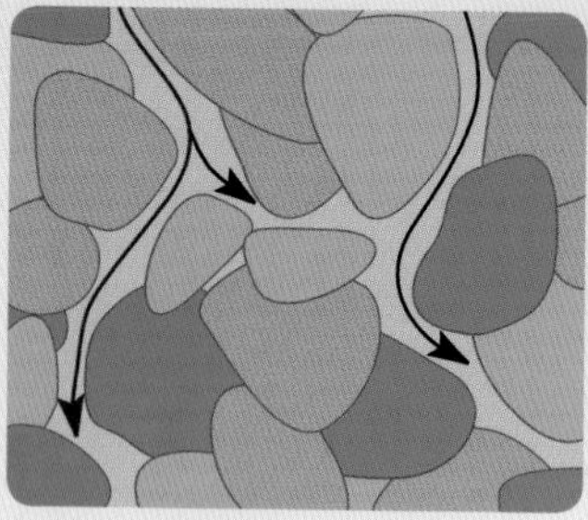
The movement of moisture when pore spaces are connected

## Testing Stone

A range of Natural Stone Testing Methods are also provided by the British Standard Institution and Building Research Establishment (BRE) and these are listed in the table on the following pages. These test methods were developed for specifying stone for new buildings rather than selecting stone for replacement or repair projects. Nevertheless, providing the data is up to date, this information can be used for informing decisions when selecting material for replacement, particularly if similar testing can be carried out on stone from the original source. Outlined below is the information we can obtain from the three main categories of testing methods: water absorption, resistance and strength tests and how the results relate to stone properties.

## Water Absorption Tests

### Porosity

This is usually expressed as a percentage value and refers to the amount of pore space (free space) within the stone fabric. However, a porosity value does not indicate how connected the pore spaces are and therefore how quickly a stone will absorb water. Knowledge of the connectivity of pore spaces through measurement of permeability or water absorption is useful information as it gives an indication how driving rain will be absorbed and travel through stone.

### Water absorption

Water Absorption is also usually expressed as a percentage value and refers to the uptake of water by a particular stone type. Tests measure the proportion of water absorbed by stone under specific immersion conditions. Value for water absorption, together with porosity and density provides an indication of performance in service, particularly, durability and stain resistance.

### Saturation coefficient

The Saturation Coefficient provides an indication of moisture retention within stone. As a general rule, the higher the Saturation Coefficient, the less durable the building stone. According to BRE, stone types with Saturation Coefficients greater than 0.8 tend to be more susceptible to frost.

## Resistance Tests

### Salt crystallisation test

This test measures the amount (by weight) of material loss from stone samples subjected to harsh saturated sodium sulphate crystallisation tests. The lower the value of weight loss the more resistant the stone is believed to be. However, many relatively good quality stone types fail this test. The value of this test has been questioned by some researchers as the salt solution used is very concentrated and test samples are fully immersed in the solution, a method which does not simulate the ingress and movement of salt in stone on a building.

### Acid immersion

This test, in conjunction with other tests (for example, water absorption, flexural strength), is useful for assessing the durability of stone exposed in areas of high atmospheric pollution. This method is a severe acid test and is only applicable to sandstone and slate. A pass indicates material with relatively good resistance to acidity.

### Frost resistance

This monitors the change in a stone type following cycles of freeze-thaw. The test is often combined with the flexural strength test to assess the percentage change in strength before and after frost action. A loss of strength greater than 20% is often regarded as significant.

## Strength Tests

### Compressive and flexural strength

The compressive and flexural strength of stone is critical in both the design and detailing of building façades, and also for flooring material. Compressive strength is an indication of the strength of stone when loaded perpendicular to the main bedding direction.

Flexural strength is a measure of the tensile strength when subjected to bending.

Testing flexural strength of Carboniferous Limestone

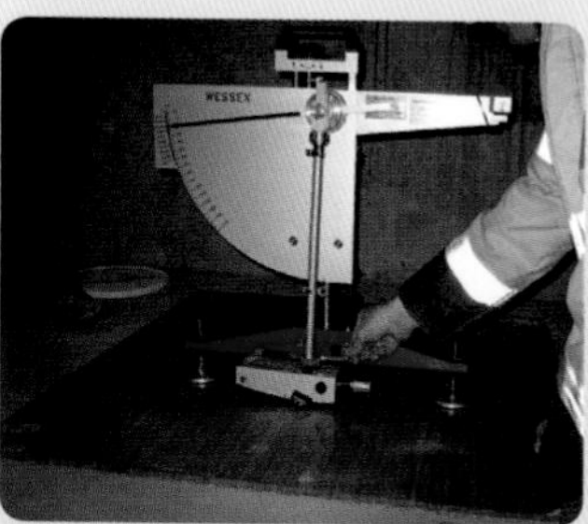


The British Pendulum Tester is the recognised British Standard method for measuring slip resistance of stone surfaces

**BS EN and BRE Test Methods for Natural Stone.**

| Test method |
|---|
| Denomination of Natural Stones |
| Petrographic Description |
| Determination of:<br>Total Porosity<br>Open Porosity<br>Real Density<br>Apparent Density |
| Determination of Water Absorption at Atmospheric Pressure |
| Compressive Strength of Dimension Stone |
| Flexural Strength of Dimension Stone |
| Determination of Frost Resistance |
| Flexural Strength following Frost Resistance |
| Unpolished Slip Resistance |
| Determination of Saturation Coefficient |
| Acid Immersion Test |
| Salt Crystallisation Test |

| Reference | Description |
|---|---|
| EN 12440 | Provides a list of all quarried natural stone types in Europe |
| BS EN 12407:2000 | Provides a standardised identification together with mineralogical and textural description of a rock type |
| EN 1936 | Porosity is the amount of free space within the stone fabric |
| BS EN 13755:2002 | Measures water uptake under specific immersion conditions |
| BS EN 1926 | Strength in MPa of stone when loaded perpendicular to main bedding direction |
| BS EN 12372:1999 | Tensile strength when subjected to bending |
| BS EN 12371:2001 | Monitoring change following cycles of frost resistance |
| BS EN 12372:1999 | Tensile strength following frost cycle conditioning. Generally reductions in strength by less than 20% are acceptable |
| BS EN 1341:2001 | Measures the slip resistance of a stone surface |
| BRE Digest 269 | A measure of the retention of moisture (and dissolved salts) within stone. According to BRE saturation coefficient greater than 0.8 tend to be more susceptible to frost. Most good quality building sandstones used within the UK have values less than 0.68 |
| BRE Digest 269 | Provides a measure of durability under acidic conditions |
| BRE Digest 269 | Provides a measure of durability under salt-rich conditions |

## Guidelines for Selecting Replacement Stone

Whilst there are no set protocols for the selection of replacement stone decisions should be made using the following broad guidelines:

### Chemical and physical compatibility of existing and replacement stone – 'like for like'

It is essential that the replacement stone selected is both chemically and physically compatible with the existing stone. In general, it is not advisable to mix stone types. For example, whilst some limestones appear to be a good match for weathered sandstones in terms of colour and texture, they will weather differently over time. In addition, when exposed, rain wash from limestone to sandstone can promote the formation of gypsum salts more rapidly through the mobilisation of calcium carbonate and under certain circumstances this can lead to accelerated decay of the sandstone.

It is also important that the physical properties of the stone types are similar. As shown above, installing a replacement sandstone with higher permeability compared to that of the existing stone can cause problems of differential

Biological growth on replacement sandstone

water absorption and biological growth on the stone surface. Relevant tests to assess chemical and physical compatibility include: petrography, XRD analysis, water absorption and probe permeability.

### Durability – 'fit for purpose'

Replacement stone should be 'fit for purpose' as a construction material. If large quantities of stone are required for a scheme, the quarry selected should be visited and assessed for quality and quantity of stone available, and the variability in chemical, physical and visual attributes of that stone to be quarried. Relevant stone tests to assess durability include resistance tests such as acid immersion and salt crystallisation. Also, for new buildings and stone flooring, flexural and compressive strength tests before and after cycles of freeze-thaw are useful.

There has been an influx of overseas granites and gabbros used for paving and cladding in the UK and Ireland as imported stone is a significantly cheaper alternative to local stone. Imported stone is usually good quality and fit for purpose. However, there is often a misconception among many architects and specifiers that 'granite is granite' wherever in the world it originates. This is not necessarily the case as granites vary widely in terms of composition, texture and strength – all factors that determine durability. In comparison with local granite, some Chinese granites have a relatively high surface porosity and permeability and relatively low abrasion resistance. When used for paving, this can cause issues of surface staining and loss of surface texturing and slip resistance due to wear which in turn can lead to significantly higher maintenance costs than those anticipated at the outset of the project.

Natural stone test data can be provided on any rock type, however, there is no substitute for a proven track record of use of a stone in the setting and environment that the material has been specified for.

## Weathering

The term 'weathering' is often quoted in literature with stone test data. This is a subjective performance indicator based on a general assessment and anecdotal evidence on the historical performance of building stones. Nevertheless, this information is important as it aids understanding of how stone performs as a building material (cladding, dressed stone, carved detail) and how stone adjusts over time.

Any comment on weathering performance should be backed up with analysis but it does provide a useful indication of expected rates of deterioration, nature of stone soiling and performance with different mortars and renders.

## Visual convergence (matching colour and texture) – blending in

It is important that the replacement stone matches existing material aesthetically and will blend in over time. Ultimately, the properties of colour and texture are determined by the physical and chemical make up of the stone which will also control how the appearance changes over time. In many cases this will mean accepting quite a visual difference as newly quarried stone is inserted into a building, in the

Clay layers in replacement sandstone will weather quickly over time

Colour difference between outer weathered stone surface and recently exposed subsurface material

knowledge that over time it will weather to match the original.

Basing selection of replacement stone solely on visual attributes will almost always turn out to be misguided. This is especially true for stone types that contain iron-rich minerals that can often weather quite rapidly following emplacement with the release of elements such as iron resulting in significant colour change as shown above, right.

Simulated exposure in an environmental chamber can provide information on how stone types change over time and under different environments. However, the best indication of weathering response to environmental conditions is observation of how the stone has behaved on other buildings.

Where the original stone is highly variable in colour (for example, some Scrabo Sandstones) it may be necessary to use several replacements to achieve the same variation.

## Stone Cleaning

In 1959 Monsieur Andre Malraux the Minister of Cultural Affairs in France, revived the 'Paris Cleaning Order' dating from 1852. This Order insisted that it was a civic responsibility of a town or city to clean all prestigious buildings. This action was followed in London during the 1960s with the first large-scale cleaning of buildings in the UK and witnessed the dramatic effect of jet black Portland Limestone buildings emerging 'sparkling white' from behind sheeted scaffolding. This was both striking and well received by the public and the desire to clean buildings spread rapidly throughout the country.

In the late 1980s stone cleaning increased significantly, particularly in Scotland. The city of Edinburgh,

## Stone Analysis and Matching

Restoration of existing stonework and choosing the most appropriate replacement stone is an essential element of historic building and monument restoration. The wrong building stone or conservation method can impact on the aesthetics of structures and in worst cases cause accelerated deterioration of stonework.

Soiled surface and sub-surface of weathered Scrabo Sandstone

In Northern Ireland we have the added complexity of the use of both local and imported stone, much of which is no longer quarried. Thus, appropriate replacement stone types must be carefully sourced.

### Analysis

| | |
|---|---|
| **Petrography** | Microscopic examination of thin-sections of stone in transmitted light. Essential to identify mineral composition of building stone. |
| **X-Ray Diffraction** | Mineral identification and information on clays within stone (when required). |
| **Ion Chromatography** | Essential to assess the salt content within the existing stonework (when required). |
| **Porosity/Permeability** | A range of methods used to assess porosity and permeability of building stone. |
| **Stone Tests** | Diagnostic stone testing including durability tests, artificial ageing tests. |

### Report

A report should provide detailed information about the stone used and, if possible, where it was quarried. Data on composition, porosity and texture should be used to specify appropriate replacement stone in terms of chemical, structural and visual compatibility, permeability and how the new stone will weather over time.

Thin section of Scrabo Sandstone

Unveiling of Sir Thomas Brock's Carrara Marble Statue of Sir Edward Harland in June 1902. Belfast City Hall is under construction in the background and the photo shows how soiled the white Portland Limestone was even before the building was finished

once described as a 'symphony of greys' – a reference to the colour of the weathered and soiled stone buildings – underwent widespread cleaning. However, a piecemeal, uncoordinated approach, and the wide variety of chemicals and techniques used, led to an often unsightly 'checkerboard pattern' of cleaning – particularly of tenements – and significant damage to stone fabric. For the most part, cleaning methods lacked both proper specification and site control and contractors cleaned without regard for the type of building or stone types.

The late 1980s and early 1990s also saw widespread stone cleaning in Northern Ireland. Like Scotland, techniques were being used without full knowledge or regard for the fabric being cleaned and the consequences of the chemicals and abrasives used are still visible today.

Due to the largely unsatisfactory and occasionally disastrous results of widespread stone cleaning in Scotland, what was dubbed the 'Anti-Stone Cleaning' lobby emerged from a conference held in Edinburgh in 1992. This led to major changes in Scotland including the agreement that stone cleaning was to be regarded as an 'alteration' to a building. As a result all stone cleaning now requires listed building consent.

Currently, the policy of Historic Scotland recommends repair and replacement of stone without cleaning the whole building. However, this practice has its own issues in that when stone is replaced, it will take many years, if ever, for new stone to blend in and

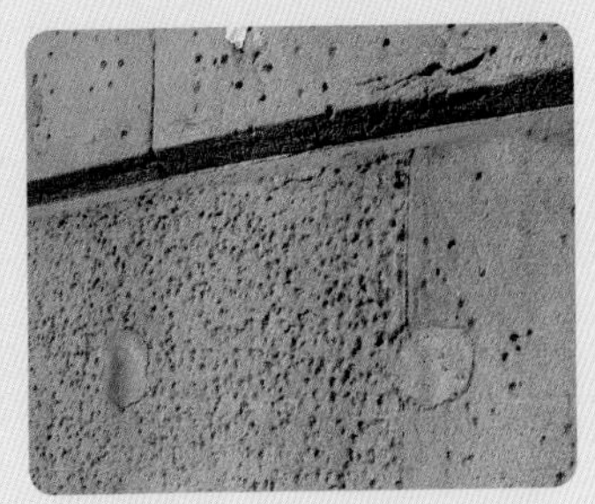

Pitting of surface due to aggressive water abrasive and chemical cleaning

Uncleaned and cleaned tenement buildings in Edinburgh

weather to a colour and texture that is similar to the original. This is because the pattern of pollution has changed significantly and new stone surfaces may never weather or soil to produce a patina similar to the remaining original stonework because they are not exposed to the same pollution conditions.

In the 21st century, cleaning of stone buildings remains a contentious issue between those who believe that cleaning is important for aesthetics and improvement of the streetscape and those who believe that cleaning is an alteration that physically changes the stone fabric. Aesthetic and perceptual studies carried out by the Robert Gordon University in Aberdeen of buildings that were soiled and those that were cleaned illustrated complex attitudes to cleaning. People feel that some buildings are aesthetically enhanced by soiling while

Patchwork effect due to inappropriate cleaning of sandstone in Belfast City Centre

other buildings are improved by cleaning especially with clarification of architectural details and brightening of the façade. There are, however, also some negative perceptions and effects following cleaning. These included loss of depth and detailing, defects and flaws were revealed on removal of patinas. On some occasions, confusion of historical context occurred with some buildings being perceived as being significantly younger following cleaning.

Stone replacement in Edinburgh. Original stone not cleaned

Stone replacement on the Scott Monument on Prince's Street in Edinburgh

Carved detail revealed following cleaning using low pressure steam. Stone was pre-treated with biocide before cleaning. Statue by Francis Derwent Wood at St Mary's Church, Ponsbourne, Hertfordshire

**Stone cleaning in a changing climate**

No stone cleaning can be performed without some changes to the stone surface. Consequently, stone cleaning must be assessed as a balance between aesthetic improvement and physical damage to the original fabric both in the short and long term. Most cleaning methods (with the exception of laser cleaning) remove the natural patina and open up the surface pore structure of the stone making re-soiling much easier and colonisation by algae and bacteria significantly more rapid. Climate models show that in Northern Ireland winters are getting wetter and warmer with stone surfaces staying wetter for longer thereby creating conditions conducive to the 'greening' of surfaces through algal growth. In addition, pollution patterns have changed with a significant reduction in sulphur dioxide and other pollutants that contribute to the formation of black crusts and grey soiling that typified the early 20th century.

A new challenge faces stone in the 21st century; perhaps unexpectedly, in that the reduction in atmospheric pollution can lead to more frequent and aggressive cleaning of stonework. This is illustrated in the images on the following pages of the Gate Pillars to

Ormeau Park in Belfast taken between April 2002 and February 2003 before and after abrasive cleaning. Aggressive water jet cleaning in June 2002 removed the biological growth but resulted in significant loss of carved detail and opening up of pores in the sandstone. This surface was re-colonised with algal material within months of cleaning. This cycle of cleaning and re-growth continued for a number of years. In these cases, the specification of a fully breathable biocide may be advisable as it slows down biological regrowth and therefore reduces the perceived need to clean abrasively.

## Methods and materials for stone cleaning

There are a large number of methods and products available for cleaning and treatment of stone façades. An in-depth discussion of stone cleaning is beyond the scope of this book, and the reader is referred to the excellent publications available listed in the 'Sources of Further Information'. However, it is important that the selection of cleaning methods and chemical products should be based on an understanding of the properties of the stone as this will dictate the suitability and efficacy of the method. It is also essential that test panels of methods are performed in advance of work starting on site and that the work is carried out by experienced personnel with a track record of good practice.

Cleaning external stonework can be grouped under the following headings:

- **Steam cleaning** – a low pressure cleaning method which is often used for cleaning sandstone and limestone
- **Nebulous spray** – a specialist method that uses a fine mist spray emitted from sprayers evenly spaced along a hose. The nebulous spray method is used for cleaning limestone (particularly Portland Limestone) with well-developed black crusts
- **Chemical products** – a variety of alkali and acid cleaners are available and can be used for heavily soiled stone elements. However, these products should be used with care as they can be detrimental to the stone fabric and in some cases leave a reservoir of chemicals that can cause problems in the future
- **Abrasive cleaning** (wet and dry grit) – this varies depending on the pressure, type of grit and equipment used. Abrasive cleaning should only be carried

Stone Cleaning trials (Low Pressure Steam) at Danesfort House, Belfast

out with use of a lancet or spiral jet system and needs careful supervision.

As soiling of stone surfaces on buildings is never evenly distributed a combination of methods outlined above may be most appropriate for cleaning a particular stone façade. An experienced consultant can advise on combining cleaning methods. It is important to remember that the option to leave stone uncleaned may, in some instances, be in the best long term interests of the stonework on a building.

**Biocides**

A 'biocide' is a treatment designed to reduce the rate of colonisation of the surface of stone by biological material. A biocide wash can be used on stonework to remove biological material. It may also be appropriate to apply a biocide following stone cleaning as disruption of the surface can open up pores and encourage algal growth. Biocide washing and treatment should be specified and applied by experienced personnel only and it is essential that the treatment that is used is breathable and causes no damage to the stone. The average length of time before re-application is needed is three to five years depending on the treatment used and the exposure conditions.

## Adverse Effect of Cleaning Sandstone on Ormeau Gate Pillars

**1** April 2002. Biological growth on the red sandstone surface

**2** June 2002. Red sandstone surface after cleaning

**3** June 2002. Significant loss of carved detail due to aggressive cleaning

**4** Within less than a year of cleaning regrowth of unsightly surface algae

## Nebulous Spray Cleaning of the Portland Limestone of Ballymena Town Hall (2007)

## Mortars and Renders

The connection between stone and mortar on a building façade or monument is inextricable and it is important that stone is viewed in association with the mortar that holds it in place. There is a wide variety of mortars and renders and a good knowledge of application is essential when specifying repairs to stonework.

In Ireland, the use of lime began during the 7th century when dry stone structures gave way to mortared rubble construction. Traditionally limestone was burned in local lime kilns to produce 'quicklime' (Calcium Oxide). Quicklime was slaked (mixed with water) on site to produce lime putty then mixed with aggregate and other additives. Lime putty was used as a binder in a variety of mixes to build, bed, point, render, harl and limewash stonework. It was made daily on site and building work was carried out in spring, summer and early autumn avoiding very wet, dry or freezing weather conditions to ensure adequate curing to provide a good set and leave a sound and stable structure.

The 20th century saw a change in construction with the use of cement mortars and renders (Ordinary Portland Cement). Portland cement (patented by Joseph Aspdin in 1824) cured more quickly, provided more strength in a shorter period of time and was easier to apply than lime mortars and renders. It soon surpassed lime as the preferred material for construction. The demand for Portland Cement increased significantly after the Second World War and its use was widespread for new building works, but it also became commonplace to use cement mortars for repairing and repointing stonework on existing buildings and monuments.

However, without doubt the use of cement mortars and renders for repairing and pointing stonework has been a major contributor to the decay of stone on historic buildings and monuments. This is particularly the case for sandstones and soft limestones as most varieties are softer than cement. Evidence shows that cementitious mortar used for repointing and repairs can cause preferential deterioration of stonework and this can be attributed to two main factors:

**Cement is less permeable than lime and many building stone types.** When moisture penetrates through joints into the stone and into the core of the wall it cannot dry out easily through cement mortar joints. Consequently the mortar joint ceases to act a as drainage channel, instead retaining moisture with salts both in the pores of the stone and in the core of the wall where the moisture and salts cause damage to the stone and often the internal render or plasterwork.

**Cement is harder and more rigid than lime and many stone types.** This hardness can cause accelerated weathering of stone blocks as the mortar joints are no longer sacrificial and restrict the natural expansion and contraction of stone blocks. When used to repair deteriorated faces of stone, the cement acts as a barrier to moisture egress and causes accelerated sub-surface stone decay.

Due to the overwhelming evidence of the damage caused by cement mortar and renders, there has been increasing use of lime for repairing and repointing historic buildings and monuments. In comparison with cement, lime is a more complex material and the application of lime requires experience and a good understanding of its properties. There are many types of lime available for mortars and renders, including 'fat' or pure lime putty and a range of naturally hydraulic limes. These binders can be used in a variety of mixes depending on the requirement of the repair work. Nowadays, as we build all year round, it is essential that stonework that is repointed or rendered with lime is properly protected from excessive rain, sun and frost to ensure that it cures properly.

Whilst there are many publications that describe the uses and benefits of lime, few take into account the type of stone it is being used with. However, the properties of stone affect how lime cures and so are also important to consider when deciding on which mortar type to use. For instance, very impermeable stone such as granite or basalt have low suction potential for mortar in joints compared to more porous sandstones and limestones. This means that it can take longer for certain types of lime mortar to dry out and more protection may be required. If the mortar does not cure correctly, in times of very heavy rain, moisture will be forced through the joints and may cause damp ingress to the internal fabric. A variety of investigative techniques can be used to analyse historic mortars and help inform decisions regarding the matching of new mortars with old.

## Mortars in Use

Cement mortar repairs applied to Scrabo Sandstone

Decay of sandstone adjacent to cement pointing

Inappropriate repointing of basalt with cement mortar

Repointing of basalt with lime mortar

Repointing sandstone with lime mortar

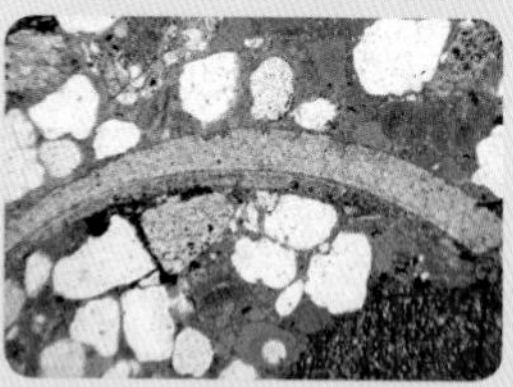

Microscope view of lime mortar

'Fat' Lime used to re-point impermeable greywacke rubble stonework. Lime mortar has not cured correctly and driving rain is penetrating the building fabric as a result

## Mortar Analysis and Matching

Choosing the right mortar mix is an essential element of historic building and monument restoration. The wrong mortar or application method can cause accelerated deterioration of structures with expensive and often irreversible consequences.

Decay and leaching of new lime mortar

Specialist mortar analysis and practical advice on mortars is essential for high quality conservation. The following analytical methods can be performed at Universities and UKAS accredited laboratories:

### Analysis

| | |
|---|---|
| **Acid Digestion/ Grain Size** | Information on binder and grading of aggregate. Essential for designing replacement and replica mortars, renders and plasters. |
| **Petrography** | Microscopic examination of thin-sections of mortar in transmitted light. Essential to identify binder and aggregate components in mortars older than 19th century. |
| **Atomic Absorption Spectroscopy** | Proportions of lime and/or cement in mortars from 19th century onwards. Mix proportions determined by the methods described in BS 4551 Part 2 1998. |
| **X-Ray Diffraction** | Mineral identification and information on hydraulic components within mortars (when required). |
| **Ion Chromatography** | Provides an assessment of salt content within the existing mortar (when required). |

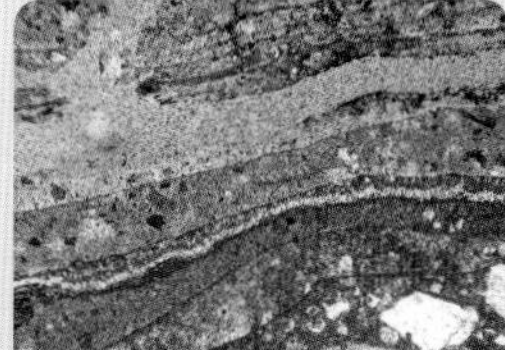
Microscope view of lime plaster and lime wash

Albert Memorial Clock, Belfast

Dawson Stelfox

# Making it Happen

## Introduction

The previous chapter focused on 'what' to do – getting the detail and specification right, but just as important is the 'how' to make it all happen – the subject of this chapter.

## Consents

Most work to listed buildings and scheduled monuments requires consent from the Northern Ireland Environment Agency (NIEA), before work starts. It is important to contact them as early as possible in the process as they are able to offer advice on good practice as well as formal consultation and approvals.

Straightforward 'like for like' repairs to listed buildings may not require a formal consent but it is still good practice to check with NIEA. Listed Building Consent application forms are available on the Planning Service website:
**www.planningni.gov.uk**

Work to scheduled monuments always requires consent from NIEA. Application forms and guidance notes can be requested on the NIEA website:
**www.ehsni.gov.uk**

NIEA also publish a 'Guide to the Repair of Scheduled Monuments' and a series of Technical Notes (See Appendix C).

Even if your building is not 'listed' or 'scheduled', historic masonry structures still deserve to be treated as if they are and the same specifications are relevant.

Repair works involving structural alterations, drainage etc., may also come under Building Regulations, under the control of your local Council. Details and application forms can be found on each Council website. Access is also covered under the Building Regulations in terms of the design of steps, ramps etc, and the scope of these may also come under the Disability Discrimination Act (DDA). It is important to note that the DDA only requires owners of buildings where the public has access, to make 'reasonable' alterations, taking into account the legal requirement to maintain the character of the listed building as well as economic factors.

Almost all construction work now comes under the remit of the Construction Design and Management Regulations (CDM) which are aimed at improving the Health and Safety record of the building industry. Projects involving any demolition work or construction work involving more than 500 person days of labour or longer than 30 days come under the scope of these regulations, though domestic work is not notifiable. The client has a responsibility to appoint a CDM coordinator to help them discharge their duties under the regulations.

The CDM regulations identify five parties who have specific duties – Clients; CDM Coordinators; Designers; Principal Contractors and Contractors. The Health and Safety Executive have produced a guidance document explaining the duties of Clients entitled, 'Want Construction Work Done Safely?'. Copies of the document, further information in respect of the regulations, and general Health and Safety information, may be downloaded from the Health and Safety Executive website: **www.hse.gov.uk** or the HSE Northern Ireland website: **www.hseni.gov.uk**

## Procurement

The selection and appointment of the contractor or contractors is one of the most important decisions in any repair project.

Unless you are a very experienced client with a lot of spare time, then it is nearly always best to appoint a single main contractor who will take full responsibility for all aspects of the project. Few contractors employ all the trades and skills likely to be required on anything but the most simple of projects and so a range of sub-contractors will be required, principally stone masons, fixers of lightning conductors, anti-bird measures, leadworkers etc.

Some stone masons and other specialists have the skills to run a full restoration job, but not many. To maintain control and choice of these appointments, it is recommended to list, say three, approved sub-contractors and give the main contractor a limited choice as to who to appoint as

St. Patrick's RC Cathedral, Armagh City

Portland Limestone used as cladding on the Bar Library, Belfast

their 'domestic' sub-contractor. Publicly funded projects must be open to all, and relevant, specific and objective criteria must be used to make a selection.

The Ulster Architectural Heritage Society (UAHS) Directory of Traditional Building Skills and the Irish Georgian Society Conservation Register lists contractors and sub-contractors along with named examples of their work that you can check or visit, but it is important to note that inclusion in these lists does not imply endorsement by those bodies.

This system effectively balances cost and quality, but leaves full responsibility for coordination and programme implementation with the main contractor. By contrast, if the client employed each sub-contractor directly they would leave themselves open to claims of delay and disruption of work if any one of the sub-contractors defaulted. The selection process is critical to achieving the best contractor for the project and there are many variants which aim to balance cost and quality of services and provision.

The principles of a good selection process are that the advertisement or supporting information lists the criteria by which a selection is to be made and relevant weighting, for example:

- Experience in undertaking this type of work
- Required skills available
- Understanding of the project
- Experience of the relevant scale of work
- Awards received for similar work
- Resources available
- Health and Safety record

Once a select list is drawn up then the final choice can be made on cost alone on the basis that a minimum threshold

Parliament Buildings, Stormont

of competence has already been proved. This is generally in accordance with the NICC single stage code of selective tendering. However, there are more sophisticated models for achieving 'best value'; such as balancing cost with quality. This requires a more specific list of criteria to be prepared and a detailed 'quality' tender to accompany the price tender. The Construction Procurement Directorate (CPD) has built up a considerable expertise in these methods and are available to advise client bodies on projects where significant government funding is involved.

## Documentation

The documentation needed on which to base a tender process will depend on the type of procurement method chosen but in almost all cases the greatest level of price certainty will be achieved by the costs being based on a detailed 'Schedule of Works', 'Activity Schedule' or 'Bill of Quantities' and a 'Specification', all of which are founded on the knowledge gained from the condition survey and stone analysis.

A 'Schedule of Works' is commonly used for smaller projects. Written descriptions of work items are outlined and the contractor will put a price against each item, in effect producing a series of mini lump sums. The items will typically combine a number of materials and actions, not individually itemized. If this is to be in any way accurate, a detailed stonework schedule should be provided that is related to the elevation drawings and cross referenced to large-scale details of each stone element to be replaced.

For more complex projects a 'Bill of Quantities' is more common. This breaks down work items into measured individual components and the contractor provides a price for each element. A 'Bill' allows for more flexibility in agreeing rates for works not individually measured and it is more likely there will be a similar or related item on which costs can be based. A 'Bill' is more time consuming to put together but is standard practice on most complex projects. A detailed stonework schedule, cross referenced to elevations and details is still required.

In all cases a detailed 'Specification' of materials and workmanship is required. This should detail all materials and methods to be used and is related directly to the schedule of works and drawings provided.

Stonework restoration projects can have a bad reputation with clients and cost managers because of a legacy of projects going to tender based on minimal information, the most cursory of surveys, and excessive use of provisional sums to cover the uncertainties. By contrast, going to tender based on comprehensive surveys, stonework schedules, fully detailed and cross-referenced drawings, well-researched specifications and a Schedule of Works or Bill of Quantities, provides cost certainty and ensures the quality of what is delivered.

## Roles and relationships

Projects work best when all partners: client, design team, contracting team, funders, statutory bodies etc., fully understand their position and responsibilities and clear lines of communication are agreed from the outset. Conservation is a collaborative process and no one party will have a monopoly of knowledge, so it is important to create an atmosphere of mutual respect and acknowledgement of expertise across the whole team. This is especially important on stonework restoration projects because inevitably there will be a significant amount of decision making to take place on site, on the scaffold, and that works best when there is trust between the design team and the contractors. However, it is important that one person, normally the conservation architect, is the core decision maker and communication hub for the whole site – positioned centrally between the client, design team and the contractors team. This ensures there is one repository for all contract documentation and there is

View from House of Fraser (Stanton Moor Sandstone cladding) to Albert Memorial Clock in Belfast

no confusion as to who issues instructions and why.

**Good practice**

No matter how good the survey, how tightly drawn up the contract documents, stone repair and restoration projects need a high level of site presence by the professional to ensure proper interpretation of information to deal with the inevitable variations, and assist with tight cost control. There are a number of good practice methodologies which can avoid mistakes and save a lot of time and money:

- Be available to the contractor, especially during the first few weeks of site when 'opening up' is underway, to answer queries and deal with small variations in the scope of work
- At the initial project meeting highlight all the specialist skills and trades required and seek identification of domestic sub-contractors to deliver those skills
- Talk to sub-contractors, identifying previous work and lessons learnt, explaining the requirements of specification and brief as required
- Ask for the sample panels or sample items requested in the tender document to be provided as soon as possible in the project and make sure all relevant parties see and approve items to avoid unnecessary problems later
- Arrange for specific training as required
- Ensure all the specialist sub-contractors understand and will follow the specification
- Keep comprehensive records.
- Ensure the Quantity Surveyor makes active checks and

Holy Cross Church, Crumlin Road, Belfast

Carved Lion on the Albert Memorial, Belfast

regular progress reports to keep costs up to date and accurate

- Remember that the aim is 'repair' and 'conservation' not restoration and re-building. If in doubt, when presented with the contractor's inevitable desire for increased replacement, go back to first principles
  - Maximum retention of historic fabric and minimum replacement
  - Make clear what is new and what is original
  - As far as is possible, ensure reversibility of historic fabric.

Long-term conservation is built on a solid foundation of knowledge about what has happened to a building over its life and it is important to know every chapter to understand the whole story. It is rare to start a repair project with full information about the nature of all work that has been carried out over the preceding years, because records were either not kept or lost as buildings changed hands or personnel changed. Inevitably, consultant teams find themselves starting from scratch and wastefully repeating survey information. This could be significantly improved by proper record keeping which becomes part of a comprehensive building manual, copies of which could be deposited with the Irish Architectural Archive or NIEA's Historic Monument and Building Record, as a resource available for all future owners.

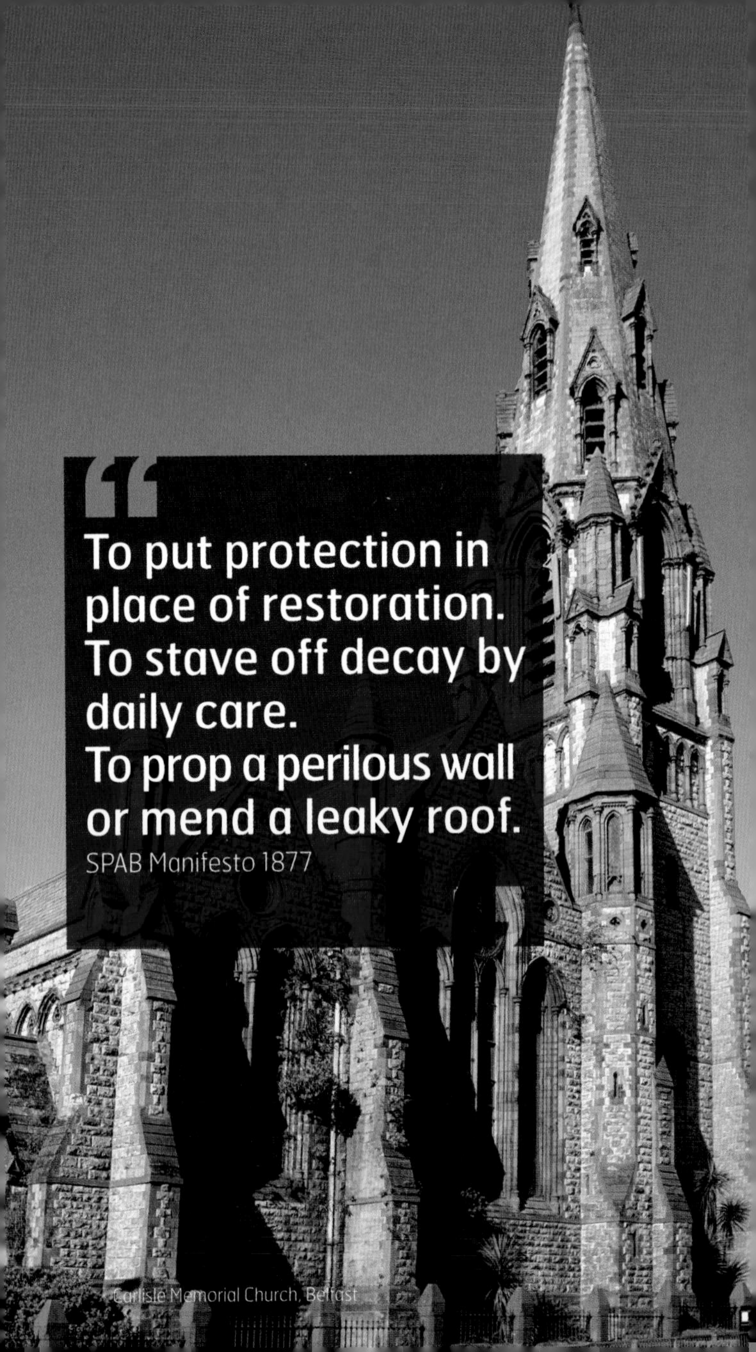

Carlisle Memorial Church, Belfast

Dawson Stelfox, Joanne Curran and John Savage

# Monitoring and Maintenance

## Introduction – The Value of Maintenance

All buildings require regular maintenance to avoid premature decay and expensive repairs and this is particularly true of stonework.

Maintenance is most beneficial when it is preventative and frequent with regular monitoring and maintenance resulting in significant long-term savings in overall costs as well as ensuring the long-term survival of historic fabric. Maintenance is thus a key factor in ensuring social, environmental and economic sustainability.

However, the sad reality is that most buildings are not properly maintained and most funding, including historic building grant aid, goes to those buildings in the worst condition and rarely goes towards preventative maintenance measures, even where it can be confidently predicted that inaction will result in expensive long term damage. Research in the UK has shown that there are a number of factors contributing to this including;

- Lack of research on maintenance issues
- Limited industry maintenance services convenient to owners
- Lack of published guidance
- Focus on major repair schemes, including grant aid
- Minimal use of life-cycle costing techniques to justify investment in maintenance
- An overall attitude where there is reluctance to spend money until there is no choice
- Maintenance and repair costs being subject to VAT

This led to a research programme by 'Maintain our Heritage' – the results of which are available on **www.maintainourheritage.co.uk**

There is now considerable guidance for building owners on maintenance, for example, through the UAHS/NIEA 'Look Before you Leak' campaign (see right) and publications such as the Historic Scotland short guide for homeowners *Maintaining Your Home*. The central message is that by planning the maintenance of your property you can save money and prolong its life.

Leaflet published by UAHS

## Building Maintenance – Gutters Checklist

### Maintain your home

'Prevention is better than cure', whether your home is historic or modern, basic maintenance is essential if minor problems are not to become major headaches.

### Clean your gutters and gullies

Your home provides shelter. In the Northern Irish environment water can cause serious damage to the structure and fabric if it is not controlled properly. Internal finishes are affected by damp, roof timbers damaged by water ingress and blocked gullies can cause flooding. Gutters and gullies are the main escape route for rainwater and should be maintained.

### Top tips:

- Check gutters twice a year: in Spring due to vegetation growth and Autumn after leaf fall
- Clean (or get cleaned) all gutters, hopper heads and roof valleys regularly
- Fix broken and damaged rainwater goods at the earliest opportunity. Repaint cast iron regularly to avoid rusting
- When on the roof inspect vulnerable areas such as chimneys and flashings. Binoculars are useful for hard to check places.

### Follow an inspection checklist

Investing a little time and money up-front on home maintenance can lead to long-term savings. This is best achieved by following a planned checklist. It is essential that the checklist records 'Must Do's', the frequency of tasks and the person responsible for completing them.

Keep the checklist in a safe place and note actions that have been taken. Over time this will help build up a comprehensive picture of the vulnerable parts of your building and the best ways to look after them.

## Built Heritage at Risk in Northern Ireland

Carlisle Memorial Church, Belfast

Vegetation growth on parapet

The Built Heritage at Risk in Northern Ireland project was first established in 1993 to identify historically important buildings and sites at risk of falling into a severe state of disrepair. Those structures considered 'at risk' are featured on the comprehensive online BHARNI Register compiled by the Ulster Architectural Heritage Society in partnership with the Northern Ireland Environment Agency.

The project aim is to highlight vulnerable buildings and structures and to act as a catalyst for conservation and re-use. This is achieved through heightened public awareness, providing help and advice for owners who wish to undertake repair schemes and assisting potential restoring purchasers who are looking for suitable properties.

Many of the buildings featured on the BHARNI Register might still be in use had intervention through maintenance occurred.

**www.ni-environment.gov.uk**
**www.uahs.org.uk**

**Be safe**
Safety is always of the utmost importance, particularly if working at height. Wear appropriate protection clothing and never work alone when using ladders. Assess all risks in advance and employ a reliable and competent contractor if necessary. Engaging professional help such as a conservation surveyor or architect may reduce concerns.

## Maintenance Plans

Every building should have a maintenance plan, which can be as basic as a simple checklist for most houses, up to a comprehensive combination of drawings and schedules for more complex buildings.

The starting point for preparing a maintenance plan is to understand your building – what

Inspecting building from Cherry Picker

Inspecting stonework on a building by abseil

materials it is made of, how it performs and, in particular, how it is affected by rainfall and other weather. Traditional, solid wall buildings perform very differently from cavity wall or framed buildings and require different maintenance and repair policies. Different stones weather and perform very differently, and the same stone can weather differently in different microclimates, influenced by orientation, vegetation etc.

The next stage is to identify the areas or elements of the building vulnerable to decay and the causes of that decay. In the case of stonework, the major decay factors are normally based on environmental conditions. Water, and in particular an excessive concentration of water, is the enemy of stonework; accelerating decay of both stone and mortar and increasing the likelihood of penetrating water ingress. Excessive dampness also encourages plant growth which both further holds moisture and can create physical damage by root growth.

Many maintenance issues can be seen from the ground, but by no means all, and a comprehensive survey should involve a close visual inspection – perhaps from an adjoining building or structure but more normally from a mobile hoist or when this is not practical, by using rope access techniques. It is also good practice to build in access for maintenance, not the least to improve the chances of it being regularly carried out. Ladders are not recommended as a means of access but if they are to be used, it must be with sensible safety precautions including a competent person on the ground to stabilize the ladder.

Record keeping is crucial. Stone can often weather slowly over a period of time, but as we have seen in the chapter entitled 'Mapping Stone Decay', can enter a period of rapid, catastrophic

## Research – Industry Partnership

Stone Conservation Services (Consarc Design Group) and the Weathering Research Group (Queen's University Belfast) are part-funded by DTI (Department of Trade and Industry) to run a two-year project to develop techniques for non-destructive testing and monitoring of stone structures.

The aim is to translate non-destructive technologies, specifically laser scanning (LiDar and High Definition Object Scanning), probe permeametry and ground penetrating radar, into novel methods for monitoring historic buildings and monuments. The combination of all three techniques will transform current surveying techniques and provide an assessment of the rate of weathering of stone and scientific rationale for forecasting how historic materials perform over time.

3D Image of laser scan (LiDar) data 'point cloud'

High Definition Object Scan of one carved stonework panel

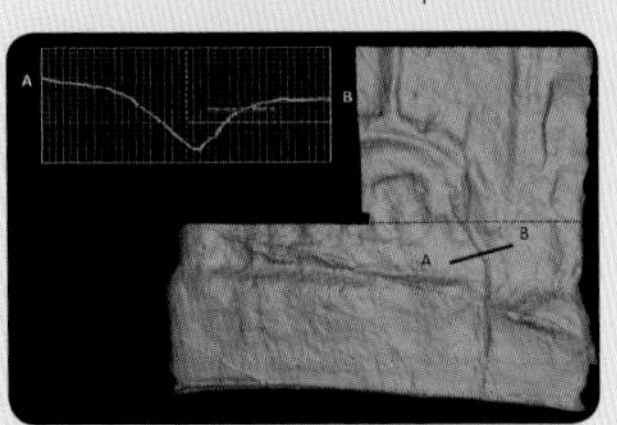

Re-scanning at regular intervals allows measurement of the rate of surface change, for example, across fractures. This can provide an indication of the rate of weathering

Non-destructive Ground Penetrating Radar (GPR) to assess for voids and planes of weakness

decay. Monitoring of stone decay over time, in particular highly carved stones of cultural significance, is the focus of a KTP (Knowledge Transfer Partnership) programme between QUB and Consarc Design Group/Stone Conservation Services, using high definition laser and object scanners to provide highly accurate records of the building's condition, repeated over time to build up an immediate and accurate picture of weathering decay.

Some items, like gutters and downpipes, need to be checked regularly, at least every six months and more often if there is a lot of vegetation or other debris around to block outlets. An annual inspection should be sufficient for most stone elements unless there is a process of catastrophic weathering underway.

## Summary of the Maintenance Plan Process

- Appraise your property and prepare a list of the areas/ materials for inspection
- Decide on the frequency of inspections for each item
- Identify areas where you might need help to gain access
- Prepare a list of relevant and experienced tradespeople who can do the work
- From the list of recorded defects, draw up a list of preventative or remedial actions
- Agree on frequency of maintenance surveys

The most reliable way to ensure maintenance is actually carried out is by putting in place a maintenance contract or by making sure it is on somebody's job programme.

A basic maintenance plan checklist is detailed below and in **Table 1**. It is normally best to start at the top of the structure and work downwards.

## Maintenance Checklist for Stone Buildings

### Gutters and downpipes

**6 month check**

Blocked, overflowing and leaking gutters and downpipes are the commonest causes of damp and need to be checked regularly. Tell-tale signs in the early stages are staining down the walls on either side of a downpipe or rusty joints. Traditional cast iron gutters can rust away in hidden areas causing considerable water ingress over a period of time before it is noticed, so it is worth checking the effectiveness of gutters and downpipes when it is actually raining.

### Junctions, cracks and joints

**Annual check**

Joints between materials, such as

Vegetation growth at parapet level

Poorly maintained downpipe

window and door jambs, inevitably produce differential movement between stone, mortar and timber, potentially opening up cracks which can lead to water ingress and subsequent rot or other decay. Maintenance should check the soundness of junction flashings and sealants. Small cracks are inevitable and are rarely a problem. Any significant cracking (greater than 2mm wide) should be monitored to ensure there is no progressive movement.

**Fixings**
Annual check

Rusting fixings for window guards, aerials, signs etc, can cause both unsightly staining and, more critically, damaging expansion cracking.

**Drains and ground levels**
6 month check

Once the water gets to ground level it is essential that it gets away to avoid rising damp or splashback, both of which will lead to a concentration of damaging salts and water ingress. Drains need to be regularly rodded and checked. Hard surfaces immediately against stone walls should be avoided as they encourage splashback in heavy rain. Ground level should be at least 150mm below inside floor level. Lowering of outside ground level is a very effective way of reducing internal damp, helped by removal of external vegetation against the walls.

**Projections, drips, flashings**
Annual Check

Stone façades should ideally shed water as quickly as possible, but window cills, cornices, stringcourses and drips can all allow water to slow and gather. Over time this can create pockets or dips where water can accumulate and more easily penetrate inwards. Regular cleaning of leaves or other debris will help but in many cases the fitting of protective lead flashing with drip edges may be necessary

Fracturing of render and stonework on a mausoleum due to ivy roots (ivy now removed)

to allow water to run off more quickly and stop penetrating damp.

### Pointing
Annual Check

Pointing in masonry walls is designed to be 'sacrificial', i.e. softer and more porous than the surrounding stone, so it will slowly recede back from the stone face. This is not a problem until significant ledges appear which encourages water ingress, and at this point re-pointing will be required, but this should be no more frequent than 25-30 years, depending on exposure.
Pointing must be done in a 'sacrificial' or lime mortar. Much damage has been done to historic character by use of hard sand: cement repointing mortars.

### Chimneys
Six months

Chimney stacks are particularly susceptible to decay given the conditions of sporadic heating and cooling, exposure to weather and relatively thin construction. They also provide an easy way for water to enter a building. Few historic buildings have lead trays to prevent water soaking through the flue and so the quality of the mason's skill is very high in detailing out damp. Flues not in use should be capped using a ventilated pot top piece.

### Plant growth, algae and moss
Six months

Vigorous plant growth: ivy, buddleia, grasses etc, should be removed immediately to avoid root damage to mortar joints.

Algae and mosses may not be seriously damaging, depending on the stone type, but they do encourage moisture retention and accelerate decay. Algae and moss can be removed by application of biocides.

### Stone pitting, pocketing and uneven decay

#### Annual Check

Some stones, typically Scrabo Sandstone, can decay erratically with one stone 'receding' significantly while its neighbours stay relatively pristine. This can lead to ledges developing in stones which again can encourage water retention and ingress. Sloping fillets of lime mortar are the easiest solution. Similarly, early application of a lime mortar filler to isolated holes can significantly slow down decay.

### Sealing and 'waterproofers'

There is a temptation to treat water penetration with one of the many propriety waterproofing sealers on the market, but this is nearly always a bad idea, without thorough analysis and testing. In most cases, application of a surface sealer will only serve to trap moisture within the structure – moisture which will have entered through cracks and junctions. If this moisture cannot easily migrate out through the stone it is more likely to move inwards or to cause long-term damage to the surface of stonework.

## Conclusion

A building is made up of many different elements, whether that building be the humblest stone-built cottage or the grandest cathedral. A knowledge of these elements and what keeps them in good order along with regular monitoring of their condition is central to good stewardship. Our historic buildings have, for the most part, been in existence for longer than us and it is the responsibility of the building owners and those with a 'duty-of-care' to ensure that best practice monitoring and maintenance increases the chance that they will still form an important part of our urban and rural landscapes for future generations to enjoy.

Table 1 **Example of Completed House Maintenance Checklist**

| **Date of inspection:** | **Your name:** |
|---|---|
| | John Savage |

| **Element** | **Component/ material** | **Defect present** | |
|---|---|---|---|
| | | **Yes** | **No** |
| **Pitched Roofs** | Slates/Tiles | ✓ | |
| | Dormer windows | ✓ | |
| | Rooflights | ✓ | |
| | Cupolas | | ✓ |
| | Ridges | ✓ | |
| | Hips | ✓ | |
| | Metal flashings | ✓ | |
| | Parapet | | ✓ |
| | Iron Cresting | | ✓ |
| | Coping | ✓ | |
| | Skews/Crowsteps | ✓ | |
| | Other features | | |
| **Flat roofs** | Roof covering | ✓ | |
| | Upstands/Parapets | ✓ | |
| | Junction with main roofs/walls | | ✓ |
| | Built-in drainage | ✓ | |
| | Verges | ✓ | |
| | Eaves | ✓ | |
| **Roof drainage** | Valley gutters | ✓ | |
| | Parapet gutters | ✓ | |
| | Hopper outlets | ✓ | |
| | Eaves gutters | ✓ | |
| | Downpipes | ✓ | |
| **Chimneys** | Chimney stacks | ✓ | |
| | Copes | ✓ | |
| | Pots | ✓ | |

| **Elevation** (use appropriate identification for example, North etc.) | |
|---|---|
| North-West | |
| **Nature of defect** | **Notes:** add any extra information for example, precise location, seriousness of defect, urgency of repair. |
| 20 broken, slipped, loose | Urgent – H and S risk, and water ingress |
| Split lead to side cheeks | Left side of right-hand dormer – water ingress |
| Rusted frame and broken glass | Original split pane cast-iron rooflight |
| | No cupola |
| Loose and uneven – mortar missing | Urgent – 2 loose ridge tiles likely to fall |
| Lead roll hip – section missing | Urgent – water ingress |
| Lead – cracked and split | West end of roof edge |
| | Parapet sound |
| | No cresting |
| 1 coping stone loose | In middle of wall – stable but loose |
| Open mortar joints | Likely water ingress at joints |
| | |
| Split and bubbled felt | Rear return – later addition |
| Upstand separated from wall | Potential water ingress at junction |
| | Junction flashings seem sound |
| Ponding | Dip in roof away from gully |
| Split felt | Likely water ingress along west wall |
| Fascia rotted and split | Timber fascia beard needs replaced |
| Holes in lead | Old lead is thin and forming holes |
| Lead separated from wall | Gap allowing water ingress |
| 1 split cast iron hopper | Left-hand side hopper |
| Sagging UPVC gutter to extension | Water spilling out and soaking wall |
| 1 blocked downpipe | Left-hand side cast iron downpipe blocked |
| Stones split and joints open | Urgent – stonework expanding and loose |
| Stones split and loose | Urgent – coping stone dislodged |
| 1 chimney pot dislodged | Urgent – H and S risk of falling |

| Example of Completed House Maintenance Checklist continued... | | | |
|---|---|---|---|
| **Date of inspection:** | **Your name:** | | |
| | John Savage | | |

| Element | Component/ material | Defect present | |
|---|---|---|---|
| | | Yes | No |
| Walls | Stonework | ✓ | |
| | Joints/Pointing | ✓ | |
| | Harl/Render | | ✓ |
| | Margins (openings) | | ✓ |
| | Sub-floor vents | ✓ | |
| | Ground level | ✓ | |
| | Other features | ✓ | |
| Bay/Oriel windows | Masonry walls | ✓ | |
| | Stone mullions | ✓ | |
| | Corbels | ✓ | |
| | Roof covering | | ✓ |
| | Blocking course | ✓ | |
| | Flashings | ✓ | |
| | Roof drainage | ✓ | |
| Windows | Window 1,2,3 etc. | ✓ | |
| Doors | Door 1,2,3 etc. | ✓ | |
| Other elements | Porch | | ✓ |

**General comments:** Note any additional information you consider relevant.

| **Elevation** (use appropriate identification for example, North etc.) | |
|---|---|
| North-West | |
| **Nature of defect** | **Notes:** add any extra information for example, precise location, seriousness of defect, urgency of repair. |
| 30% spalling stones | Urgent – some exfoliated stones likely to fail |
| 65% open joints | Some hard cement mortar in west corner |
| | No rendered walls |
| | No defects |
| Blocked by raised ground | |
| Split against building too high | |
| Split moulding | Hood mould over doors |
| Dislodged stones at jambs | Signs of rusting iron cramps |
| Loose and out of plumb | Rusting iron rods |
| Settled and uneven | Caused by movement in stonework |
| Lead | Lead – seems sound |
| Joints open | Caused by settlement below |
| Lead split where stones moved | |
| Outlet blocked | Outlet too small |
| Rotted cill members | Refer to detailed window checklist |
| Rotted frame bottoms | Refer to timber door inspection checklist |
| | No porch |

> Rain! whose soft architectural hands have power to cut stones and chisel to shapes of grandeur the very mountains
>
> Henry Ward Beecher (1813–1887)

Armagh Limestone

# Appendices

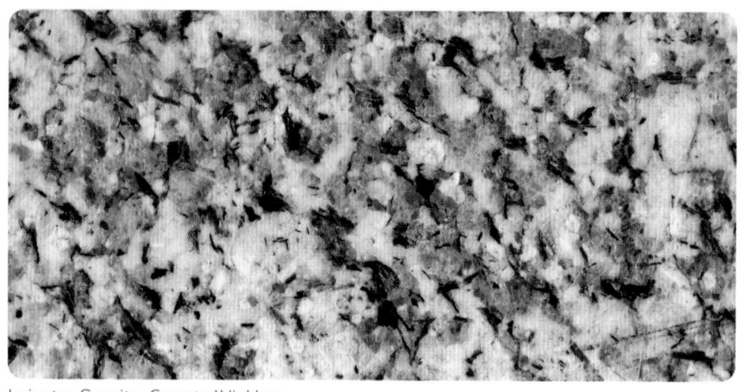

Leinster Granite, County Wicklow

## Appendix A.
## Glossary of Terms

For reasons of clarity, the glossary of terms has been sub-divided into architectural terms and geological terms. The lists for both are not comprehensive but contain the most commonly used terminology with the glossary of architectural terms being complemented by drawings of stonework details, stone wall construction, window details, column orders and stone surface finishes provided on the pages following the descriptions.

## Glossary of Architectural Terms

| | |
|---|---|
| **Applied or engaged column** | A column which is attached to a wall as opposed to being freestanding. |
| **Apse** | A vaulted semi-circular or polygonal space usually found at the (eastern) end of a church. |
| **Arcade** | A series of arches carried on columns. If attached to a wall (as opposed to being freestanding) it is known as a 'blind arcade'. |
| **Arris** | A sharp edge at the junction of two surfaces. |
| **Ashlar** | Smooth faced stone blocks in regular courses and sizes. |
| **Baldacchino** | A canopy over an altar, tomb or throne, which is carried on columns, supported on brackets. |
| **Balusters** | Small columns or posts forming part of a balustrade (see 'Stonework terms – Classical style'). |
| **Balustrade** | A wall edge feature made up of balusters and a coping (see 'Stonework terms - Classical style'). |
| **Band** | A flat horizontal course around a building which is less projecting, moulded or decorated than a 'string course'. |
| **Banker-mark** | A stone mason's personal mark cut into a dressed stone, named after the 'banker' or bench that the mason worked at. |
| **Battlement** | A notched or indented parapet. The high points are called 'merlons' and the gaps, 'embrasures'. A wall with a battlement is described as being 'crenellated' or 'castellated'. |
| **Bartizan** | A small turret projecting from the corner of the top of a tower. |
| **Bay** | The division of the architectural arrangement of a building, correctly based on its structural layout but commonly on window openings. |
| **Bed** | The horizontal surface on which stone lies. |

## Glossary of Architectural Terms

| | |
|---|---|
| **Bell-cote / Bell-gable** | Small turret or gable in which bells are hung. These are common in churches but also found in estate farmyards. |
| **Boss** | An enriched ornamental block at the intersection of vault ribs or ends of mouldings. |
| **Breakfront** | A slightly advanced section of a façade, typically the central bays of a classical style elevation. |
| **Broached** | A surface finish applied to stone consisting of broad diagonal parallel grooves cut with a broach or mason's pointed chisel. A broached spire has pyramidal corner blocks at the transition between an octagonal spire and a square tower (see 'Stone surface finishes'). |
| **Buttress** | A projection from a wall designed to provide additional strength and support. A diagonal buttress is set at an angle of 135° to the corner it is attached to. |
| **Canted** | Stonework that is splayed or bevelled. A polygonal column can be termed canted. |
| **Chamfer** | An arris or angle shaved off creating a splayed corner. |
| **Chancel** | The sanctuary of a church around the altar. The chancel arch marks the division between the nave and the chancel. |
| **Chisel draft or Drafted margin** | A margin around the edges of a stone comprising closely spaced fine lines at right angles to the edge (see 'Stone surface finishes'). |
| **Cills (sills)** | Sometimes 'sills' – normally projecting horizontal stone at the base of a window or door. |
| **Classical Style** | Based on precedents of Greek and Roman architecture and includes 'Palladian' and 'Renaissance' (16th century) and Neo-Classical (18th century onwards) styles. |
| **Clerestorey** | A window or row of windows in the upper part of a building, typically a church nave above side aisle roofs. |

## Glossary of Architectural Terms

| | |
|---|---|
| **Colonnade** | A long sequence of columns joined by their entablature |
| **Conservation** | The sensitive repair and consolidation of historic fabric, retaining the maximum amount of original historic material. (See British Standard; BS 7570) |
| **Coping** | A top course of stones along a wall, normally projecting and designed to throw water off the top of the wall (see 'Stonework terms – Classical style'). |
| **Cramps and Dowels** | Metal bars holding stones together – historically these were made of iron, later copper or bronze was used but now stainless steel is the metal of choice. |
| **Crow-stepped** | A stair-step type of design at the top of the triangular gable-end of a building where the gable wall extends beyond the roof line and finishes in a stepped fashion. |
| **Dentil** | A rectangular or cubic tooth-like projection used as ornamentation in classical mouldings (see 'Architectural terms – Classical style'). |
| **Dimension Stone** | Quarried stone that has been selected and cut to specific sizes or shapes. |
| **Dressings** | Projecting or ornate stonework around doors, windows and eaves. |
| **Drip** | Projecting edge of a moulding designed to throw off rain. Elaborately moulded drips are described as 'label moulds' or 'hood moulds'. |
| **Eaves** | The lower horizontal edge of a roof, usually supporting the gutters. These can be overhanging or flush. |
| **Elizabethan Revival** | The term given to early Renaissance architecture in England, during the reign of Queen Elizabeth I. |
| **Entablature** | The superstructure of mouldings and bands which lie horizontally above columns, resting on their capitals. |
| **Entasis** | The slight outward curve of a classical column used as a device to prevent them from appearing concave. |
| **Façade** | Any external elevation of a building, usually the front. |

## Glossary of Architectural Terms

| | |
|---|---|
| **Finial** | The decorative upper termination of a pinnacle, gable end, buttress, canopy, or spire (see 'Stonework terms – Gothic style tower'). |
| **Flashing** | Weatherproofing cover for joints and junctions, usually made of lead. |
| **Gable** | The end wall of a property that frequently carries a chimney. |
| **Gablet** | A small gable, often ornamental (see 'Stonework terms – Gothic style tower). |
| **Gallet** | A small stone placed in wide mortar joints for decoration and to reduce the amount of mortar used, in the technique called 'galleting'. Galleting is most frequently used in combination with uneven, hard-to-dress stonework (see 'Stone wall construction'). |
| **Georgian Style** | Architecture style associated with the period of Kings George I to IV (1714-1830). The term is also often applied to a simple form of stripped classical style. |
| **Gothic Style** | Characterised by pointed arches, vaulting and tracery. The Gothic style was the dominant European style in the 12th to 17th centuries followed by the Gothic Revival (Gothick) in the 18th century, becoming a purer, more historically based form by the mid 19th century (see 'Stonework terms – Gothic style spire'). |
| **Grout** | A semi-liquid mortar poured or forced into joints in masonry or rubble to stabilise a structure. |
| **Harling** | A lime coating or wet dash applied as an external finish to stone walls. The harling material is a combination of aggregates and lime, mixed into a slurry consistency. Historically, harling was applied directly onto masonry walls, which had previously been evened out by pointing the wall flush and filling small holes with stone pinnings. Towards the end of the 19th century it became commonplace to apply one or two trowelled undercoats to flatten the background before casting on the lime harling. |

## Glossary of Architectural Terms

|  |  |
|---|---|
| **Head** | Although this term is used to describe the top member of a door or window it is also used to describe a brick or stone exposed in a wall with its longest side set at right-angles to the face of the wall. |
| **Hipped** | A hipped (or hip) roof slopes down to the eaves on all four sides. |
| **Jacobean Revival** | The term given to the architectural style that prevailed in England during the reign of James I of England (1603-25). |
| **Keystone** | The highest central stone in an arch or ribbed vault. |
| **Kneeler** | The stone shaped to provide the springing of an arch or vault or the end stone of a parapet or skew-table, shaped to bond with the wall below and resist outward thrust. |
| **Lancet** | A tall, narrow window with a sharply pointed arched head (see 'Stonework terms – Gothic style spire base'). |
| **Lintel (also Lintol)** | The horizontal 'head' over an opening (see 'Stonework terms – Classical style'). |
| **Moulding** | The ornamental contours given to the angles and features of stonework (see 'Stonework terms – Classical style'). |
| **Mullion** | A vertical division between the lights of a window, usually subdivided by horizontal 'transoms'. Mullions are usually moulded (see also Transom). (See 'Stonework terms – Windows') |
| **Natural Bed** | Sedimentary rocks (limestones and sandstones) that are layered. These should be laid with the layers parallel to the wall bed known as naturally bedded. If laid on their edge, such stones are described as being 'face bedded' and are prone to delamination. Projecting stones should be edge bedded with the layers / laminations at right angles to the face of the wall. |
| **Nave** | The central aisle of a church, traditionally for the lay population and separated from the chancel or sanctuary. |
| **Niche** | A recess in a wall for a statue or ornament usually curved on plan and arched over. |

## Glossary of Architectural Terms

| | |
|---|---|
| **Obelisk** | A tall, tapering shaft with a pyramidal top, based on an ancient Egyptian form. |
| **Ogee** | An 'S'-shaped double curve. |
| **Palazzo** | An Italian Palace, or any large extravagant building of a similar style. |
| **Patina** | An alteration in surface colour associated with the age and exposure history of a building. This is a feature that can be lost in over enthusiastic restoration. |
| **Pediment** | A classical, low-pitched, triangular gable end supported on the entablature above a portico. The pediment often contains a coat of arms or other sculptured decoration. Similar features above doors, windows and other openings where they may be triangular or segmental (see also Tympanum) (see 'Stonework terms – Classical style'). |
| **Pilaster** | A pilaster is a slightly projecting column built into or applied to the face of a wall. Most commonly flattened or rectangular in form, pilasters can also take a half-round form or the shape of any type of column (see 'Stonework terms – Classical style'). |
| **Pointing** | The filler in masonry joints. In historic stonework a lime and sand mix was normally used. |
| **Portico** | A porch leading to the entrance of a building, or extended as a colonnade with a roof structure over a walkway supported by columns or enclosed by walls. |
| **Quoin** | The dressed corner stones of a wall frequently alternating between a header and stretcher on each side (see 'Stonework terms – Classical style'). |
| **Reveal** | The side of an opening in a wall, typically at windows and doors. |
| **Restoration** | Replacement of worn historic fabric with new material. |
| **Rubble** | Masonry consisting of undressed, rough stones, laid either as un-coursed (random) or coursed (with specific layers of horizontal blocks or stones). |
| **Rusticated** | The working of deep grooves or channels in stonework (see' Stone surface finishes'). |

## Glossary of Architectural Terms

**Scottish Baronial Style** 19th-century castle style with rough-hewn stone, turrets and bartizans, crenellations and towers, usually containing Gothic details.

**Sett** A square stone used for paving.

**Skew** The sloping coping stones on a gable wall.

**Spandrel** The triangular space between the curve of an arch and square enclosing it or any approximately triangular area (see 'Stonework terms – Gothic style spire base').

**Stretcher** A brick or stone laid with its longest face in the surface of the wall.

**String Course** Stone course or moulding projecting from the façade (see 'Stonework terms – Classical style').

**Tracery** Combination of mullions and transoms forming windows or screens, including rose-windows. In its simplest form 'Y-tracery' is a central, branched mullion in a pointed opening (see 'Stonework terms – Gothic windows').

**Tetrastyle** A portico or colonnade with four frontal columns.

**Transom** The horizontal member forming the division between the lights of a window or other opening (see also Mullion).

**Trefoil** The ornamental foliation or cusping introduced into the heads of window-lights, tracery and panellings in which the centre takes the form of a three-lobed leaf (formed from three partially-overlapping circles). The fourfold version of an architectural trefoil is called a quatrefoil (see 'Stonework terms – Gothic style spire' and 'Stonework terms – Windows').

**Tympanum** The semi-circular or triangular decorative wall surface over an entrance bounded by a lintel and arch. It often contains sculptures or other ornaments (see 'Stonework terms – Classical style').

**Vault** An arched structure over a space constructed of stone or brick. Its simplest form is a semicircular 'barrel-vault' with more complex shapes including groin-vaults, rib-vaults and fan-vaults.

## Stonework Terms – Classical Style

1 Balustrade
2 Solid End Piece
3 Classical Baluster
4 Coping
5 Cornice
6 Back Face
7 Top Mouldings: 'Cyma Recta'
8 Modillions
9 Dentils
10 Middle Moulding: 'Cyma Reversa'
11 Bottom Moulding: 'Astragal'
12 Pediment
13 Tympanum
14 Corona
15 Fascia Lintol
16 Capital and Abacus
17 Pilaster
18 Jamb or Architrave
19 Soffit
20 Rusticated Smooth Faced Quoin
21 Plain Ashar
22 Torus and Scotia Moulds
23 Pilaster Attic Base
24 Pilaster Cornice
25 Pilaster Dado or Die
26 Apron Panel
27 Cill Base
28 Pedestal

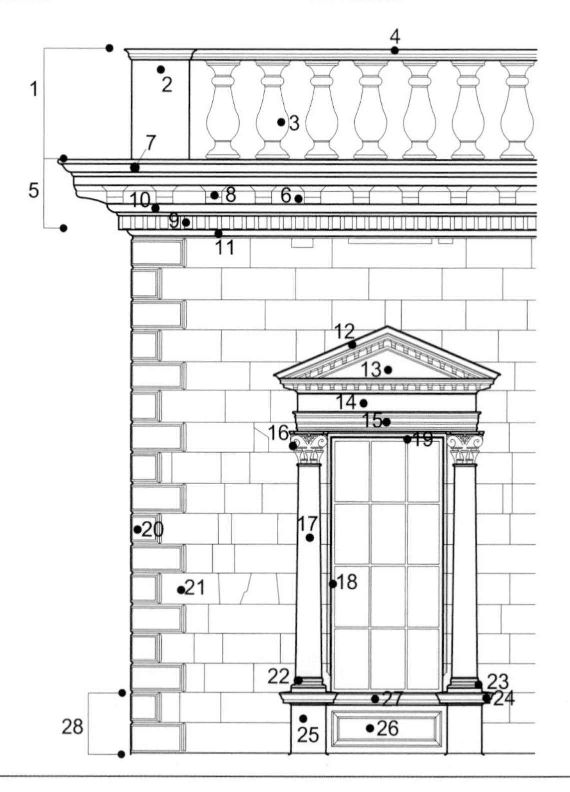

## Stonework Terms – Classical Style

1 Torus
2 Pilaster Base or Plinth
3 Cill Block
4 Base Course
5 Lower Cornice:
  **a** Top Mould
  **b** Dentils
6 Keystone
7 Diamond Headed Voussoir
8 Diamond Headed Quoin – Corner
9 Platband
10 String Course
11 Rusticated Smooth Ashlar
12 Diamond Headed Quoin – Jamb
13 Jamb Stone
14 Intrados
15 Apron Panel
16 Cill Block
17 Rope Moulding
18 Diamond Frieze Panel
19 Roll or Cable Moulding
20 Rusticated Vermiculated Plinth:
  **a** Ashlar Stone
  **b** Ashlar Quoin

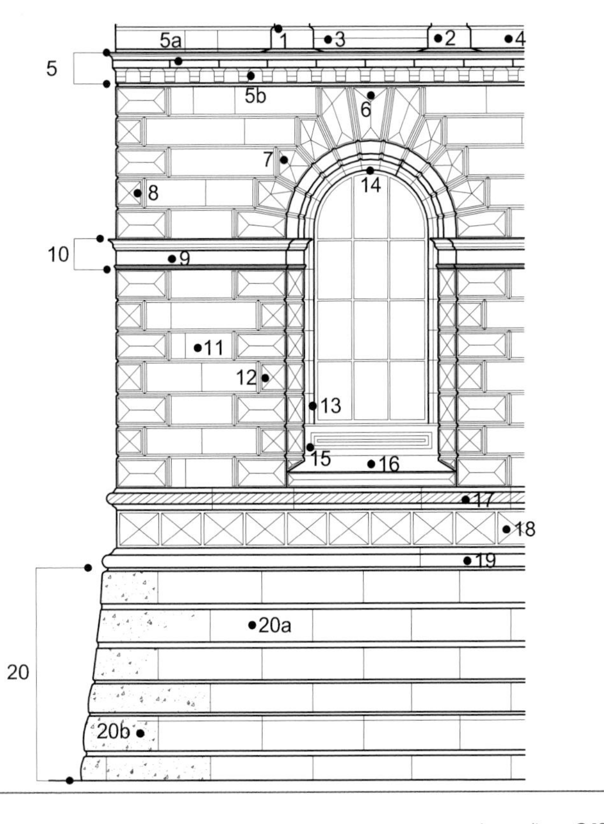

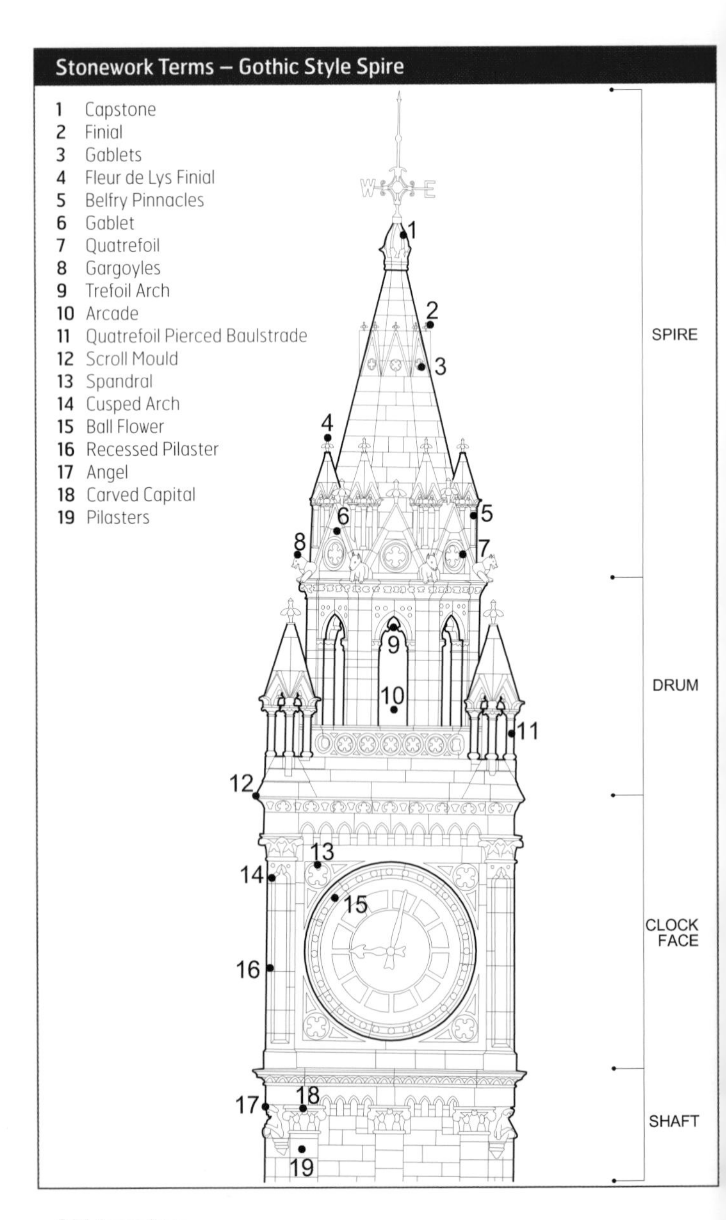
Stonework Terms – Gothic Style Spire
1 Capstone
2 Finial
3 Gablets
4 Fleur de Lys Finial
5 Belfry Pinnacles
6 Gablet
7 Quatrefoil
8 Gargoyles
9 Trefoil Arch
10 Arcade
11 Quatrefoil Pierced Baulstrade
12 Scroll Mould
13 Spandral
14 Cusped Arch
15 Ball Flower
16 Recessed Pilaster
17 Angel
18 Carved Capital
19 Pilasters
W
E
SPIRE
DRUM
CLOCK FACE
SHAFT

## Stonework Terms – Gothic Style Base

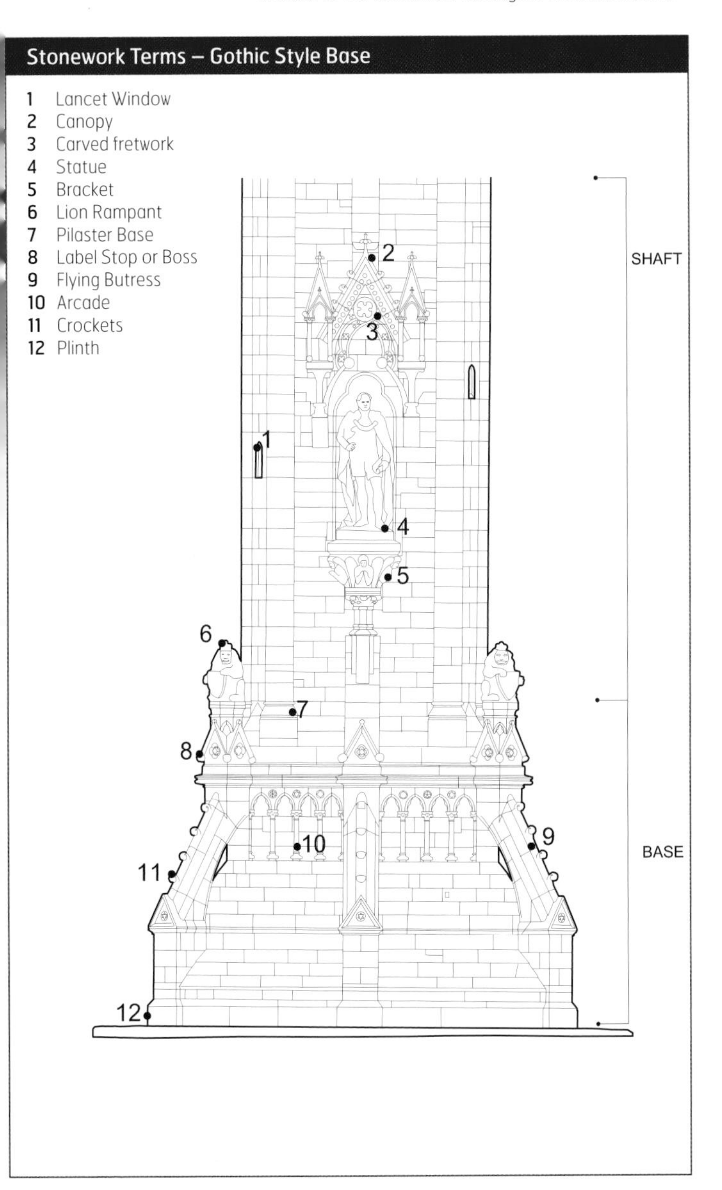

## Stonework Terms – Column Orders and Gothic Style Windows

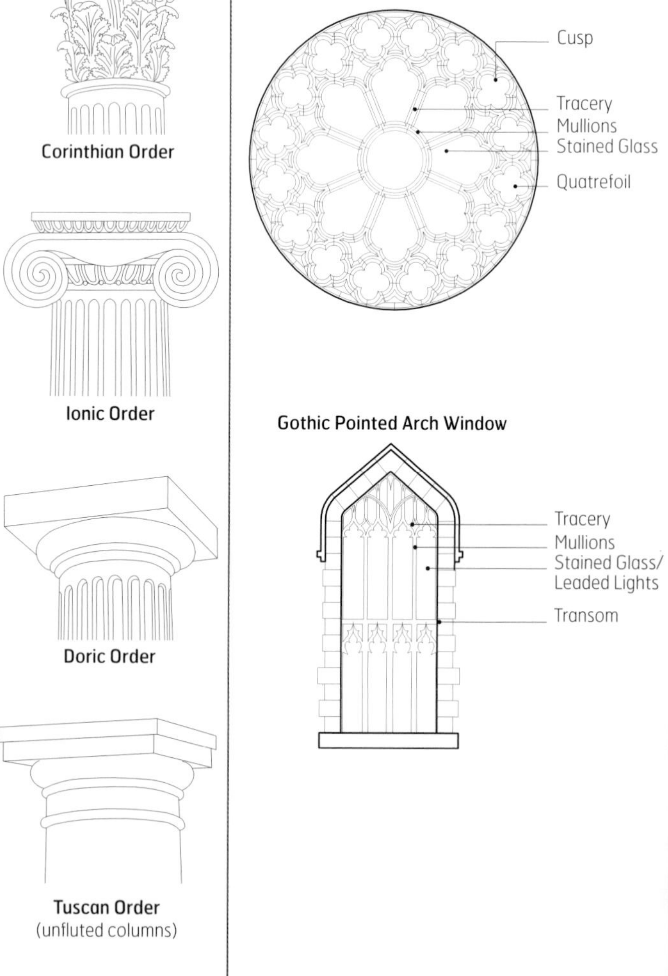

## Stonework Terms – Stone Surface Finishes

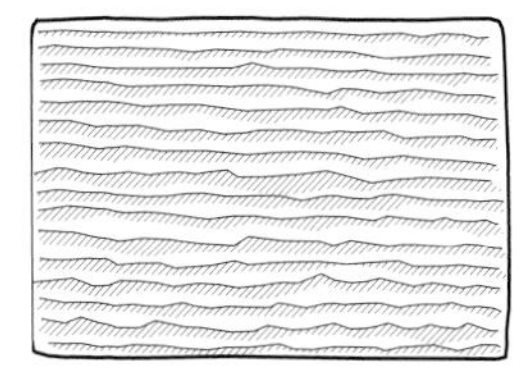

Broached

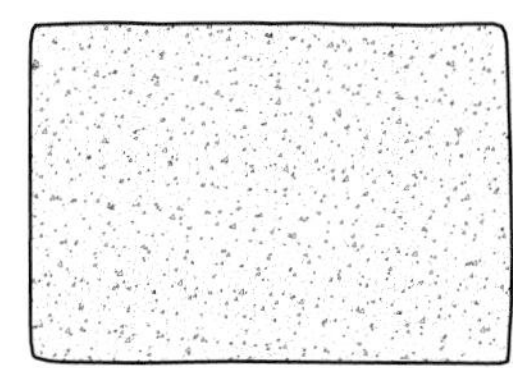

Bush Hammered

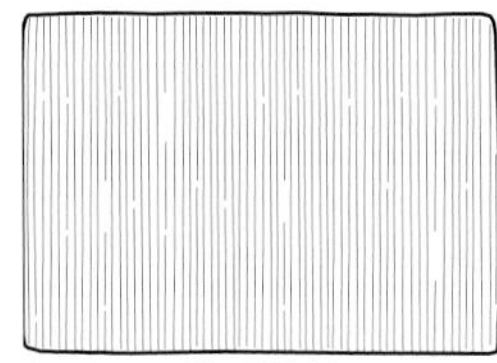

Corduroy / Tool Finish

Droved

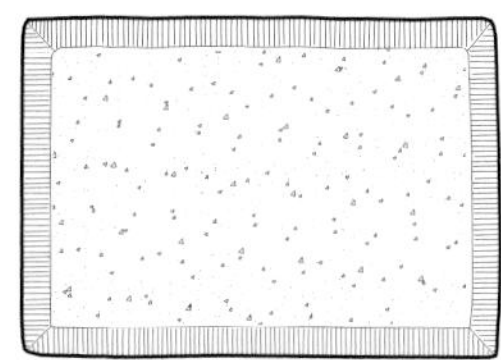

Finely Punched
With Drafted Margins

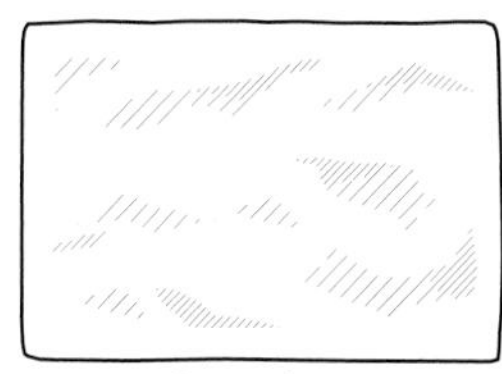

Hammer Dressed

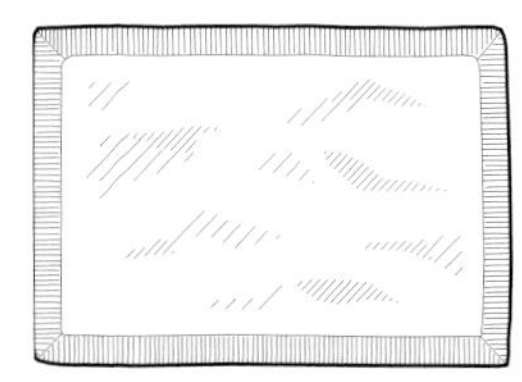

Hammer Dressed
With Drafted Margins

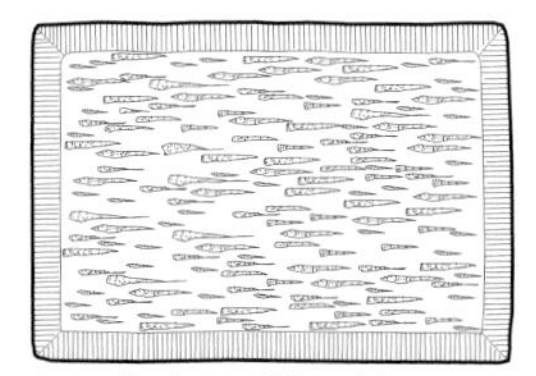

Long Horizontal Punching
With Drafted Margins

## Stonework Terms – Stone Surface Finishes

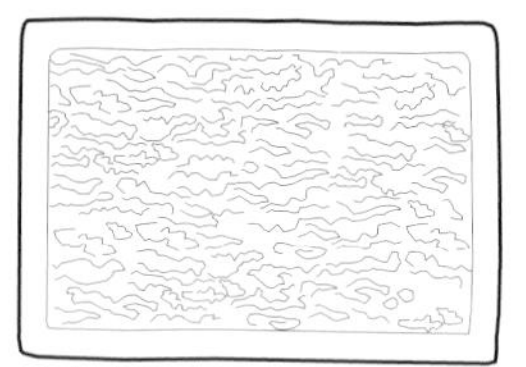

Picked With Smooth Border

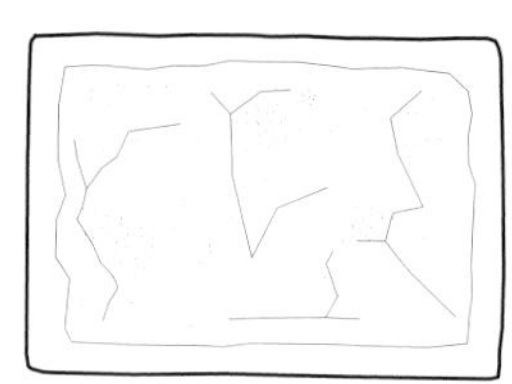

Pitch Faced

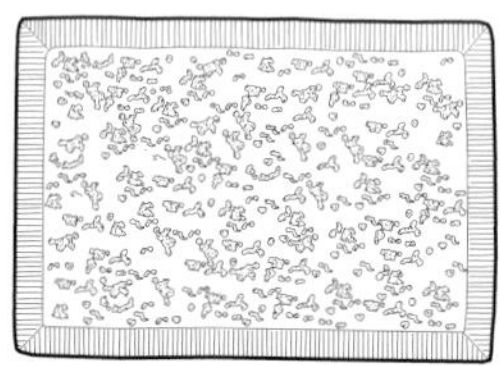

Rough Punching
With Drafted Margins

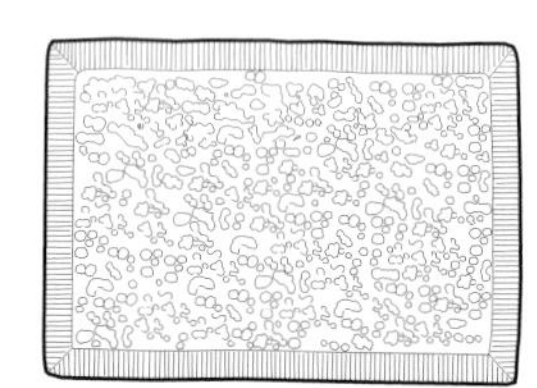

Sparrow Pecked Surface With
Drafted Margins

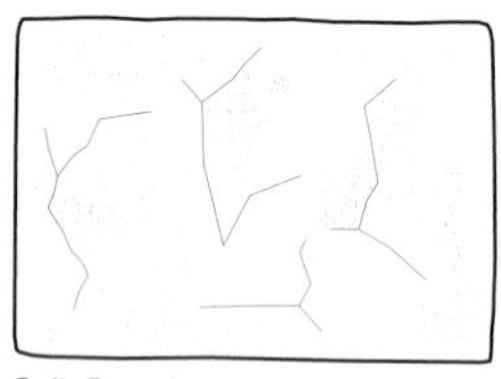

Split Faced

Stugged

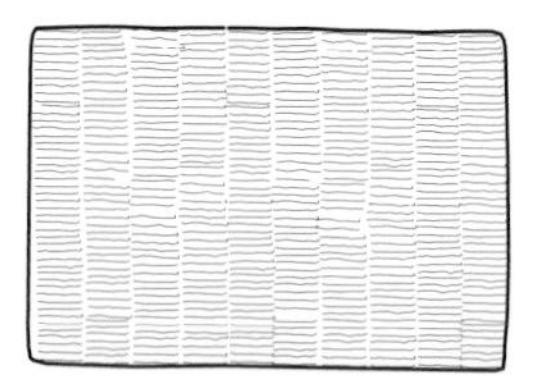

Horizontal Tooled Face

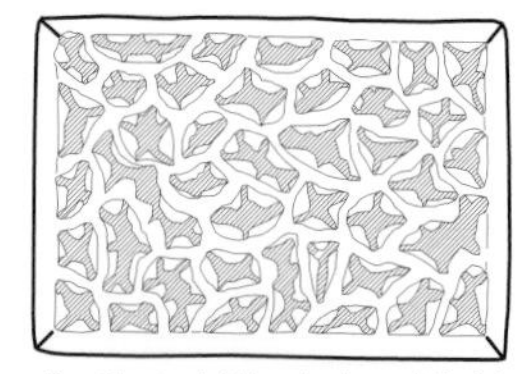

Rusticated / Verniculated Finish

## Stonework Terms – Stone Wall Types

Random Rubble Wall

Coursed Random Rubble Walling

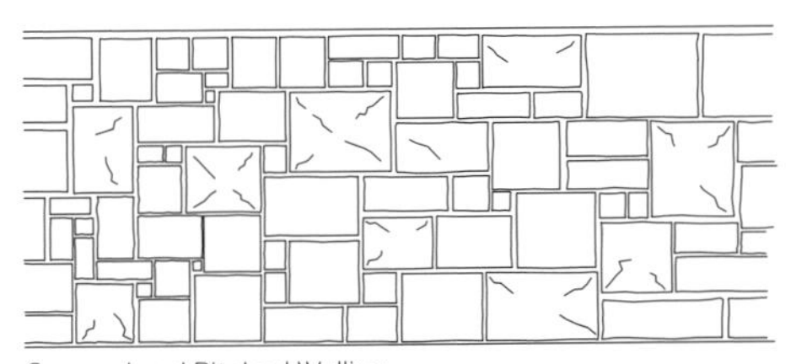

Squared and Pitched Walling

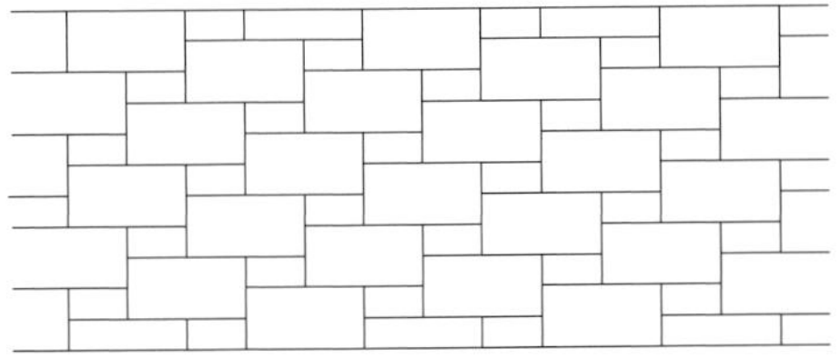

Block and Sneck Walling

## Stonework Terms – Stone Wall Types

### Stone Clad Walling

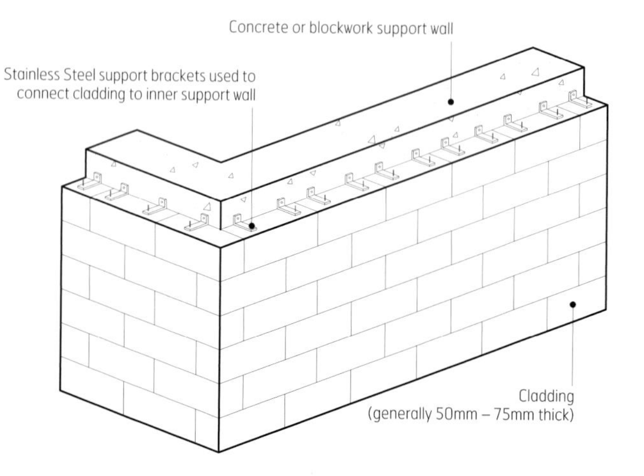


### Coursed Ashlar With Rustic Quoins

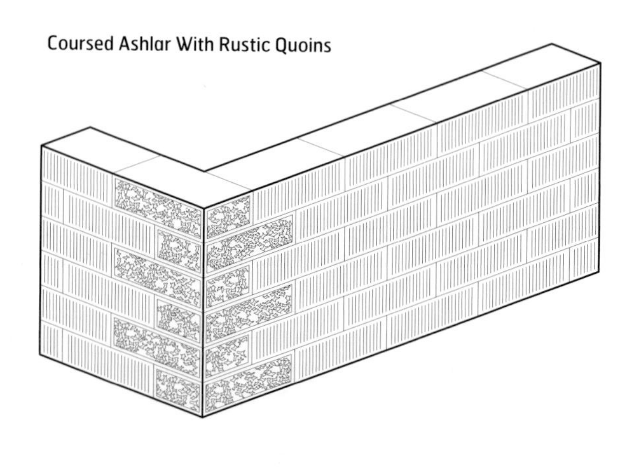

## Glossary of Geological Terms

| | |
|---|---|
| **Acid** | Defined as being a substance that has a pH of less than 7. |
| **Acid Deposition** | A term used to describe the chemical characteristics of precipitation in polluted environments where the combination of gaseous pollutants such as sulphur dioxide and nitrous oxides with moisture in rain, snow or fog reduce the pH value below that expected for precipitation in unpolluted environments. |
| **Aeolian** | A term used to describe the action of wind in eroding and transporting sediment. |
| **Aggregate** | Sand, gravel, crushed stone, shells and other materials that are used to mix with a binder and water to produce mortars and renders. |
| **Alkaline** | Defined as being a substance that has a pH of more than 7. In the context of geology, rocks predominantly composed of alkaline minerals are described as being basic rocks. |
| **Alluvial fan** | A cone-shaped mass of sand, gravel, cobbles and boulders that is deposited by a stream as it emerges from the confines of a mountain or upland valley. Loss of stream power results in sediment deposition and a spreading out of sediments across a plane or valley floor. |
| **Anorthoclase** | A mineral composed predominantly of alkali feldspars. |
| **Anoxic** | Conditions in which oxygen is absent. |
| **Banding** | Striped appearance of some rock types in which the stripes or bands have different structural and / or mineralogical characteristics. |
| **Basalt** | A finely crystalline basic igneous rock. It is primarily dark grey to black in colour when fresh and is usually fine-grained due to rapid cooling of lava at the Earth's surface. Basalts can be porphyritic or vesicular with the former containing large visible crystals (phenocrysts) set in a fine grained matrix while the latter contains visible holes or vesicles caused by gas bubbles. |
| **Basic / Ultra-basic rock** | Igneous rocks that have very low silica content but are rich in ferromagnesian minerals. |

## Glossary of Geological Terms

**Bedding (planes)** Visible layering of sediments within sedimentary rocks.

**Biotite Mica** A common rock-forming mineral found in many igneous and metamorphic rocks. It is rich in the elements aluminium, silica and iron with magnesium and potassium. It is dark in colour, soft and splits readily into thin sheets along crystal cleavage planes.

**Boxwork** A term used to describe the feature formed when stone blocks have almost been completely eroded away leaving a lattice or 'boxwork' pattern of mortar indicating the original block dimensions (see Fig. 1).

**Breccia** A sedimentary rock consisting of individual clasts set within a finer-grained matrix. The clasts are usually angular in appearance and are differentiated from conglomerates which consist of rounded clasts. The clasts are larger than sand (>2mm).

**Capillary Rise** The mechanism by which water is drawn upwards through porous material.

**Cement/Matrix** Material which binds grains and/or fossil fragments together to form coherent rock. Common examples include; clay, iron, calcium carbonate and silica.

**Clast** A fragment of rock. Clastic rocks are those that contain fragments of pre-existing rock.

**Clay lamination** A thin continuous layer of clay minerals visible within sedimentary rock.

**Clay Lens** A visible lens-shaped concentration of clay minerals within sedimentary rock.

**Clay Minerals** These are finely crystalline minerals rich in aluminium and silica. They have a propensity to absorb and retain moisture and because of their platy, layered crystal structures they have a tendency to swell when wet and shrink when moisture is lost.

**Cleavage (plane)** This refers to the tendency for a rock or mineral to break along a predefined plane. In minerals this is determined by the crystal structure while in rock these lines of

## Glossary of Geological Terms

fracture are secondary structural features related to the effects of either metamorphism or deformation.

**Cobbles** Sediment that is between 64–256mm in diameter as defined by the Wentworth Scale.

**Coefficient of Thermal Expansion** The amount that a material expands as a result of heating. Individual minerals and rock types differ considerably with regard to this property.

**Compressive Strength** This is the capacity of material to withstand pressure (compressive load) applied along a single axis before it fails. The compressive strength of rock tends to be much greater than its tensile strength.

**Conglomerate** A sedimentary rock consisting of individual clasts within a finer-grained matrix. The clasts are usually rounded fragments and are differentiated from breccias which consist of angular clasts. The clasts are larger than sand (>2mm).

**Cross Bedding** A feature found in granular sedimentary rock, typically sandstone, that is caused by changes in the direction of currents of wind or water when the sediments were originally laid down. They are visible as laminations that run transverse to, or are obliquely inclined to the main bedding planes.

**Crystalline** Comprising an interlocking network of crystals. Crystalline rocks are usually formed by solidification of molten rock (granite, gabbro, basalt) or metamorphic action (marble).

**Curing** When certain rock types such as limestone are quarried they are relatively 'soft' and need to be left to 'cure' or harden for some time before they can be worked.

**Cyanobacteria** Also known as blue-green algae these are a form of bacteria that obtain energy through photosynthesis.

**Delamination** This is the separation of layers of rock which results from exposure to repeated stress such as repeated wetting and drying, heating and cooling or repeated cycles of salt crystallisation.

## Glossary of Geological Terms

**Diagenesis** The processes, such as compaction and cementation, that take place within an unconsolidated sediment as it is turned into rock.

**Dissolution** The chemical weathering process whereby susceptible minerals are dissolved and removed from rock in solution over time by the action of water.

**Eh Scale (Redox Potential)** A measure of the gain of an electron (reduction) or the loss of an electron (oxidation) in a chemical reaction.

**Feldspars** A very common group of rock-forming minerals rich in aluminium silicates linked with calcium, potassium and sodium. Those with sodium and/or calcium are described as plagioclase feldspars while those with sodium and/or potassium are classified as alkali feldspars. Feldspars are essential constituents of igneous rock but also occur in metamorphic and some sedimentary rocks.

**Flaking** This is the formation and release of thin layers or flakes of stone that typically develop in fine-grained stone and are usually no more than 20–30mm in diameter and 1–2mm in thickness.

**Foliated/ Banded** Alternating bands of minerals arranged in parallel planes. This arrangement is due to the rock having developed under great pressure and heat. The bands or foliations are often contorted (see Fig. 2).

**Foliation** This feature is common in metamorphic rocks and describes the preferred orientation of minerals forming parallel platy layers.

**Fossils / Fossiliferous** The remains of plants and animals. These are usually visible shell and coral fragments. In some limestones such as Portland Basebed, spherical particles called ooids are visible (see Fig. 3). Fossiliferous means containing fossils.

**Fragmental** Comprising large (more than 5mm in diameter) fragments of rock and/or fossils bound together. Fragments can be of any shape.

## Glossary of Geological Terms

**Freestone** A building stone that is fine-grained, uniform in structure and can be worked easily in any direction.

**Gabbro** A dense, dark grey-green, coarse-grained intrusive igneous rock.

**Gneiss** A coarse-grained, banded, crystalline metamorphic rock.

**Granodiorite** A light-coloured, coarse-grained intrusive igneous rock. Granodiorite is very similar to granite and typically made up of tightly interlocking crystals of quartz, feldspar, mica and hornblende. It usually contains abundant biotite mica and hornblende, giving it a darker appearance than true granite.

**Granite** A light-coloured, coarse-grained intrusive igneous rock typically made up of tightly interlocking crystals of quartz, feldspar and mica.

**Granular** Comprising individual grains or fossils that are visible and set in a binding material. This term describes sandstones and limestones.

**Granular Disintegration** This is the weathering related breakdown of rock through the loosening and dislodgement of individual mineral grains.

**Granule** A particle of rock that has a diameter of between 2–4mm as defined by the Wentworth Scale.

**Greywacke** A type of sandstone or gritstone characterised by its hardness, dark colour, and poorly-sorted, angular grains of quartz, feldspar, and small rock fragments set in a compact, fine grained matrix. It is a texturally-immature sedimentary rock commonly of Palaeozoic age.

**Gritstone** A sedimentary rock composed of a combination of coarse sand grains and small pebbles. It is a form of sandstone but is more coarse-grained than most sandstones used in construction.

**Haematite (hematite)** One of the most important sources of iron, haematite is also one of the main cementing agents of sandstones.

## Glossary of Geological Terms

**Hard Mortar** A term typically used to describe Portland cement mortar which is less flexible than lime mortar and which is cited as contributing to the accelerated breakdown of comparatively 'softer' sedimentary stone when it has been used to replace degraded lime mortar. As it is less flexible, it constrains the natural tendency of the stone to expand and contract which eventually triggers breakdown of the block surface.

**Honeycomb Weathering** Also known as alveolar weathering, as the name suggests it results in the formation of a 'honeycomb-like' assemblage of hollows typically up to 10cm in diameter and several centimetres in depth. There is uncertainty about the precise mechanism of their formation but they are usually associated with the action of salt and moisture.

**Hydraulic Lime** A variety of slaked lime used to make lime mortar. 'Hydraulicity' is the ability of lime to set under water. Hydraulic lime is produced by heating calcining limestone that contains clay and other impurities. Calcium reacts in the kiln with the clay minerals to produce silicates that enable the lime to set without exposure to air. Any unreacted calcium is slaked to calcium hydroxide. Hydraulic lime is used for providing a faster initial set than ordinary lime in more extreme conditions (including under water).

**Igneous Rock** Igneous rock forms from magma and can be either intrusive (for example granite) or extrusive (for example basalt). The former cools slowly beneath the Earth's surface and is typically coarse-grained with large visible crystals while the latter is extruded on to the Earth's surface where it cools quickly forming very fine-grained rock.

**Inter-bedding** This occurs when beds of one rock type lie between beds of a different rock type.

**Larvikite** A well-known variety of syenite quarried from around Larvik near Oslo in Norway. It is valued for decorative purposes as polishing enhances the colours of the feldspar minerals.

## Glossary of Geological Terms

| | |
|---|---|
| **Layers / Laminations** | Rocks such as sandstone and shale are often laid down in layers. Layers are usually several millimetres in thickness. |
| **Lime Putty** | Lime Putty or Non-Hydraulic Lime is produced by slaking Quicklime in an excess of water which is then left to mature for at least three months. The resulting fat lime putty hardens or cures as a result of exposure to the air / carbonation and does not set under water. This lime is often regarded as the most appropriate lime to use where maximum permeability is required. |
| **Limestone** | Limestone is a sedimentary rock composed largely of the mineral calcite (calcium carbonate: $CaCO_3$) formed as biochemical or biological precipitates of carbonate minerals. The principal sources of the carbonate minerals are the skeletons of organisms including algae, corals and shells. |
| **Lithification** | The process of turning unconsolidated sediment into rock through compaction and cementation. |
| **Lustre** | Sheen or shimmering reflectance from the rock surface that is enhanced in polished rock. Its intensity can vary from dull to splendid and it can have a glassy, metallic, pearly or silky appearance. |
| **Magma** | A substance generated by melting of the Earth's crust or mantle and which provides the raw material for the formation of igneous rock. |
| **Marble** | This is a non-foliated metamorphosed limestone mostly composed of calcium carbonate and which is hard enough to take a polish. |
| **Megacrysts** | Any crystal within crystalline rock that is much larger than those surrounding it. |
| **Micaceous** | Stone that comprises or contains mica minerals (biotite or muscovite). |
| **Micro-fractures** | Small-scale fracture development in rock with fractures typically being less than 0.1mm wide but can be several millimetres in length. |

## Glossary of Geological Terms

**Micron** A micron or micrometer (US) is a unit of length in the metric system with 1000 microns in a millimetre and 10,000 microns in a centimetre.

**Minerals** Inorganic rock-forming substances that are typically crystalline with characteristic chemical compositions. Minerals can be described as being primary or secondary with the former crystallising out directly from magma while the latter represent minerals that have formed from the subsequent alteration of primary minerals.

**Mohs Scale** A test designed to assess the hardness of rock based on Mohs Scale in which there are 10 levels of hardness. In Mohs Scale a fingernail has an approximate hardness of 2.5, a copper coin 3.5, a knife blade 5.5 and a steel file 6.5. Therefore, if a rock can be scratched using a fingernail then it will have an approximate hardness of 2.5. Calcite, the mineral in limestone, can be scratched with a stainless steel blade giving it a hardness of less than 6.5. To try this test: scratch the stone surface in different places with a steel blade and a copper coin. Then wet the stone surface and if the steel blade scratch remains but the copper coin scratch disappears the rock can be said to have a hardness of between 3.5 and 6.5.

**Mortar** A mixture of aggregate (sand), a binder such as cement or lime, and water and is applied as a paste which then sets hard. Mortar can be used to fix, or point masonry (see also Hard Mortar).

**Non-crystalline (amorphous)** Lacking a crystalline structure.

**Olivine** One of the most common minerals on Earth, olivine is so-called because of its typical olive green colour. The main elements that form this mineral are silica, magnesium and iron.

**Ooids** Spherical concretion of calcium carbonate not exceeding 2mm in diameter (see Fig. 3).

## Glossary of Geological Terms

**Oolitic** Composed of spherical grains of calcium carbonate (ooids) not exceeding 2mm in diameter (Fig. 3).

**Ordinary Portland Cement** Ordinary Portland Cement (OPC) is one of several types of cement being manufactured throughout the world. It is a hydraulic binder which, when mixed with water, forms a paste which sets and hardens by means of hydration reactions and processes. After hardening it retains its strength and stability even under water.

**Oxidation** A chemical reaction in which either oxygen combines with, or hydrogen is lost from a substance. A common example of this is the rusting of iron.

**Pebbles** Sediment that falls into the size range 4–64mm in diameter as defined by the Wentworth scale.

**Permeability** The ability of a rock to allow fluids (air or liquid) to flow through it. This property is basically a measure of how connected pore spaces are within a rock.

**pH Scale** This is a measure of the acidity or alkalinity of a substance where pure water represents the mid-point of the scale with a value of 7 while substances with values higher than this (up to pH 14) are described as being alkaline and those with values of less than 7 are described as being acidic. The pH scale is logarithmic and therefore each whole pH value below 7 is ten times more acidic than the next higher value with, for example, pH 4 being ten times more acidic than pH 5 and 100 times more acidic than pH 6. The same holds true for pH values above 7.

**Phenocrysts** Large, well-formed crystals set in a much finer-grained matrix. Rocks that contain large numbers of phenocrysts are described as being porphyritic.

**Porosity** A measure of the spaces between individual mineral grains within a rock.

**Pyroxene** An important group of silica-rich rock-forming minerals found in many igneous and metamorphic rocks.

**Quartzite** A very hard, silica-rich metamorphic rock that was originally sandstone.

## Glossary of Geological Terms

**Quicklime** Calcium oxide (CaO), also known as burnt lime. It is made by the burning of limestone that contains calcium carbonate ($CaCO_3$; mineral name: calcite) in a lime-kiln. This is accomplished by heating the material to above 825°C, a process called calcination or lime-burning, liberating carbon dioxide ($CO_2$) thus leaving CaO. This process is reversible, once the quicklime has cooled it immediately starts to absorb carbon dioxide from the air and, after enough time, reverts back to calcium carbonate.

**Reduction** A chemical process in which oxygen is removed from a substance. For example, in waterlogged conditions ferric iron can be converted into ferrous iron, which is much more mobile.

**Render** Render is a lime- or cement-based coating applied to the external or internal surfaces of walls. It is made of aggregate, a binder (lime or cement) and water.

**Sandstone** Sandstones are sedimentary rocks composed mainly of sand-size mineral grains (up to 2mm). Sandstones are the consolidated and cemented deposits of grains (mostly quartz and feldspar) that are laid down in beds. Sandstones represent ancient desert, river and marine deposits.

**Scaling** Formation and release of thin 'plates' of stone typically several centimetres in diameter and more than 5mm in thickness. Scales are bigger than 'flakes' and can developed in fine, medium and coarse-grained stone types. Scales often follow the surface detailing of a stone and this is described as 'contour scaling'.

**Schillerization** Development of rod-like intrusions along certain planes within minerals such as feldspars that through reflection and play-of-light create a 'Schiller' effect.

**Schistose** Having the characteristics of schist with often flaky, parallel layers of micaceous minerals.

**Scratch Test** A test designed to assess the hardness of a rock or mineral (see also Mohs Scale).

## Glossary of Geological Terms

**Serpentinite** Metamorphic rock formed from alteration of basic and ultra-basic igneous rock. Tends to have a greenish variegated colour and is used for decorative stonework.

**Silicates** Minerals in which silica is the major component.

**Slaking** Slaking of lime refers to the reaction between calcium oxide (quicklime) and water to form calcium hydroxide. This process is represented by the following equation:

$$CaO + H_2O = Ca(OH)_2 + Heat$$

(Calcium Oxide) + (Water) = (Calcium Hydroxide)

**Stylolites** Jagged, irregular suture-like feature that occurs in limestone and forms in response to pressures during rock formation (diagenesis).

**Syenite** A group of coarse-grained intrusive igneous rocks rich in alkali feldspars (for example Larvikite) but in which quartz content is either extremely low or absent.

**Tabular Mineral** A mineral that has a tablet-shaped rectangular form.

**Tafoni** Weathering hollows in vertical rock faces larger than alveolar or honeycomb weathering features.

**Tensile Strength** The ability of a material to withstand tension (pulling load) applied along a single axis before failure occurs. In comparison to compressive strength, the tensile strength of rock is negligible reflecting its 'brittle' characteristics as an engineering material.

**Texture** This refers to the size, shape and arrangement of mineral grains or larger particles that make up rock.

**Thermal Conductivity** The ability of a material to conduct or transfer heat through its fabric. In comparison to metals, rock is a poor conductor of heat.

**Tuff** Medium to fine-grained rock that consists of compacted fragments of volcanic ash.

**Vesicles** Spherical cavities (gas bubbles) within rocks such as basalt (see Fig. 4). Sometimes these are infilled with white minerals such as zeolites and calcite.

## Glossary of Geological Terms

**Weathering** The decomposition and breakdown of rock and minerals by chemical, physical and biological processes at or very near the Earth's surface.

**Wentworth Scale** A quantitative method of classifying particle size. The Wentworth Scale, or more accurately the Udden-Wentworth Scale, was devised by J.A. Udden in 1898 and modified by C.K. Wentworth in 1922.

**Xenoliths** A term used almost exclusively for igneous rock to describe a fragment of older rock that has failed to melt and has become enveloped by magma that subsequently cools to form a different rock type.

## Images for Glossary

**Fig 1**. Image shows the erosion of sandstone blocks in the presence of hard mortar leaving a lattice or 'boxwork' pattern

**Fig 2**. Image shows 'foliation' in Derry Schist. The green schist rock shows alternating bands of minerals arranged in parallel planes. Image also shows hard cement mortar plastered over the joints between stones

**Fig 3.** Image shows spherical ooids and remnants of fossil shells visible in Portland Basebed Limestone

**Fig 4.** Image above shows vesicles (gas bubbles) in the black basalt stone

# Appendix B. Sources of Further Information

## Professional Bodies

**Royal Institute of British Architects (RIBA)**

**www.architecture.com**

**Architects Accreditation in Building Conservation (AABC)** Register:

**www.aabc-register.co.uk**

**Royal Institute of Architects of Ireland (RIAI)**. Conservation Accreditation Scheme.

**www.riai.ie**

**The Royal Society of Ulster Architects (RSUA)** offers a Diploma in Historic Building Conservation and those gaining this post graduate qualification who are practicing architects are listed in the RSUA Handbook and website.

**www.rsua.org.uk**

**Royal Institute of Architects of Scotland (RIAS)**

**www.rias.org.uk**

**Royal Institution of Chartered Surveyors (RICS) Scheme**, the RICS has a Building Conservation Forum which runs an accreditation scheme for surveyors in conservation. The Building Conservation section of the website contains a lot of useful and relevant material on conservation good practice. Institute of Civil Engineers (ICE) also have a conservation engineer accreditation scheme

**www.rics.org**

**The Institute of Historic Building Conservation (IHBC)** is a professional body combining all relevant conservation professions including: architects, engineers, planners etc.

**www.ihbc.org.uk**

**The Chartered Institute of Architectural Technologists (CIAT)**

**www.ciat.org.uk**

**International Council of Monuments and Sites (ICOMOS)**

**www.icomos.org**

**Europa Nostra** – a forum for cultural heritage in Europe, representing individuals and organizations active in the field of cultural heritage

**www.europanostra.org**

## Bibliography

**Allen, G. 2003.** *Hydraulic Lime Mortar for Stone, Brick and Block Masonry: A Best Practice Guide* (Donhead)

**Amery, C. (ed.) 1974.** *Period Houses and Their Details* (The Architectural Press, London)

**Ashurst, N. 1994.** *Cleaning Historic buildings Volume 1:* 'Substrates, Soiling and Investigation' (Donhead)

**Ashurst, N. 1994.** *Cleaning Historic buildings Volume 2:* 'Cleaning materials and Processes' (Donhead)

**Ashurst, J. and Ashurst, N. 1988.** *Practical Building Conservation, English Heritage Technical Handbook Vol. 1:* 'Stone Masonry' (Gower Publishing)

**Ashurst, J. and Ashurst, N. 1988.** *Practical Building Conservation, English Heritage Technical Handbook Vol. 2:* 'Brick, Terracotta and Earth' (Gower Publishing)

**Ashurst, J. and Ashurst, N. 1988.** *Practical Building Conservation, English Heritage Technical Handbook Vol. 3:* 'Mortars, Plasters and Renders' (Gower Publishing)

**Brereton, C. 1991.** *The Repair of Historic Buildings – Advice on Principles and Method* (English Heritage, London)

**Brett, C.E.B. 1996.** *Buildings of County Antrim* Ulster Architectural Heritage Society (UAHS)

**Brett, C.E.B. 1999.** *Buildings of County Armagh* Ulster Architectural Heritage Society (UAHS)

**Brett, C.E.B. 2002.** *Buildings of North County Down* Ulster Architectural Heritage Society (UAHS)

**CIBSE 2002.** *Guide to Building Services for Historic Buildings* Chartered Institution of Building Services Engineers (CIBSE)

**CIBSE 2005.** *Natural Ventilation in Non-Domestic Buildings* Chartered Institution of Building Services Engineers (CIBSE)

**Collings, J. 2002.** *Old House Care and Repair* (Donhead)

**Council for the Care of Churches 2003.** *A Stitch in Time: Guidelines for the care of Churches*

**Curl, J.S. 1992.** *Encyclopaedia of Architectural Terms* (Donhead)

**Davey, A. 1995.** *Care and Maintenance of Georgian Houses – A Maintenance Manual for Edinburgh New Town* (4th Revision) (Architectural Press)

**Davey, A., Heath, B., Hodges, D., Ketchin, M. and Milne R. 1978.** *The Care and Conservation of Georgian Houses – A Maintenance*

*Manual for the New Town of Edinburgh* (Edinburgh New Town Conservation Committee)

**Dixon, H. 2008.** *An Introduction to Ulster Architecture* (2nd edition) Ulster Architectural Heritage Society (UAHS)

**Earl, J. 2003.** *Building Conservation Philosophy* (Donhead)

**English Heritage 2006.** *Identifying and Sourcing Stone for Historic Building Repair: An approach to determining and obtaining compatible replacement stone* Technical Advice Note. Available for download from: **http://www.english-heritage.org.uk/upload/pdf/HISTORIC_REPAIR_WEB.pdf**

**Environment and Heritage Service 2001.** *The Conservation of Scheduled Masonry Monuments – A Guidance Booklet for Owners and Builders* Available for download from: **http://www.ni-environment.gov.uk/conservation_of_scheduled_masonry_monuments.pdf**

**Felden, B.M. 1982.** *Conservation of Historic Buildings* (Cornwall)

**Gaffikin, P. 1999.** *Set in Stone – A Geological Guide to the Building Stones of Belfast* (Environment and Heritage Service)

**Geological Survey of Northern Ireland (2nd Edition), 2004.** *The Geology of Northern Ireland – Our Natural Foundation* (Department of Enterprise, Trade and Investment)

**Henry, A. (ed.) 2007.** *Stone Conservation Principles and Practice* (Donhead)

**Historic Scotland 2007.** *Maintaining Your Home. A Short Guide Information for Homeowners.* Technical Conservation, Research and Education Group (Historic Scotland) Available for download from: **http://www.historic-scotland.gov.uk/maintaining-your-home.pdf**

**Holland, C. and Sanders, I. (eds.) 2009.** *The Geology of Ireland* (2nd edition) (Dunedin Academic Press)

**Holmes, S. and Wingate, M. 1997.** *Building with Lime – A Practical Introduction* (Donhead)

**Honour, H., Fleming, J. and Pevsner, N. 2004.** *The Penguin Dictionary of Architecture* (5th edition) (Penguin)

**Howe, J.A. 2001.** *The Geology of Building Stones* (Donhead)

**Jackson, P.W. 1993.** *The Building Stones of Dublin – A Walking Guide* (Town House and Country House)

**Kinahan, G. K., 1886–1889.** *Economic Geology of Ireland* Scientific Proceedings of the Royal Society of Dublin

**Kincaid, D. 2002.** *Adapting Buildings for Changing Uses: Guidelines for Change of Use Refurbishment* (Spon Press)

**Larmour, P. 1987.** *Belfast: Illustrated Architectural Guide* (Friar's Bush Press)

**Lyle, P. 1996.** *A Geological Excursion Guide to the Causeway Coast* (Environment and Heritage Service)

**Lyle, P. 2003.** *The North of Ireland – Classic Geology in Europe* (Terra Publishing)

**McAffee, P. 1998.** *Stonewalling – a guide to the building and repair of traditional stone walls in Ireland* (O'Brien Press)

**McClelland, A. 2004.** *Directory of Traditional Building Skills* (4th edition) Ulster Architectural Heritage Society (UAHS) Available for download at: **http://www.uahs.org.uk/shop/extract.php?book=72**

**Mills, E. D. 1994.** *Building Maintenance and Preservation* (2nd revised edition) (The Architectural Press)

**Mitchell, W.I. (ed.) 2004.** *The Geology of Northern Ireland: Our Natural Foundation* (2nd edition) (Geological Survey of Northern Ireland, Belfast – GSNI)

**Morriss, R.K. 2000.** *The Archaeology of Buildings* (Tempus)

**Oxley, R. 2003.** *Surveying and Repair of Traditional Buildings* (Donhead)

**Patton, M. 1993.** *Central Belfast: An Historical Gazetteer* Ulster Architectural Heritage Society (UAHS)

**Patton, M. 1999.** *Bangor: An Historical Gazetteer* (2nd edition) Ulster Architectural Heritage Society (UAHS)

**Pavia, S. and Bolton, J. 2000.** *Stone, Brick and Mortar: Historical Use, Decay and Conservation of Building Materials in Ireland* (Wordwell)

**Powyss, A. R. 1995.** (3rd Edition, first published in 1929) *Repair of Ancient Buildings* (SPAB, London)

**Price, M.T. 2007.** *The Source of Decorative Stone – An Illustrated Identification Guide* (Firefly)

**Prikryl, R. (ed.) 2004.** *Dimension Stone – New Perspective of a Traditional Building Material* Proceedings of the International Conference on Dimension Stone 2004 Prague, Czech Republic (AA Balkema)

**RIBA 2009.** *RIBA Conservation 09 – Directory of Chartered Practices* (Royal Institute of British Architects)

**Schaffer, R. J. 2004.** *The Weathering of Natural Building Stones* (Donhead)

**Schofield, J. 1995** (2nd Edition). *Lime in Building: A Practical Guide* (Cullompton Press)

**Smith, B.J. and Warke, P.A. 1996.** *Processes of Urban Stone Decay* (Donhead)

**US. Gov. 1997.** *The Historic Lighthouse Preservation Handbook* Available for download from: **http://www.nps.gov/history/maritime/handbook.htm**

**Vicat, L.J. 1997.** *Mortars and Cements* (Donhead)

**Warke, P.A., Curran, J.M., Turkington, A.V. and Smith, B.J. 2003.** *Condition assessment for building stone conservation: a staging system approach. Building and Environment, Vol. 38: 1113–1123* (Elsevier)

**Watt, D. 1999.** *Building Pathology: Principles and Practice* (Blackwell)

**Watt, D. and Colston, B. 2003.** *Conservation of Historic Buildings and their Contents: Addressing the Conflicts* (Donhead)

**Watt, D. and Swallow, P. 1996.** *Surveying Historic Buildings* (Donhead)

**Webster, R. G. M. (Ed.) 1992.** *Stone Cleaning and the Nature of Soiling and Decay Mechanisms of Stone* Proceedings of the International Conference held in Edinburgh UK 14-16 April 1992 (Donhead)

**Wilson, P. 2004.** *Maintaining our Churches: A Short Guide* (Ulster Historic Churches Trust)

**Wilson, P. 2005.** *Building with Scottish Stone* Natural Stone Institute (Arcamedia)

**Wilkinson, G. 1845.** *Practical Geology and Ancient Architecture of Ireland* (John Murray, London)

**Young, M.E., Murray, M. and Cordiner, P. 1999.** *Stone Consolidants and Chemical Treatments in Scotland* Report to Historic Scotland Summary available at **http://www2.rgu.ac.uk/Schools/mcrg/miconsol.htm**

| Historic Scotland | |
|---|---|
| 'Inform' series | • Masonry Design<br>• Use of Lime and Cementing Traditional Buildings<br>• Graffiti and its safe removal<br>• Damp – Causes and Solutions |
| **Technical Advice** | |
| TAN 1<br>TAN 9<br>TAN 10<br>TAN 25 | • Preparations and use of lime mortars<br>• Stone cleaning of granite buildings<br>• Biological growths on sandstone buildings – control and treatment<br>• Maintenance and repair of cleaned stone buildings |

| Building Research Establishment (BRE) Reports | |
|---|---|
| BR84 | • The building sandstones of the British Isles |
| BR141 | • Durability tests for building stone, Ross, K and Butlin, RN 1989 |
| BR195 | • The building slates of the British Isles, Hart, D (1990) |
| SO36 | • The building limestones of the British Isles, Leary, E (1983, reprinted with corrections 1989) |

| Building Research Establishment (BRE) Digests | |
|---|---|
| No. 177 | • Decay and conservation of stone masonry |
| No. 280 | • Cleaning external surfaces of buildings |
| No. 420 | • Selecting natural building stone |

| Stone Federation Great Britain Leaflets | |
|---|---|
| TI 3 93 | • Care and maintenance of stone in buildings for building owners |
| TD 2 96 | • Mortar and pointing |

| The Society for the Protection of Ancient Buildings (SPAB) | |
|---|---|
| **Information Sheet 1** | • Basic Limewash |
| **Information Sheet 4** | • The need for old buildings to 'Breathe' |
| **Information Sheet 5** | • Pointing stone and brick walling |
| **Information Sheet 9** | • An introduction to building limes |

| Environment and Heritage Service (now Northern Ireland Environment Agency, NIEA) | |
|---|---|
| **Technical Note 5** | • Mortars |
| **Technical Note 38** | • Cleaning stonework |
| **Technical Note 39** | • Stonework repairs |
| **Technical Note 45** | • Masonry walls |
| **Technical Note 46** | • Wall finishes external |
| **Technical Note 52** | • Cleaning masonry buildings |
| **Guidance Booklet** | • The Conservation of Scheduled Masonry Monuments – A Guidance Booklet for Owners and Builders |

**Websites**

Architects Accredited in Building Conservation (AABC)
**www.aabc-register.co.uk**

Building Research Establishment (BRE) **www.bre.co.uk**

Historic Scotland
**www.historic-scotland.gov.uk**

Institute of Historic Building Conservation (IHBC)
**www.ihbc.org.uk**

Irish Architectural Archive
**www.iarc.ie**

Maintain our Heritage
**www.maintainourheritage.co.uk**

Northern Ireland Environment Agency (NIEA)
**www.ni-environment.gov.uk**

Northern Ireland Natural Stone Database
**www.stonedatabase.com**

National Inventory of Architectural Heritage (NIAH)
**www.buildingsofireland.ie**

Planning Service (Northern Ireland) **www.planningni.gov.uk**

Royal Institute of British Architects (RIBA)
**www.architecture.com**

Royal Institution of Chartered Surveyors (RICS)
**www.rics.org**

Royal Society of Ulster Architects (RSUA) **www.rsua.org.uk**

Scottish Lime Centre Trust
**www.scotlime.org**

The Society for the Protection of Ancient Buildings (SPAB)
**www.spab.org.uk**

Ulster Architectural Heritage Society (UAHS)
**www.uahs.co.uk**

The Edinburgh Group *
**www.understandingconservation.org**
* The Edinburgh Group comprises most of the statutory and professional bodies involved in conservation that have come together to co-ordinate training and accreditation standards.

## Appendix C. Inventory of Buildings and Monuments in this Book

The following inventory lists buildings and monuments referred to in this book. The inventory provides an architectural description, stone type identification and other general information for each building and monument.

The buildings and monuments are listed for Belfast first and then for each county in alphabetical order: Antrim, Armagh, Down, Fermanagh, Londonderry and Tyrone. The information has been extracted from 'The Natural Stone Database for Northern Ireland' (**www.stonedatabase.com**), where the reader can obtain information about other historic buildings and monuments in Northern Ireland not mentioned in this book.

Monuments that feature in the inventory are designated 'MON' following the protocol set by the Northern Ireland Environment Agency (NIEA). Listed buildings are those buildings of special architectural or historic interest that are registered by NIEA. The register of listed buildings can be viewed on the 'Buildings Database' on the NIEA website: **www.ni-environment.gov.uk**. The listing covers the complete interior and exterior of the building and can also extend to fixtures and free standing objects within the curtilage of the building. Based on the criteria set out in Annex C of Planning Policy Statement 6, the listing takes into account the age and significance of the building and architectural features such as style, proportion, ornamentation, plan form, spatial organisation, structural system, innovatory qualities, degree of alteration, quality and survival of interiors, setting and group value.

Based on age, significance and architectural interest, buildings within Northern Ireland are given a listing 'grade' ranging from Grade A, B+, B1 and down to B2. These grades are used to determine the percentage of grant-aid available for eligible repairs and conservation works.

For more information on listing grades see:
**www.ni-environment.gov.uk/guidance_notes.pdf**

| Building | Architectural Description | Stone Types |
|---|---|---|
| **Belfast** | | |
| <br>**Albert Memorial**<br>High Street,<br>Belfast | A freestanding square clock tower in High Victorian Gothic with eclectic mix of styles. The memorial stands 113 feet tall with a base of flying buttresses surmounted by crowned lions. Most of the original ornamental stonework was removed between 1924 and 1950 due to deterioration but was reinstated during a major restoration project in 2000 by Belfast City Council. | Scrabo Sandstone, Dukes Sandstone and Stanton Moor Sandstone<br>**Building Information**<br>**Date of construction:** 1865<br>**Architect:** W. J. Barre<br>**Listing:** B+ |
| <br>**The Bank Buildings**<br>(Primark)<br>Castle Place,<br>Belfast | Classical style five storey commercial building with large pedimented clock on top of main face. Ground and first floors have polished granite and top three are in red sandstone. Large square entrance with vast fanlight above. Second and third floor have six sets of paired windows with two storey Corinthian columns. Top floor has smaller casement windows with pilasters in between. | Locharbriggs Sandstone and Balmoral Granite Columns<br>**Building Information**<br>**Date of construction:** 1899<br>**Architect:** W.H. Lynn<br>**Listing:** B |

| Building | Architectural Description | Stone Types |
|---|---|---|
| **Bar Library**<br>91 Chichester Street, Belfast | Two five storey buildings built around an atria. Sculptural elevations of Portland limestone, brick and glass constructed to echo the adjacent Royal Courts of Justice. | Portland Limestone<br>**Building Information**<br>**Date of construction:** 2003<br>**Architect:** Robinson McIlwaine<br>**Listing:** N/A |
| **Belfast Central Library**<br>Royal Avenue, Belfast | Classical style three storey, seven bay library. Broad end bays, enclosing a piano nobile of windows under round headed arches, set behind Corinthian columns. Three arches lead into entrance porch, above this stone balustrade spans full width of central bays at first floor level. | Locharbriggs Sandstone and Gabbro Plinth<br>**Building Information**<br>**Date of construction:** 1883<br>**Architect:** W.H. Lynn<br>**Listing:** B |
| **Carlisle Memorial Church,**<br>Carlisle Circus, Belfast | Gothic Revival style church in early English style. A tall tower with stone spire at north east corner. Tall lancet windows at east and west end gables. Corresponding arched porch doorway on south side. Rose windows in transept gables. Pitched slate roof. | Armagh Limestone and Dundonald Sandstone<br>**Building Information**<br>**Date of construction:** 1872<br>**Architect:** W. H. Lynn<br>**Listing:** B+ |

| Building | Architectural Description | Stone Types |
|---|---|---|
| **Chapel, Good Shepherd Complex**<br>Ormeau Road,<br>Belfast | Large red-brick Gothic style chapel with limestone dressing. Central nave and two parallel wings. Entrance on North wing, pointed arch doorway with matching window either side, statue above. Central section gable has very large tracery window, large pinnacles at edges and cross finial. | Kilkenny Limestone<br>**Building Information**<br>**Date of construction:** 1916<br>**Architect:**<br>W and R Byrne<br>**Listing:** B1 |
| <br>**Chapel of the Resurrection**<br>Innisfayle Park,<br>Belfast | Decorated Gothic style which was originally a mortuary chapel of the Donegall family. Circular side tower with conical slate roof. Tall nave is four bays in length with apsidal end. Mortuary underneath nave floor. The chapel was derelict for many years but has since been made weathertight. | Scrabo Sandstone and Portland Limestone<br>**Building Information**<br>**Date of construction:** 1865<br>**Architect:**<br>Lanyon, Lynn and Lanyon<br>**Listing:** B+ |
| <br>**Christ Church**<br>College Square North,<br>Belfast | Late Neo-Classical façade with Greek Revival styling. Ionic 'in antes' porch. Stone façade only, rest brick. Pedimented entrance door set in porch. | Binny Sandstone and Boden Grey Sandstone<br>**Building Information**<br>**Date of construction:** 1833<br>**Architect:**<br>William Farrell<br>**Listing:** B+ |

| Building | Architectural Description | Stone Types |
|---|---|---|
| **Church of the Most Holy Redeemer**<br>Clonard, Clonard Gardens,<br>Belfast | A Gothic, early French style. Nave and aisles with shallow transepts, semi-circular apse and side chapels. Octagonal turrets flank entrance. Main front has large bar traceried rose window set above triple Gothic arched recessed entrance doors, all deeply carved. | Donegal Quartzite and Donegal Sandstone<br>**Building Information**<br>**Date of construction:** 1908<br>**Architect:** J.J. McDonnell<br>**Listing:** B+ |
| <br>**City Hall**<br>Donegall Square,<br>Belfast | A large Baroque Revival, three storey over basement, public building, square in plan with four wings around a central courtyard. Two storey Ionic order detailing above rusticated ground floor. Great central dome over main entrance on North wing with smaller corner cupolas. The building is set in park area with only south side directly onto the road. | Portland Limestone<br>**Building Information**<br>**Date of construction:** 1896<br>**Architect:** Sir Alfred Brumwell Thomas<br>**Listing:** A |
| <br>**Crescent Arts Centre**<br>Lower Crescent,<br>Belfast | Three storey building with hipped roof, gabled dormers and lower wing on north side. Stone porch entrance with slate roof and two storey canted bay on West gable. Former Victoria College. The building underwent major stone restoration in 2009. | Scrabo Sandstone<br>**Building Information**<br>**Date of construction:** 1873<br>**Architect:** Young and Mackenzie<br>**Listing:** B1 |

| Building | Architectural Description | Stone Types |
|---|---|---|
| <br>**Custom House**<br>Custom House Square,<br>Belfast | Two storey over basement, plus attic, Italian Renaissance Palazzo of Giffnock Sandstone on a deep battered plinth. Upper floors plain ashlar with diamond pointed quoin stones. On an E-shaped plan enclosing an elevated courtyard reached by a flight of stairs between a balustraded screen wall. River frontage has a central advanced bay and pediment with tympanum carving. Round headed windows on ground floor with pedimented ones above. | Giffnock Sandstone and Newry Granodiorite<br>**Building Information**<br>**Date of construction:** 1854<br>**Architect:** Lanyon, Lynn and Lanyon<br>**Listing:** A |
| <br>**Danesfort Gate Lodge**<br>Malone Road,<br>Belfast | Gothic style gate lodge to Danesfort House. Two storey with tower. Random coursed, rock-faced limestone. Fine face finish on stringcourses and window surrounds. | Armagh Limestone and Giffnock Sandstone<br>**Building Information**<br>**Date of construction:** 1875<br>**Architect:** William Batt<br>**Listing:** B1 |
| <br>**Danesfort House**<br>Stranmillis Road,<br>Belfast | Gothic-Italianate country house with large central three storey square tower above porte cochère. Tower has a mansard roof and is decorated with carved balconettes and parapets. Porch comprises four rounded arches to the front with two larger arches to each side with a chamfered corner next to porch. | Armagh Limestone and Giffnock Sandstone<br>**Building Information**<br>**Date of construction:** 1864<br>**Architect:** William Barre<br>**Listing:** B+ |

| Building | Architectural Description | Stone Types |
| --- | --- | --- |
| **11-15 Donegall Square North**<br>Belfast | Classical style, three storey, eleven bay building. Central entrance is rounded arch with keystone, other two are square-topped, all with Corinthian columns. Ground floor topped by balconies and balustrade. First floor has square-topped windows, pediment at both ends and balcony over central window. Second floor windows have segmental arch heads with keystone. Balustrade at top. | Corsehill Sandstone and Gabbro<br>**Building Information**<br>**Date of construction:** 1900<br>**Architect:** W.H. Lynn<br>**Listing:** B1 |
| <br>**Ewart's Building**<br>Bedford Street, Belfast | Venetian Renaissance style, three storey warehouse with curved corner bay, segmental arch windows on ground floor, rounded arch with keystone on first and second floor, pilasters in between on first, Corinthian columns on second. Main façade has near centre doorway with surround, one Corinthian column and one pilaster either side, rounded arch window with column and carved head keystone above. Corner entrance bay, extending into a cupola with copper roof on fourth floor. Balustrade and dormers at roof level. | Giffnock Sandstone<br>**Building Information**<br>**Date of construction:** 1869<br>**Architect:** James Hamilton<br>**Listing:** B1 |

| Building | Architectural Description | Stone Types |
| --- | --- | --- |
| <br>**Gordon House**<br>22-24 Lombard Street and 26-28 Rosemary Street, Belfast | Classical style, three storey plus attic commercial building. Shop fronts on ground floor with stone pilasters. Square-topped windows on first floor with small carvings above and pilasters, second floor windows are segmental with keystones. Dormer windows, square and fish-scale slates to attic. | Dundonald Sandstone and Polished Black Granite<br>**Building Information**<br>**Date of construction:** 1878<br>**Architect:** Thomas Jackson and Son<br>**Listing:** B1 |
| <br>**Greg Mausoleum**<br>Knockbreda Churchyard, Church Road, Knockbreda, Belfast | Square Classical style monument with domed cap on a concave base. Each face has a central blind archway with plaque and pilasters either side. A pair of detached Doric columns is set at each chamfered corner. These originally had urn finials but only one remains in place, the rest are on the ground. | Binny Sandstone and Marble Plaques<br>**Building Information**<br>**Date of construction:** 1796<br>**Architect:** Not Assigned<br>**Listing:** B+ |
| <br>**Headline Building**<br>10-14 Victoria Street, Belfast | Venetian Renaissance palazzo style, three storey building with basement, in chamfered sandstone on a limestone plinth, rounded at corners. Central projecting section, rounded arch windows with keystones on all floors. Built for Scottish Amicable Life Assurance Company, later the Heyn Shipping Company. | Dungannon Sandstone and Local Carboniferous Limestone<br>**Building Information**<br>**Date of construction:** 1863<br>**Architect:** Thomas Jackson and Son<br>**Listing:** B1 |

| Building | Architectural Description | Stone Types |
|---|---|---|
| **Holy Cross Church**<br>Crumlin Road,<br>Belfast | A Lombardic Romanesque style church with distinctive twin towers to main front, flanking the nave. The Lady chapel to North side is by Rudolph Butler with classically detailed front. The south side chapel was added 1961 by W.D. Bready. | Scrabo Sandstone and Doulting Limestone<br>**Building Information**<br>**Date of construction:** 1900<br>**Architect:** Doolin, Butler and Donnelly<br>**Listing:** B+ |
| **House of Fraser**<br>Victoria Square,<br>Belfast | Four storey department store at the corner of Chichester and Victoria Street. | Stanton Moor Sandstone<br>**Building Information**<br>**Date of construction:** 2008<br>**Architect:** BDP Architects<br>**Listing:** N/A |
| **Lanyon Building**<br>Queen's University Belfast,<br>University Road,<br>Belfast | Extensive two storey range in Tudor Gothic style with large central square tower, with main entrance at base. Pitched slate roof behind battlement with pinnacles. Built in red-brick with stone dressings. | Giffnock Sandstone and Dungannon Sandstone<br>**Building Information**<br>**Date of construction:** 1846<br>**Architect:** Charles Lanyon<br>**Listing:** A |

| Building | Architectural Description | Stone Types |
|---|---|---|
| **Lyttle's and McCausland's Warehouses**<br>34-38 Victoria Street,<br>Belfast | Palazzo style, four storey warehouses. McCausland's (right) in Italianate Classical style and Lyttle's in a Romanesque style. Famous for its ground floor carvings by Michael Fitzpatrick in particular the carved heads representing the five continents. | Giffnock and Dungannon Sandstone<br>**Building Information**<br>**Date of construction:** 1867<br>**Architect:** William Hastings<br>**Listing:** A |
| <br>**Nelson Memorial Church,**<br>Nelson Square,<br>Belfast | A Classical style stone front elevation (North) built onto red brick 'hall' church. A central advanced, pedimented front with square side bays. Pilasters with Corinthian capitals and a large cornice and balustrade. A double door entrance and slate hipped roof behind. | Corsehill Sandstone<br>**Building Information**<br>**Date of construction:** 1893<br>**Architect:** William J. Gilliland<br>**Listing:** B |
| <br>**Northern Bank Building**<br>Royal Avenue,<br>Belfast | Italianate style four storey plus attic, five bay building in cream sandstone on a Newry Granodiorite plinth. Central three bays have giant order Ionic columns in Shap Granite at first and second floor above arcaded ground floor, flanked by slightly advanced side bays, which rise to attic level in pedimented dormers. Corbelled stone chimney-stacks. Balustrade along cornice. | Giffnock Sandstone and Newry Granodiorite<br>**Building Information**<br>**Date of construction:** 1883<br>**Architect:** John Lanyon<br>**Listing:** B1 |

| Building | Architectural Description | Stone Types |
|---|---|---|
| **Northern Whig**<br>Bridge Street,<br>Belfast | Late Georgian three storey, one bay public building with fine ashlar façade. Ground floor has small Doric porches in rusticated stonework. First floor has a row of Ionic columns across central five bays. | Leinster Granite<br>**Building Information**<br>**Date of construction:** 1820<br>**Architect:** John McCutcheon<br>**Listing:** B+ |
| <br>**Ormeau Park Gates and Pillars**<br>Ormeau Road,<br>Belfast | Classical archways combined with railed gates and central stone pillar. Red sandstone ashlar blocks, flanked by park walls which have metal railings atop ashlar capstone, above rubble stone random course. The pillars have been cleaned very aggressively which has caused significant deterioration of stonework and carved coat of arms. | Red Scottish Sandstone<br>**Building Information**<br>**Date of construction:** 1871<br>**Architect:** Timothy Hevey<br>**Listing:** B+ |
| <br>**Parliament Buildings**<br>Stormont,<br>Belfast | A large, Neo-Classical, four storey plus attic and basement, building, oblong in plan. A central full height portico with attic storey rising above portico. The ground floor has square rusticated columns supporting six giant Ionic columns and pediment. The first floor forms a balcony with balustrade between the Ionic columns. Ground floor consists of rusticated stonework set on a granite plinth. Symmetrical in design with side entrances in East and West elevations. | Portland Limestone and Mourne Granite<br>**Building Information**<br>**Date of construction:** 1927<br>**Architect:** Arnold Thornley<br>**Listing:** B+ |

| Building | Architectural Description | Stone Types |
|---|---|---|
| **(Former) Provincial Bank of Ireland (Tesco)**<br>2 Royal Avenue, Belfast | Two storey, seven bay former bank with large pediment and interlaced balustrade. Centre three bays set forward with three tall doorways on ground floor. All windows are sash set in a rounded arch with carved spandrels (foliage and carved heads) on first and centre ground floor. First floor has columns with Venetian capitals, pilasters on ground floor. | Cookstown Sandstone<br>**Building Information**<br>**Date of construction:** 1869<br>**Architect:** W.J. Barre<br>**Listing:** A |
| <br>**St Anne's Cathedral**<br>Donegall Street, Belfast | A Neo-Romanesque cathedral worked on by a succession of architects. Tall central gable flanked by octagonal towers, with lower towers at ends of screen walls in front of aisle. The main stonework is a mix of Doulting and Portland Limestone. | Portland Limestone and Doulting Limestone<br>**Building Information**<br>**Date of construction:** 1898<br>**Architect:** Thomas Drew<br>**Listing:** A |
| <br>**St Malachy's RC Church**<br>Alfred Street, Belfast | Large Tudor Revival church in dark red brick with slender octagonal corner turrets. Central gable has panelled and studded Tudor entrance doors with label moulding and quatrefoils in spandrels. Stonework painted over. Mourne Granite steps. Gate posts and railings have a Newry Granodiorite base topped with Giffnock Sandstone. | Giffnock Sandstone and Mourne Granite<br>**Building Information**<br>**Date of construction:** 1840<br>**Architect:** Thomas Jackson<br>**Listing:** A |

| Building | Architectural Description | Stone Types |
|---|---|---|
| **St Mark's Church C of I**<br>Holywood Road, Belfast | Mix of Gothic styles with English tracery. Traditional plan with tall square tower flanked by side porch entrances. Nave with side aisles and North/South transepts up to chancel. On North aisle behind porch is a modern choir vestry and toilets. Pitched slate roof with gable ends. Tower topped by belfry and pyramidal slate roof. | Dundonald Sandstone and Scrabo Sandstone<br>**Building Information**<br>**Date of construction:** 1876<br>**Architect:** William Butterfield<br>**Listing:** A |
| <br>**St Matthew's RC Church**<br>Bryson Street, Belfast | A Gothic Revival style church with high nave, low side aisles with clerestory above and apsidal chancel. A tall stone spire to the front of the church. The church is constructed of Scrabo sandstone that deteriorated very rapidly in the polluted, maritime environment of this area of the city. The church underwent major restoration including significant stone replacement and treatment in the late 1990s. | Scrabo Sandstone, Dundonald Sandstone and York Stone (spire)<br>**Building Information**<br>**Date of construction:** 1881<br>**Architect:** Alexander McAllister<br>**Listing:** B |
| <br>**St Patrick's RC Church**<br>Donegall Street, Belfast | Romanesque style church with substantial tower and spire forming west wall of the nave and entrance. Early French detailing. The flanking aisles have smaller entrances at west face. Has been re-pointed with (1970's) cement-based mortar, cleaned and treated but re-soiling is very evident. | Dungannon Sandstone<br>**Building Information**<br>**Date of construction:** 1877<br>**Architect:** Timothy Hevey/ Mortimer Thompson<br>**Listing:** B |

| Building | Architectural Description | Stone Types |
|---|---|---|
|  **St Peter's Cathedral** St Peter's Square North, Belfast | Large Gothic Revival style church. Twin western towers and spires with large tracery window in west gable above double recessed door with tympanum sculpture. Nave with aisles and lean-to roofs. Side porches enlarged to form chapels. Apse ended on west face. | Scrabo Sandstone and Giffnock Sandstone<br>**Building Information**<br>**Date of construction:** 1860<br>**Architect:** Jeremiah McAuley<br>**Listing:** A |
|  **Scottish Mutual Building** 15-16 Donegall Square South, Belfast | Scottish Baronial style five storey commercial building in dark red sandstone, with large turrets corbelled out at each corner and smaller turrets flanking a central crow-stepped gable on Belfast façade. Larvikite pilasters and stall risers to ground floor shops. Open arcading under deep eaves at fourth floor. | Locharbriggs Sandstone and Larvikite facing stone<br>**Building Information**<br>**Date of construction:** 1904<br>**Architect:** Henry Seaver<br>**Listing:** B |
|  **Scottish Provident Building** Donegall Square West, Belfast | Baroque Late Victorian style in Glasgow Blonde Sandstone. Rusticated granite pilasters between shops. Chamfered corners rising to octagonal turrets with fish-scale copper roofs. Central bay set forward in shallow bow under pediment. Channelled first floor, giant order semi-fluted attached Corinthian columns on plinth supporting cornice to balustraded parapet. | Glasgow Blonde Sandstone and Swedish Granite<br>**Building Information**<br>**Date of construction:** 1879<br>**Architect:** Young and Mackenzie<br>**Listing:** B |

| Building | Architectural Description | Stone Types |
|---|---|---|
|  **Sinclair Seaman's Church** Belfast | An Italian Lombardy style church on an 'L' shaped plan with a tall corner campanile, linked to nave gallery by an arcaded flying buttress. The church was built to serve visiting seamen with a distinctly nautical interior. The stonework is in poor condition with significant bedding-plane erosion, face loss and hollowing of individual blocks, exacerbated by the use of hard cement mortar. | Scrabo Sandstone and Dundonald Sandstone<br>**Building Information**<br>**Date of construction:** 1857<br>**Architect:** Lanyon, Lynn and Lanyon<br>**Listing:** B |
|  **Stormont Castle** Stormont Estate, Upper Newtownards Road, Belfast | Scottish Baronial style castle which is an 1858 re-working of the original castle. Centre of main face has a two storey canted bay window, rest of windows square-topped sashes, with bartizan turrets at either end. Taller tower at East end with large door surround and balustrade on top, turrets on tower corners, crow-stepped castellation and three rounded arch windows at top. | Scrabo Sandstone<br>**Building Information**<br>**Date of construction:** 1830/1858<br>**Architect:** Thomas Turner<br>**Listing:** B+ |
|  **Titanic Memorial** City Hall Grounds, Belfast | Marble statue to commemorate the loss of the Titanic, on a tall granite plinth and steps. Fountain on East face.<br><br>It is the last work of the acclaimed sculptor Thomas Brock. In the memorial, the female figure looks down upon two sea nymphs rising from the waves with the body of a drowned seaman in their arms. | Cornish Granite (De Lank) and Marble Statuary<br>**Building Information**<br>**Date of construction:** 1920<br>**Architect:** Not Assigned<br>**Listing:** A |

| Building | Architectural Description | Stone Types |
|---|---|---|
| **Ulster Reform Club**<br>4-6 Royal Avenue, Belfast | Classical style three storey red sandstone building with tall corner turret and iron balcony at first floor. Corner entrance inside open porch with red granite columns. Tall first floor windows arranged in canted bays between deep pilasters. Balustrade in front of second floor windows, pedimented dormers and domed corner lantern. | Corsehill Sandstone and Peterhead Granite columns<br>**Building Information**<br>**Date of construction:** 1883<br>**Architect:** Maxwell and Tuke of Manchester<br>**Listing:** A |
| <br>**Union Theological College**<br>Botanic Avenue, Belfast | Renaissance Revival style two storey college with attic storey above central entrance, framed by four double height Doric columns. Later wings form a square around an open central courtyard, with rear sections in three storeys.<br>Constructed of grey Scrabo Sandstone and stonework is in reasonable condition but heavily soiled. Previous cement repairs are unsightly and causing preferential deterioration of sandstone, particularly to rear elevations. A modern Stanton Moor sandstone extension has been added recently. | Scrabo Sandstone, Cookstown Sandstone and Stanton Moor Sandstone<br>**Building Information**<br>**Date of construction:** 1852<br>**Architect:** Charles Lanyon<br>**Listing:** A |

| Building | Architectural Description | Stone Types |
|---|---|---|
| **Victoria Monument**<br>City Hall Grounds,<br>Belfast | Classical style plinth with marble statue of Queen Victoria, by the sculptor Thomas Brock. Set in front of Belfast City Hall. Carved bronze figures around upper plinth. Granite steps. | Sicilian Marble and Carrara Marble<br>**Building Information**<br>**Date of construction:** 1903<br>**Architect:** Not Assigned<br>**Listing:** A |
| **War Memorial**<br>Queen's University,<br>University Road,<br>Belfast | Tall Classical style granite pedestal with bronze statue of an angel and soldier on top. Date plaques in bronze and stone. | Grey Aberdeen Granite<br>**Building Information**<br>**Date of construction:** 1924<br>**Architect:** Sir Thomas Brock<br>**Listing:** B1 |
| **County Antrim** | | |
| **Boat House**<br>The Station,<br>Rathlin Island,<br>Co. Antrim | A small two storey boat house with hipped slate roof and dressed quoins. The boat entrance is on west front. Brick dressing surround wooden slat windows with slate cills. It is now a tourist office and the boat entrance is cemented up with the entrance on East side. | Antrim Chalk and Antrim Basalt<br>**Building Information**<br>**Date of construction:** 19th century<br>**Architect:** Not Assigned<br>**Listing:** B1 |

| Building | Architectural Description | Stone Types |
|---|---|---|
| **Billy Parish Church C of I**<br>1 Cabragh Road Bushmills,<br>Co. Antrim | Gothic style chapel fronted by three stage tower with battlements, corner pinnacles, and arched windows with hood-moulds. Nave has three Y-tracery arched windows on each side. Side door in arched recessed on tower with hood-mould. Pitched slate roof. Later addition of apse style chancel (basalt with red sandstone dressing) three bays long. Yellow sandstone on original window dressing, red sandstone on courses. Recently repointed in lime, cleaned, and new rainwater goods fitted. | Basalt and Ballycastle Sandstone dressings<br>**Building Information**<br>**Date of construction:** 1815<br>**Architect:** Not Assigned<br>**Listing:** B+ |
| **Bonamargy Friary**<br>Ballycastle,<br>Co. Antrim | Roofless remains of friary consisting of church, east range, gate house and later vault. Walls to full height and dressing remains in place on most windows and doors. | Ballycastle Sandstone<br>**Building Information**<br>**Date of construction:** *c.* 1500<br>**Architect:** Not Assigned<br>**Listing:** MON |
| **Braid Ballymena Townhall,**<br>Museum and Arts Complex,<br>Ballymena,<br>Co. Antrim | The Braid is a new museum and arts complex built in 2008. It is constructed of Portland Limestone and forms an addition to the original neo-classical three storey Town Hall built in 1924. The Town Hall has corner entrance with attached giant columns and domed clock tower above. Deep cornice. Rusticated ashlar to two principal floors. Hipped slate roof. The building was cleaned using the nebulous spray method and the stonework restored during the project. | Portland Limestone<br>**Building Information**<br>**Date of construction:** 1924<br>**Architect:** Jones and Kelly (Dublin), Consarc Design Group<br>**Listing:** B1 |

| Building | Architectural Description | Stone Types |
|---|---|---|
| **Carrickfergus Castle**<br>Carrickfergus,<br>Co. Antrim | Situated on a basalt projection from the shore, forming a rough oval in plan. Comprises a square central stone keep with an outer and inner ward defended by curtain walls of basalt rubble. Fronted by large gatehouse flanked by two rounded towers. Internal buildings and store houses. Many changes of use and development over the centuries. | Antrim Basalt and Cultra Limestone<br>**Building Information**<br>**Date of construction:** 1180<br>**Architect:** Not Assigned<br>**Listing:** MON |
| **Clotworthy House**<br>Town Parks, Antrim,<br>Co. Antrim | A former carriage house and stabling for Antrim Castle. Jacobean style gateway with square turrets, and family coat of arms. Screen wall at each side linked to two storey ranges with Dutch-style gables, and finely carved pinnacles on each gable. Built around a courtyard. Pitched slate roof. Tardree Rhyolite ashlar quoins and dressing. | Antrim Basalt and Tardree Rhyolite<br>**Building Information**<br>**Date of construction:** *c.* 1840<br>**Architect:** Not Assigned<br>**Listing:** B+ |
| **Cushendall Presbyterian Church,**<br>Shore Street,<br>Cushendall,<br>Co. Antrim | Small church, nave and chancel. Paired lancet windows with rounded window moulds. Pitched slate roof. Side enclosed wooden porch entrance on stone plinth. | Devonian Sandstone (Cross Slieve Group) and Bangor Blue (Penrhyn) Slate<br>**Building Information**<br>**Date of construction:** 1900<br>**Architect:** W.J. Fennell<br>**Listing:** B |

| Building | Architectural Description | Stone Types |
|---|---|---|
| **Cushendun Parish Church**<br>Cushendun,<br>Co. Antrim | Gothic hall church with small vestry extension. Two paired lancet windows on nave walls. Square tower with pointed arched doorway and corner stone pinnacles. Pitched slate roof. Roughly dressed red sandstone quoins with buff sandstone to windows. | Devonian Sandstone (Cross Slieve Group) and Local Carboniferous Sandstone<br>**Building Information**<br>**Date of construction:** 1838<br>**Architect:** Not Assigned<br>**Listing:** B1 |
| **Dunluce Castle,**<br>Co. Antrim | Extensive castle ruins set on cliff face, including gatehouse, curtain walls and tower, two storey manor house and kitchen area. | Antrim Basalt and Ballycastle Sandstone<br>**Building Information**<br>**Date of construction:** 17th century<br>**Architect:** Not Assigned<br>**Listing:** MON |
| **Dunseverick Castle**<br>Co. Antrim | Remains of a small partly collapsed two storey tower. | Antrim Basalt<br>**Building Information**<br>**Date of construction:** Medieval<br>**Architect:** Not Assigned<br>**Listing:** MON |

| Building | Architectural Description | Stone Types |
|---|---|---|
| **Holy Trinity Church**<br>The Diamond,<br>Ballycastle,<br>Co. Antrim | Classical stone façade. Nave with pitched slate roof. Pedimented central doorway with attached fluted columns, flanked by two recessed keystone doorways. Central square clock tower with stone spire. Balustrade around top of tower. Eastern apse ended chancel. Rendered on sides. Cleaned 1990. | Ballycastle Sandstone<br>**Building Information**<br>**Date of construction:** 1756<br>**Architect:** Christopher Myers<br>**Listing:** A |
| **Maud's Cottages**<br>Cushendun,<br>Co. Antrim | Two storey, ten bay terrace. The upper storey is hung slate cladding and the ground floor is rendered. The terrace has a pitched slate roof. | Bangor Blue (Penrhyn) Slate<br>**Building Information**<br>**Date of construction:** 1926<br>**Architect:** Clough Williams Ellis<br>**Listing:** B |
| **Roark's Kitchen**<br>Ballintoy Harbour,<br>Co. Antrim | A one storey, five bay cottage, extensively renovated in 1975 and now a shop, one bay wide. A pitched roof with central chalk chimney. Situated at the edge of the harbour with North wall facing the sea. Wooden window frames and concrete cills. | Antrim Chalk<br>**Building Information**<br>**Date of construction:** 1978<br>**Architect:** Not Assigned<br>**Listing:** Not Listed |

| Building | Architectural Description | Stone Types |
|---|---|---|
| <br>**St Louis' Convent**<br>Cullybackey Road,<br>Ballymena,<br>Co. Antrim | Two storey with attic. Large six bay house with multiple Dutch gables with finials. Large portico entrance with square columns topped by balustrade with carved lions. A bell tower to the north west corner. Two extended wings to North. Pitched slate roof. | Cookstown Sandstone<br>**Building Information**<br>**Date of construction:** 1862<br>**Architect:** Lanyon, Lynn and Lanyon<br>**Listing:** B1 |
| <br>**St Thomas' Church**<br>Rathlin Island,<br>Co. Antrim | A Gothic style church. The nave has three large arched windows along side, with pitched slate roof. Fronted by a square, three bay tower with battlements. Arched doorway in the same style as windows to south side of tower. A small gabled vestry in north east corner. Walls are a mixture of chalk and basalt rubble stonework and windows and door have sandstone dressings. | Antrim chalk, Antrim Basalt and Ballycastle Sandstone<br>**Building Information**<br>**Date of construction:** 1815<br>**Architect:** Not Assigned<br>**Listing:** B+ |
| <br>**Stephenson Mausoleum**<br>Kilbride Churchyard,<br>Doagh,<br>Co. Antrim | Family mausoleum in the style of a miniature Moghol tomb. | Tardree Rhyolite and Kilkenny Limestone<br>**Building Information**<br>**Date of construction:** 1837<br>**Architect:** Not Assigned<br>**Listing:** B1 |

| Building | Architectural Description | Stone Types |
|---|---|---|
| <br>**Town Hall,**<br>Upper Cross Street,<br>Larne,<br>Co. Antrim | Ruskinian Gothic style Town Hall, two storey, eleven bay. Central square tower with clock. Pitched slate roof. Gabled upper windows. Red sandstone string courses. Slate columns on windows and entrance. | Scrabo Sandstone<br>**Building Information**<br>**Date of construction:** 1868<br>**Architect:** Alexander Tate, S.P. Close<br>**Listing:** B+ |
| **County Armagh** | | |
| <br>**Armagh Court House**<br>The Mall,<br>Armagh City,<br>Co. Armagh | Classical style, symmetrical courthouse. Fronted by pedimented tetrastyle portico with Doric columns and pilasters to façade. Central doorway with semi-circular arch, keystone and fanlight. Plain round headed windows to each side bay. Conglomerate on plinth. | Armagh Limestone and Drumarg Conglomerate<br>**Building Information**<br>**Date of construction:** 1809<br>**Architect:** Francis Johnston<br>**Listing:** A |
| <br>**Armagh First Presbyterian Church**<br>The Mall West,<br>Armagh City,<br>Co. Armagh | Decorated Gothic Revival style church consisting of a two storey, five bay nave with stepped buttresses and gableted finials. Five paired lancet windows below tall pointed windows. Steep gabled porch with pointed arch door. Front corner square tall tower with octagonal stone spire. | Armagh Limestone and Dungannon Sandstone dressings<br>**Building Information**<br>**Date of construction:** 1878<br>**Architect:** Young and Mackenzie<br>**Listing:** B+ |

| Building | Architectural Description | Stone Types |
|---|---|---|
| <br>**Armagh Gaol**<br>Armagh City,<br>Co. Armagh | Classical style three storey, fourteen bay Gaol. Two projecting, pedimented gabled entrance bays with semi-circular fanlight surround and blocked ashlar stonework at ground level. First floor windows are tripartite, below triple arched window. Main block has ground floor semi-circular windows with recesses. First and second floor have segmental arch windows with keystones. Topped by cornice and blocked parapet with hipped slate roof. | Drumarg Conglomerate and Armagh Limestone<br>**Building Information**<br>**Date of construction:** 1780<br>**Architect:** Thomas Cooley<br>**Listing:** B+ |
| <br>**Armagh Observatory**<br>College Hill,<br>Armagh City,<br>Co. Armagh | Classical style two storey over basement, three bay square plan, double pile main house. Tuscan style porch with block parapet and cornice. Sash windows. Stepped quoins. Upper cornice and blocked parapet. Single storey wing to east leading to Observatory tower. | Drumarg Conglomerate and Armagh Limestone<br>**Building Information**<br>**Date of construction:** 1789<br>**Architect:** Francis Johnston<br>**Listing:** A |
| <br>**Armagh Technical Institution**<br>Market Street,<br>Armagh City,<br>Co. Armagh | Classical style three storey, five bay, square plan building. Rusticated ground floor. Three bay breakfront with pediment on west face. Cornice and parapet around roof. | Armagh Limestone<br>**Building Information**<br>**Date of construction:** 1815<br>**Architect:** Thomas Duff/ Francis Johnston<br>**Listing:** B |

| Building | Architectural Description | Stone Types |
|---|---|---|
|  **Brownlow House**<br>Windsor Avenue,<br>Lurgan,<br>Co. Armagh | Large Elizabethan Revival style country house, two storey with attic, forming a three sided courtyard. Multi-gabled with carved stone finials, mullioned windows and full height canted bay windows. Two storey gabled porch entrance. Tall carved stone chimneys are a particularly distinctive feature. Small square copper domed tower. | Binny Sandstone<br>**Building Information**<br>**Date of construction:** 1833<br>**Architect:** William Playfair<br>**Listing:** A |
|  **Lurgan War Memorial**<br>Market Street,<br>Lurgan,<br>Co. Armagh | Bronze winged statue on top of an open domed temple. Hexagonal plan on stepped plinth, with columns supporting frieze, cornice and domed roof. | Grey Aberdeen Granite and polished Red Granite<br>**Building Information**<br>**Date of construction:** 1928<br>**Architect:** Not Assigned<br>**Listing:** B1 |
|  **St John's Church of Ireland**<br>Newtownhamilton Road, Lisnadill,<br>Co. Armagh | Plain Gothic style church. Rendered nave with three stage square bell tower at front with corner buttresses and octagonal corner pinnacles and crenellation. Pointed arch recessed door. | Drumarg Conglomerate and Armagh Limestone<br>**Building Information**<br>**Date of construction:** 1772<br>**Architect:** Thomas Cooley<br>**Listing:** B |

| Building | Architectural Description | Stone Types |
|---|---|---|
|  **St Patrick's RC Cathedral** Armagh City, Co. Armagh | A large French Gothic Revival style church, consisting of nave with clerestory, side aisles and transepts. Front façade has multi-recessed central entrance below row of alcoved statues, and large gable tracery window, flanked by tall square towers with broached stone spires. The church has a pitched slate roof. | Armagh Limestone and Dungannon Sandstone<br>**Building Information**<br>**Date of construction:** 1840<br>**Architect:** Thomas Duff and J.J. McCarthy<br>**Listing:** A |
|  **St Peter's RC Church,** North Street, Lurgan, Co. Armagh | Large Gothic Revival style church consisting of nave with clerestory, lean-to aisles with pointed arch windows, and transepts. Slim gabled porch with pointed arch door. Tall square tower in southwest corner with corner buttresses, and octagonal turret with spire. Slim gabled porch to tower with two Corinthian columns each side. Pitched slate roof. | Basalt and Armagh Limestone<br>**Building Information**<br>**Date of construction:** 1867<br>**Architect:** Ashlin and Coleman<br>**Listing:** B |
|  **Ulster Bank** 14-16 Market Street, Lurgan, Co. Armagh | Classical style, three storey, five bay bank. Two side bays with entrances projecting above cornice, with semi-circular topped blocked parapet. Ground floor ashlar granite, upper floors sandstone. Central bay has canted window at first floor level. | Donegal Sandstone and Grey Aberdeen Granite<br>**Building Information**<br>**Date of construction:** 1910<br>**Architect:** Vincent Craig<br>**Listing:** B1 |

| Building | Architectural Description | Stone Types |
|---|---|---|
| **County Down** | | |
| **Ballydugan Flour Mill**<br>Ballydugan,<br>Downpatrick,<br>Co. Down | Six bay, six storey mill building. Granite segmental archway with keystone right of centre, single doorway at left. Six sash windows on each floor, diminished on top floor. Was largely derelict before recent restoration. | Greywacke and Mourne Granite<br>**Building Information**<br>**Date of construction:** 1792<br>**Architect:** Not Assigned<br>**Listing:** B1 |
| **Bangor Abbey Parish Church**<br>Bangor,<br>Co. Down | Gothic style church fronted by a tall square tower, which is rubble built with tall square stone octagonal spire in regular coursed plain ashlar. West door: rounded arch recessed door with carved head below window. Clock-face high up wall. Balustrade and corner pinnacles. Sandstone dressings, rest of church rendered. | Greywacke and Scrabo Sandstone<br>**Building Information**<br>**Date of construction:** 15th century–1830's<br>**Architect:** Not Assigned<br>**Listing:** A |
| **Bangor Castle**<br>(Town Hall),<br>Bangor,<br>Co. Down | Elizabethan Revival style mansion. Rectangular two storey plus attic and basement, with three storey tower topped by corner clock and turret beside porch. Windows are a mix of canted, square, and bowed with mullions. Tall gables with triple windows. Carved fretwork on stone of bay windows. | Giffnock Sandstone<br>**Building Information**<br>**Date of construction:** 1848<br>**Architect:** William Burn<br>**Listing:** A |

| Building | Architectural Description | Stone Types |
| --- | --- | --- |
| **Castleward House**<br>Strangford,<br>Co. Down | Large country house, three storey over basement. Seven bays long, four wide. Divided in style; West façade classical, East façade Strawberry Gothic. Later Classical style enclosed stone porch to South façade with balustrade and set of two columns on either side. Classical face has set of four giant Corinthian columns attached above entrance. | Bath Stone and Giffnock Sandstone<br>**Building Information**<br>**Date of construction:** 1760<br>**Architect:** Not Assigned<br>**Listing:** B1 |
| <br>**Castlewellan Castle**<br>Castlewellan,<br>Co. Down | Scottish Baronial style castle. Three storey plus attic. A round tower with battlements to the south west corner. The north west corner has a gabled wing with crow steps forward of main face. Pedimented dormers at roof level. On the north face a two storey house and outbuildings with side corner turrets. On the east face a central square attached tower with shallow porch stone enclosed entrance porch. | Newry Granodiorite<br>**Building Information**<br>**Date of construction:** 1856<br>**Architect:** William Burns<br>**Listing:** B+ |
| <br>**Drumgooland Parish Church**<br>Ballyward,<br>Co. Down | Gothic church with nave, North/South transepts, side-corner vestry, and square tower with pinnacles. Recessed pointed arch side door and Y-tracery. Granite dressing (plain ashlar) on doors and windows. Pitched slate roof. | Newry Granodiorite and Mourne Granite<br>**Building Information**<br>**Date of construction:** 1820<br>**Architect:** Not Assigned<br>**Listing:** B |

| Building | Architectural Description | Stone Types |
|---|---|---|
| **Gillespie Monument**<br>Comber, Co. Down | A tall square column with statue on platform, supported on large square pedestal with inserts on each face for plaques. Stepped plinth on all sides of the column. | Scrabo Sandstone and Castle Espie Limestone<br>**Building Information**<br>**Date of construction:** 1845<br>**Architect:** Not Assigned<br>**Listing:** B1 |
| **Grey Abbey**<br>Co. Down | Cistercian abbey consisting of ruins of nave, chapter house and refectory. Fine doorway to nave with four orders with dog tooth ornament. Sandstone dressing and quoins. | Greywacke and Scrabo Sandstone<br>**Building Information**<br>**Date of construction:** 1193<br>**Architect:** Not Assigned<br>**Listing:** MON |
| **Holy Trinity Cathedral**<br>English Street, Downpatrick, Co. Down | A Gothic style cathedral with tall nave and lean-to side aisles with large pinnacles atop buttresses. The church is fronted by a large four stage square tower with pointed pinnacles and castellated top. There is a recessed doorway into church via tower. | Greywacke and Scrabo Sandstone<br>**Building Information**<br>**Date of construction:** 1790<br>**Architect:** Charles Lilly (LA)<br>**Listing:** A |

| Building | Architectural Description | Stone Types |
|---|---|---|
| <br>**Holywood Friary**<br>Bangor Road,<br>Holywood,<br>Co. Down | Roofless rectangular church. West gable has a recessed pointed arch doorway with hood-mould below a narrow window. Tower has a square base with clock face supporting a smaller square section with chamfered corners, pointed arch vents and crenellation. Nave side; blocked-up rounded arch windows. East gable partial dressing survives. 17th century windows. | Cultra Limestone and Scrabo Sandstone<br>**Building Information**<br>**Date of construction:** 13th century–1651<br>**Architect:** Not Assigned<br>**Listing:** MON |
| <br>**Kilhorne Church**<br>Annalong,<br>Co. Down | Small Gothic church, consisting of nave, projecting chancel and side-corner modern vestry. Fronted by a square three stage tower with crenellation, and corner pinnacles. Front pointed arched recessed door with moulding and clock face. Tall lancet windows along nave. Ashlar quoins, and modern Chinese granite disability ramp. Pitched slate roof. Strap pointing. Granite plinth, ashlar at front and string course. | Mourne Granite and Giffnock Sandstone<br>**Building Information**<br>**Date of construction:** 1840<br>**Architect:** Not Assigned<br>**Listing:** B1 |
| <br>**Main Street**<br>Moira,<br>Co. Down | Georgian style house, two storey above basement, seven bays long. Central doorway, pedimented with attached columns and fanlight. West side doorway with fanlight and keystone. Fluted band course under cornice. Rubble walls with galleting, sandstone quoins and banding. | Antrim Basalt and unspecified Sandstone<br>**Building Information**<br>**Date of construction:** *c.* 1770–1835<br>**Architect:** Not Assigned<br>**Listing:** B1 |

| Building | Architectural Description | Stone Types |
|---|---|---|
|  **The Priory** Newtownards, Co. Down | 17th century church built on ruins of a Priory. Gothic in style with lancet windows and a pointed arch doorway with attached columns. A tall square bell tower on North wall with mix of slit and rounded arch windows. At the base is a finely carved Italian Renaissance rounded arch door surround with coat of arms. The Nave is rubble-built with sandstone ashlar quoins. | Greywacke and Scrabo Sandstone<br>**Building Information**<br>**Date of construction:** 1244<br>**Architect:** Not Assigned<br>**Listing:** MON |
|  **St Brigid's RC Church** Glassdrumman, Newry, Co. Down | Classical Italianate style church. A two storey nave with classical pediment and deep cornice, decorated with mosaic to South front. Large rose window above a slim portico with four tall Ionic columns, three doors with fanlight, rounded arch with keystone, pilasters at rear to columns. Side-aisle façades have breakfront narrow rectangular windows. South east corner is tall square bell-tower finished with large cornice and shallow hipped roof. | Newry Granodiorite and Giffnock Sandstone<br>**Building Information**<br>**Date of construction:** 1928<br>**Architect:** W. H. Byrne and Son<br>**Listing:** B+ |

| Building | Architectural Description | Stone Types |
|---|---|---|
| **St Colman's RC Church**<br>Newry Road, Kilkeel, Co. Down | Gothic style church consisting of nave, transepts, chancel and vestry. Fronted by attached square tower with corner pinnacles and corner buttresses. Nave has tall lancet windows and buttresses. Transept is double gabled on each side with porch doorway on each. Single storey vestry buildings at rear of chancel. Pitched slate roof. | Mourne Granite<br>**Building Information**<br>**Date of construction:** 1879<br>**Architect:** O'Neill and Byrne<br>**Listing:** B1 |
| **St Colman's Old Church Ruin**<br>Bridge Street, Kilkeel, Co. Down | Rectangular gabled ruin with rough dressed split-stone quoins. Sandstone dressing on windows. | Mourne Granite and Scrabo Sandstone<br>**Building Information**<br>**Date of construction:** 14th century<br>**Architect:** Not Assigned<br>**Listing:** MON |
| **St Matthew's RC Church**<br>Scarva, Co. Down | A Gothic style church with four bay nave and tall lancet windows with strap-moulds, projecting chancel, and South transept with side entrance. The nave is fronted by square bell tower with broached spire, and small gabled slit windows. The church has a pitched slate roof and sandstone ashlar dressing on quoins, windows and doors. | Greywacke and Dungannon Sandstone<br>**Building Information**<br>**Date of construction:** 1850<br>**Architect:** Not Assigned<br>**Listing:** B |

| Building | Architectural Description | Stone Types |
|---|---|---|
| **St Patrick's Memorial Church**<br>Saul,<br>Co. Down | Irish Romanesque style church with round corner tower and double recessed rounded central doorway on west gable beneath ocular window. Set of five rounded arch windows on sides. Pitched slate roof. Projecting chancel at east end. Rubble built with quoins and window dressings. | Mourne Granite<br>**Building Information**<br>**Date of construction:** 1932<br>**Architect:** Henry Seaver<br>**Listing:** B+ |
| <br>**St Patrick's RC Church**<br>Dromore Street,<br>Banbridge,<br>Co. Down | Gothic stone façade on rendered nave. Central Tudor arched doorway below a large tracery window with flanking tall pointed arch windows. Slim buttresses dividing bays with octagonal pointed pinnacles. Squared greywacke walls with plain ashlar granite dressing. | Greywacke and Newry Granodiorite<br>**Building Information**<br>**Date of construction:** 1838<br>**Architect:** Thomas Duff<br>**Listing:** B |
| <br>**St Patrick's RC Church**<br>Newtownards,<br>Co. Down | A Gothic style church consisting of nave, lean-to aisle and North and South transepts. A square tower with pyramidal roof and circular windows. An apse ended chancel and south east corner vestry below round turret with conical slate roof. The church has a tall gabled porch with recessed door. | Scrabo Sandstone and Dundonald Sandstone<br>**Building Information**<br>**Date of construction:** 1877<br>**Architect:** J. A. Hansom<br>**Listing:** B1 |

| Building | Architectural Description | Stone Types |
|---|---|---|
| **Scrabo Tower**<br>Scrabo,<br>Newtownards,<br>Co. Down | Square Scottish Baronial tower with four corner turrets, three corbelled, and a fourth full height for spiral staircase. Motile storey with central conical corbelled roof. Steps lead up to a tall rounded arch doorway below plaque insert and coat of arms. | Basalt (Dolerite) and Scrabo Sandstone<br>**Building Information**<br>**Date of construction:** 1865<br>**Architect:** Charles Lanyon<br>**Listing:** B+ |
| **The Temple Above Temple Water**<br>Castleward,<br>Strangford,<br>Co. Down | Folly in the form of a Greek Temple, formed of central way with lean-to wings. Central bay is fronted by a Classical pedimented portico with set of four Tuscan columns and carved frieze. Constructed mainly of brick, rear and sides rendered. Stone steps up to entrance. | Bath Stone<br>**Building Information**<br>**Date of construction:** 1755<br>**Architect:** Not Assigned<br>**Listing:** B |
| **Tullynagill Church Ruins**<br>Loughinisland,<br>Co. Down | A Gothic style church, rectangular in plan with four walls still remaining. Rounded arched windows mullioned at East face with sandstone dressing. The west façade has a large lancet window. | Greywacke and Castle Espie Limestone<br>**Building Information**<br>**Date of construction:** Medieval<br>**Architect:** Not Assigned<br>**Listing:** MON |

| Building | Architectural Description | Stone Types |
|---|---|---|
|  **Ulster Bank** Upper Square, Castlewellan, Co. Down | Two storey, two bay bank in Classical style. Corner entrance with broken pediment, gabled, with mullioned windows and hipped slate roof. Classical cornice and carved window mullions. Random coursed main wall, regular coursed plinth. | Newry Granodiorite **Building Information** **Date of construction:** 1926 **Architect:** Not Assigned **Listing:** B1 |
| County Fermanagh | | |
|  **Armagh Manor** Ballagh, Lisnaskea, Co. Fermanagh | Scottish Baronial style country house with central attached turret facing southeast, containing main doorway. Section to the left has canted bay window, three small sash windows above and bartizan on southwest corner. Crow-stepped gables. Crow-stepped archway into courtyard with outbuildings attached. Dressing less tooled than main stone. | Fermanagh Carboniferous Limestone **Building Information** **Date of construction:** 1865 **Architect:** Not Assigned **Listing:** B |
|  **Belle Isle House** Lisbellaw, Co. Fermanagh | Large country house, mostly two storey with several extensions. Main façade is seven bays long. At south end is a five storey crenellated tower, buttressed, with casement windows, and a projecting porch with Tudor arched entrance doors. Centre section has two large canted bay windows and mullioned casement. Rendered with sandstone dressings. | Fermanagh Carboniferous Limestone **Building Information** **Date of construction:** *c.* 1890 **Architect:** Morley Horder **Listing:** B+ |

| Building | Architectural Description | Stone Types |
| --- | --- | --- |
| **Belleek Porcelain Factory** 3 Main Street, Belleek, Co. Fermanagh | Classical style three storey, thirteen bay factory building, with pediment over central three bays. Rounded arch windows on ground floor, rounded arch with keystone on first, and paired rounded arch with keystone on top floor. Central three bay section has central doors with 2:3:2 pattern of round headed windows above. Hipped slate roof. | Fermanagh Carboniferous Limestone<br>**Building Information**<br>**Date of construction:** 1857<br>**Architect:** William Armstrong<br>**Listing:** B+ |
| <br>**Boa Island Figures** Boa Island, Co. Fermanagh | The Boa Island figures comprise two high relief carved stone statues thought to be pre-Christian pagan idols and are currently located within the confines of Caldragh Graveyard on Boa Island. The larger of the two statues is described as a Janus-type figure because of its two back-to-back faces and torsos. The faces are pear-shaped or oval in shape with bulging eyes and interlaced carving between the heads representing hair. The other, smaller statue, originally came from the nearby island of Lusty More and is sometimes referred to as the 'Lustyman' although it is thought that the statue may actually be a representation of the female form. | Fermanagh Carboniferous Sandstone<br>**Building Information**<br>**Date of construction:** Unknown<br>**Architect:** Not Assigned<br>**Listing:** MON |

| Building | Architectural Description | Stone Types |
|---|---|---|
| <br>**Castle Coole**<br>Enniskillen,<br>Co. Fermanagh | A nine bay, two storey Neo-Classical Country House with colonnaded wings ending in pavilions. Central block has a four-columned Ionic portico with pediment, balustrade around roof edge. Each colonnaded section has a central doorway with consoles and three alcoves either side. Pavilions have two storey sash windows at centre with a fluted column either side, and a rounded alcove either side. North façade has a segmental bow with fluted columns. | Portland Limestone<br>**Building Information**<br>**Date of construction:**<br>1790–1797<br>**Architect:**<br>James Wyatt<br>**Listing:** A |
| <br>**Cooneen Parish Church**<br>Cooneen,<br>Co. Fermanagh | Gothic style church with small attached tower in southwest corner. Tower has triple recessed side entrance, quatrefoil window, three small pointed arch windows on each side and octagonal stone spire. Main face has one course of hard limestone, lancet windows with trefoil detail, and projecting gabled entrance porch at East end with Jacobean Revival style window and cusped inset trefoil window above. | Fermanagh Carboniferous Limestone<br>**Building Information**<br>**Date of construction:**<br>1871–73<br>**Architect:**<br>Francis Farrell<br>**Listing:** B |

| Building | Architectural Description | Stone Types |
| --- | --- | --- |
| **Donaghmore Cross**<br>Donaghmore,<br>Co. Fermanagh | The cross is made up of parts of two different crosses. It is said to have been thrown down in 17th century and re-erected in the 18th. On the West side are the following scenes: a mounted horseman, Adam and Eve, Cain and Abel and the Sacrifice of Isaac. On the East side are the Annunciation, the Adoration of the Magi, the Baptism, the Miracle at Cana, the Multiplication of Loaves and Fishes, the Arrest and the Crucifixion. | Tyrone Carboniferous Sandstone<br>**Building Information**<br>**Date of construction:** Possibly 10th century<br>**Architect:** Not Assigned<br>**Listing:** MON |
| <br>**Enniskillen Castle**<br>Enniskillen,<br>Co. Fermanagh | Three storey Castle Keep, with a mixture of large rectangular sash windows with sandstone dressing, and smaller square sash windows with red-brick dressing. Any former castellation has been replaced by an M-shaped hipped slate roof. Some arrow-slits remain. No windows on south face. | Fermanagh Carboniferous Limestone<br>**Building Information**<br>**Date of construction:** 15th–16th century<br>**Architect:** Not Assigned<br>**Listing:** MON |
| <br>**Northern Bank**<br>24 Town Hall Street,<br>Enniskillen,<br>Co. Fermanagh | Classical Italianate style, two storey, five bays with stone front façade. Ground floor two rounded-arch recessed doorways at North and South sides, the left with fanlight and the right with carved stone tympanum. Plinth. Three tall rectangular windows with carved tympanum set in keystoned arch. Deep cill recess with five segmental head windows on first floor. Deep eaves with dentil detail, hipped roof. | Corsehill Sandstone<br>**Building Information**<br>**Date of construction:** 1889<br>**Architect:** Not Assigned<br>**Listing:** B1 |

| Building | Architectural Description | Stone Types |
|---|---|---|
| **St Mary's Priory**<br>Devenish Island,<br>Co. Fermanagh | 5th century abbey, divided by a crossing tower (west of centre), supported by two double-chamfered piers. The arches, tower, and north wall of choir are complete. Convent buildings are on the north of the church and were, a court around an enclosed cloister, sacristy and chapter house in East range, refectory on North, and guest house on west. East window of the abbey was taken to Devenish Parish Church, Monea. | Fermanagh Carboniferous Limestone<br>**Building Information**<br>**Date of construction:** 1449<br>**Architect:** Not Assigned<br>**Listing:** MON |
| <br>**Town Hall**<br>The Diamond,<br>Enniskillen,<br>Co. Fermanagh | Classical style, two storey, six bays along each main façade. Square tower in northwest corner with clock-face, alcoves for stone statues, topped by a round turret with copper dome. West front portico entrance with balcony below pediment and coat of arms. Rusticated ground floor with rectangular recessed windows, upper same but with sandstone dressing. | Fermanagh Carboniferous Limestone and Dungannon Sandstone dressings<br>**Building Information**<br>**Date of construction:** 1897<br>**Architect:** William Scott<br>**Listing:** B+ |

| Building | Architectural Description | Stone Types |
| --- | --- | --- |
| **County Londonderry** | | |
|  **Aghanloo Church** Aghanloo Road, Limavady, Co. Londonderry | Gothic style nave fronted by three stage tower with corner pinnacles and battlements. Nave has three gothic style paired lancets. No apse, with triple lancet in gable. Sandstone dressings and hood moulds to black basalt walls. | Basalt and Barony Glen Sandstone dressings<br>**Building Information**<br>**Date of construction:** 1823<br>**Architect:** John Bowden<br>**Listing:** B+ |
|  **Church of Ireland** Ballyquin Road, Carrick, Limavady, Co. Londonderry | Small Gothic Revival style church. Four bay nave with pointed arch tall windows with hood moulds. First bay slim projection with gable and squared buttresses with gabled octagonal pinnacles. Southwest corner vestry. Projecting chancel. Angled string course. Bell belfry and gabled enclosed porch with Tudor arched doorway with octagonal buttresses. Pitched slate roof. | Derry Schist and Barony Glen Sandstone (Dungiven) dressing<br>**Building Information**<br>**Date of construction:** 1846<br>**Architect:** Not Assigned<br>**Listing:** B1 |
|  **City Walls** Londonderry, Co. Londonderry | The walls of the city of Londonderry (Derry) enclose the old city with a circumference of approximately 1.5km. The walls vary in thickness from 3-10m and are the only surviving complete set of city walls in Ireland. | Derry Schist<br>**Building Information**<br>**Date of construction:** 1613–18<br>**Architect:** Not Assigned<br>**Listing:** MON |

| Building | Architectural Description | Stone Types |
|---|---|---|
|  **(Former) Court House** Castlerock Road Coleraine, Co. Londonderry | Greek Doric style two storey former courthouse. Main façade has full height portico with large pediment supported by four columns. Central square-topped doorway with date plaque above. One square-topped pedimented sash window either side with inset rectangular panels beneath. Rendered extension at rear. | Giffnock Sandstone<br>**Building Information**<br>**Date of construction:** 1852<br>**Architect:** Stewart Gordon<br>**Listing:** B1 |
|  **Dungiven Priory** Dungiven, Co. Londonderry | The west half of the structure is the original nave, later a chancel was added to east face. The main face has a rounded arch doorway at west end and one pointed arch window with some remains of tracery. There are two windows in South face and two narrow recessed lancets in East face. | Barony Glen Sandstone and Antrim Basalt<br>**Building Information**<br>**Date of construction:** 12th–13th century<br>**Architect:** Not Assigned<br>**Listing:** MON |
|  **Guild Hall,** Shipquay Place, Londonderry, Co. Londonderry | Tudoresque Gothic style town hall. Main façade has a gabled front flanked by narrow octagonal turrets. Central large elaborate tracery window with carving detail and ogee lancet window panels. Tall tower on south west corner with large doorway, lancet windows, clock face and corner pinnacles. Similar style on all four elevations. | Barony Glen Sandstone and Corsehill Sandstone<br>**Building Information**<br>**Date of construction:** 1887<br>**Architect:** John Guy Ferguson<br>**Listing:** A |

| Building | Architectural Description | Stone Types |
|---|---|---|
| <br>**Harbour Commissioner's Office**<br>Londonderry,<br>Co. Londonderry | A two storey, seven bay Classical style building. Comprises a square-topped doorway with pediment to the fifth bay which extends upwards above roof balustrade to form clock tower with pedimented clock and roof level balustrade. | Barony Glen Sandstone<br>**Building Information**<br>**Date of construction:** 1882<br>**Architect:**<br>John Kennedy<br>**Listing:** B |
| <br>**Mussenden Temple**<br>Downhill,<br>Co. Londonderry | Circular temple based on the Temple of Vesta at Tivoli. South side has a square-topped doorway with light, carved surround and Bishop's coat of arms above. North, east and west sides have a large rectangular sash window. Sixteen Corinthian columns run around the carved walls with carved inscription around the top. Domed slate roof with urn finial at centre. Basalt base with rounded arch entrance in east face. | Ballycastle Sandstone and Basalt Plinth<br>**Building Information**<br>**Date of construction:** 1783<br>**Architect:**<br>Michael Shanahan<br>**Listing:** A |
| **Northern Bank**<br>Shipquay Place,<br>Londonderry,<br>Co. Londonderry | Palazzo style, three storey, six bay bank building. Main façade has a shouldered doorway at each end with Northern Banking Company plaque and carving above, four rounded arch windows with carved head keystones in between. First floor has six sash windows with Ionic pilasters and segmental pediments. Second floor has plain sash windows. Balustrade on top and chamfered corners. | Giffnock Sandstone and Newry Granodiorite<br>**Building Information**<br>**Date of construction:** 1866<br>**Architect:**<br>Thomas Turner<br>**Listing:** B+ |

| Building | Architectural Description | Stone Types |
|---|---|---|
| **Rock Bakery**<br>Strand Road,<br>Londonderry,<br>Co. Londonderry | Classical style five storey, seven bay former bakery/factory, now converted into student housing. Rounded arch windows on all floors, diminished to upper floors. Central segmental arch entrance on ground floor. | Derry Schist<br>**Building Information**<br>**Date of construction:** 1846<br>**Architect:** Not Assigned<br>**Listing:** B1 |
| <br>**St Eugene's RC Church**<br>Moneyneany,<br>Co. Londonderry | Gothic Revival style church, three bay nave with paired lancets, north and south transepts forming a T-plan. Large central arch doorway below rose window. Bell belfry over West gable. Rounded apse of lower height. Vestry in northeast corner. Pitched slate roof. | Barony Glen Sandstone<br>**Building Information**<br>**Date of construction:** 1902<br>**Architect:** Not Assigned<br>**Listing:** B |
| <br>**Star Factory**<br>79E Foyle Road,<br>Londonderry,<br>Co. Londonderry | Five storey, ten bay former factory, rounded arch windows on ground floor and large central archway with "Star Factory" above. Windows on other floors are segmental arch with keystones. Clock at centre of fourth floor with stone surround, keystone and balustrade. Rest of fourth floor is metal sheeted, apart from sides. | Donegal Sandstone<br>**Building Information**<br>**Date of construction:** 1889<br>**Architect:** Daniel Conroy<br>**Listing:** B+ |

| Building | Architectural Description | Stone Types |
| --- | --- | --- |
|  **Ulster Bank** 20-22 Broad Street, Magherafelt, Co. Londonderry | Two storey plus attic, seven bay Bank in ashlar sandstone. Central square-topped entrance with light. Large sash windows, smaller on first floor, interspersed with large Ionic columns on ground floor. | Barony Glen Sandstone<br>**Building Information**<br>**Date of construction:** 1925<br>**Architect:** Blackwood and Jury<br>**Listing:** B1 |
| **County Tyrone** | | |
|  **Allied Irish Bank** 18-20 Scotch Street, Dungannon, Co. Tyrone | Gothic style two storey plus attic, five bay Bank. Hipped slate roof with eaves on brackets, cill course each floor. Rectangular recessed windows. Two dormer windows. Central segmental arched double recessed doorway with light. To the rear is a mix of various height projecting wings with tall chimney stacks, all in same style but possible later additions. | Dungannon Sandstone<br>**Building Information**<br>**Date of construction:** 1890<br>**Architect:** Not Assigned<br>**Listing:** B1 |
|  **Allied Irish Bank** 71 Main Street, Strabane, Co. Tyrone | Classical style stone façade, three storeys and four bays. Ground floor divided by pilasters. Rounded arch doorway with cornice. First floor has large pedimented sash windows, second floor are un-pedimented. Roof has balustrade and cornice. | Barony Glen Sandstone<br>**Building Information**<br>**Date of construction:** 1885<br>**Architect:** R. Watt<br>**Listing:** B1 |

| Building | Architectural Description | Stone Types |
|---|---|---|
| **Ballymagrane Presbyterian Church**<br>Crilly, Co. Tyrone | Barn style church with Gothic style dressings. Entrance gable has tall pointed arch central doorway below three lancet windows and date stone. Stepped quoins and plinth. Four tall lancet windows along sides. | Tyrone Carboniferous Limestone and Dungannon Sandstone<br>**Building Information**<br>**Date of construction:** 1839<br>**Architect:** Not Assigned<br>**Listing:** B |
| **Boer War Memorial**<br>Drumragh Avenue, Omagh, Co. Tyrone | Granite plinth and pedestal with rectangular columns to each side with bronze statues. | Cornish Granite (De Lank)<br>**Building Information**<br>**Date of construction:** 1904<br>**Architect:** Sydney March<br>**Listing:** B |
| **Castle Caulfield**<br>Castlecaulfield, Co. Tyrone | Remains of large three storey house and gate house with gun-loops. Mullioned windows with ashlar dressing and quoins, open ruin with no internal floors remaining. | Tyrone Carboniferous Limestone and Dungannon Sandstone<br>**Building Information**<br>**Date of construction:** 1611<br>**Architect:** Not Assigned<br>**Listing:** MON |

| Building | Architectural Description | Stone Types |
|---|---|---|
|  **Dyan Corn Mill** Caledon, Co. Tyrone | Large two storey mill complex, L-shaped in plan. Grilled windows with red-brick dressing. Various segmental arch doorways and slim projecting rectangular stone porch with cornice along east face. Stepped quoins. Hipped slate roof. To rear is pair of two storey, three bay houses and attached stores and outbuildings. | Tyrone Carboniferous Limestone and Dungannon Sandstone<br>**Building Information**<br>**Date of construction:** 1829<br>**Architect:** Not Assigned<br>**Listing:** B+ |
|  **Methodist Church** Loy Street, Cookstown, Co. Tyrone | Romanesque style four bay nave over basement. Steps up to door with shoulders and fanlight with semi-circular insert, flanked by columns. Above are paired round headed windows with columns surmounted by bell gable. Sides have four tall similar windows and segmental smaller windows to basement. Modern building to rear. Pitched slate roof. | Cookstown Sandstone<br>**Building Information**<br>**Date of construction:** *c.* 1860<br>**Architect:** Not Assigned<br>**Listing:** B |
|  **St Anne's Parish Church** Church Street, Dungannon, Co. Tyrone | Early English style church consisting of nave with clerestory, side aisles and north and south transepts. North gabled porch with pointed arch doorway and large gabled pyramidal pinnacles. Northeast corner has tall square tower with multi-recessed pointed arch doorway and octagonal stone spire. | Dungannon Sandstone<br>**Building Information**<br>**Date of construction:** 1865<br>**Architect:** W.J. Barre<br>**Listing:** B+ |

| Building | Architectural Description | Stone Types |
|---|---|---|
| <br>**St Laurence's Church**<br>Cookstown,<br>Co. Tyrone | A Gothic Revival style church consisting of a two bay nave with pointed arch windows and buttresses. The church comprises wide transepts and lean-to vestry to the North-West corner and a projecting three bay chancel. The church is fronted by a square tower with corner buttresses, pyramidal corner pinnacles and crenellation and topped by octagonal stone spire, pointed arch doorway. The tower and spire are originally from an 1822 church by John Nash. | Cookstown Sandstone and Dungannon Sandstone<br>**Building Information**<br>**Date of construction:** 1861<br>**Architect:** Joseph Welland<br>**Listing:** B+ |
| <br>**Trinity RC Church**<br>Chapel Street,<br>Cookstown,<br>Co. Tyrone | Early English Gothic Revival style church consisting of five bay nave with clerestory and side aisles with side chapel and vestry. Projecting chancel. Pointed arch windows with trefoils. Fronted by large tall square tower with broached stone spire. Multi-recessed doorway with columns. Corner buttresses to tower. | Cookstown Sandstone<br>**Building Information**<br>**Date of construction:** 1855<br>**Architect:** J.J. McCarthy<br>**Listing:** B+ |